FEDERAL, STATE, AND LOCAL
ADMINISTRATIVE RELATIONSHIPS
IN AGRICULTURE

Publications of the Bureau of Public Administration
University of California

+——+

Federal, State, and Local Administrative Relationships in Agriculture

By Carleton R. Ball

+——+

In Two Volumes

VOLUME I

UNIVERSITY OF CALIFORNIA PRESS
BERKELEY, CALIFORNIA
1938

CONTENTS

VOLUME I

FOREWORD

Although much has been written concerning the legal powers of State and Federal governments, little has been published hitherto on the great number and variety of administrative interrelationships arising between Federal, State, and local agencies in the performance of their respective tasks.

In 1930 the Bureau of Public Administration of the University of California undertook a series of studies of the interrelationships of the State of California and its subdivisions and the Federal government. These studies are descriptive rather than critical, but it is hoped that the information contained in them will be of assistance to government officials and students, in pointing the way toward a better coördinated performance of governmental service.

The first volume in this series, *Welfare Activities of Federal, State, and Local Governments in California, 1850–1934,* by Frances Cahn and Valeska Bary, was published in 1936 by the University of California Press. Later publications will include the results of studies in Natural Resources, by Carleton R. Ball, and Transportation, by Austin F. Macdonald.

The second publication to appear in this series is here presented: *Federal, State, and Local Administrative Relationships in Agriculture,* by Carleton R. Ball.

Samuel C. May, Director.

Berkeley, California,
December 10, 1937.

Chapter I: PRINCIPLES AND PRACTICES OF COÖPERATION

[Because each chapter covers a different subject and therefore will be used chiefly by a different constituency, it seems desirable to make each one complete and self-contained. For this reason, among others, a complete table of chapter contents is placed at the beginning of each chapter, rather than at the front of the volume. A list of all literature cited in the chapter will be found at the end of the chapter and the numbers in parentheses in the text refer the reader to the corresponding entries in the list. All entry numbers occurring in each major section of a chapter are also listed in numerical sequence at the end of that section, thus forming what is in effect a section list of literature cited. These features all should prove of great convenience to readers.]

CHAPTER CONTENTS

Chapter I

PRINCIPLES AND PRACTICES OF COÖPERATION

1. INTRODUCTION

THIS FIRST CHAPTER, as its title indicates, is a study of the principles, advantages, and practices of coöperation between official agencies at all levels of government. It is not in any sense a summary of the material found in the successive subject-matter chapters. Rather, it is an introduction to the subject of coöperation among official agricultural agencies. It has a much wider application, however, than merely to agricultural activities. Much of the material is of almost universal application.

From this viewpoint, the chapter shows first the historical development of the idea (including mental attitudes), presents the extensive discussions of coöperation which have been carried on, and exhibits the principles and advantages which have been crystallized from these discussions. Next it outlines the scope and nature of official relations. It then makes an analysis of Federal-State relations and sets forth the practice of Federal-State coöperation, as evidenced by coöperating committees, coöperative agreements, the publication of coöperative results, and the acknowledgment of coöperation in such publications. Finally, it illustrates the prevalence of coöperation in certain Federal-State fields and defines some terms commonly used.

Because this chapter, like those dealing with subject-matter applications of coöperation, is made self-containing, a detailed table of contents is prefixed and a list of literature cited is appended. Numbers in parentheses in the text refer to the Literature Cited at the end of the chapter.

2. HISTORICAL DEVELOPMENT OF COÖPERATION

TO STUDY AND PORTRAY the facts of coöperation in agriculture is not enough. Antecedent even to the record of its history is the determination of what the parties concerned are thinking. There are attitudes of mind which make for or against the acceptance of the principles of coöperation, the acknowledgment of its advantages, the development of coöperative structures, and the achievement of coöperative results.

Human relations range from active antagonism, through self-centered indifference, to friendly interest, and finally to planned coöperation. This is as true in agriculture as elswhere. Relations in agriculture are but a picture of relations in the larger world. One type of relation may prevail at one time or in one place while another prevails at the same time in another place, or in the same place at another time. Similarly, at any time or place, one individual or group may hold a certain attitude and another individual or group may feel quite differently. Attitudes precede action.

Active antagonism, regional, institutional, or individual, has not been unknown in agriculture but has become exceedingly rare. The stage of indifference is marked by self-centered action without concern for others. It may imply either concentration on the assigned problem, limited perspective, or failure to recognize the value of coöperation. Again, it may happen that coöperation is deliberately neglected or refused because of personal reasons, such as dislike or hostility, reluctance to make contacts, objections to sharing credit, or intent to gain personal advantage even at the expense of the public which pays the bills. Friendly interest is the general rule, however, evidenced by abundant contacts and conferences and the willingness to work together.

Coöperation in effort marks the dawning of a new day. It connotes willingness to surrender some personal privileges for the good of society, unselfish recognition of the rights of others, and ready assumption of the obligation to planned helpfulness. The development of coöperation in the field of agriculture is but a miniature of its development in broader fields. Human progress, whether by individuals or institutions, is measured by the ratio between insistence on individual privilege and the recognition of social values and responsibilities. Slow as this progress has been, and still is, it nevertheless is real and it is growing. The areas of its application are enlarging and the speed of its development is increasing.

DEVELOPMENT OF OFFICIAL RELATIONS

This subject may be separated conveniently into three periods, early, middle, and recent. With the increase of our national tempo the periods become successively shorter.

Early Period, 1776–1860

Governmental interrelations, particularly Federal-State relations, have been of paramount importance since the beginnings of our nation. These relations were a vital problem in formulating the Articles of Confederation and in the efficient conduct of the Revolution. The framers of the Constitution of the United States wrestled long with the same problem, and the Constitution as adopted is a compromise. Throughout our century and a half of national development, the only consistently continuous political question has been that of the relative powers and duties of the central government and the individual States.

In the whole period of about 160 years, the pendulum of popular conviction on this subject has swung almost from one extreme to the other. The Federal government has passed from the original condition of virtual impotence to the present condition of large coöperative responsibility for the welfare of the people of this nation of States. The movement started with the original Federal land grants to the States to promote education, and continued with grants for such internal improvements as canals, turnpikes, and railroads in the fifty years from 1820 to 1870. These later subsidies were strenuously resisted by one group as unconstitutional encroachments on State responsibilities, and were justified by their successive proponents under the "general welfare" clause of the Constitution. At the beginning of the next period, the Civil War, developed partly out of the States'-rights issue, officially settled the controversy in favor of centralized power in the national government.

In the early days of American agriculture there was comparatively little need or opportunity for official interrelations, and those which developed were informal. Under the pioneer conditions prevailing, most advancement was the result of activities by individual farmers or by the farmers' clubs and other organizations which developed rapidly in the first half of the nineteenth century. A few official agencies, such as the Medical Department of the United States Army, the Smithsonian Institution, and later the Federal Department of Agriculture, established some coöperation among themselves and with other official agencies in obtaining and compiling weather records. The Navy Department assisted in furnishing meteorological data from the oceans. Diplomatic and consular officers of the State Department, as well as officers of the Navy Department, helped in getting seeds, plants, and animals from foreign countries for distribution through the Treasury Department and, later, the Department of the Interior. All this entailed some coöperation with officials of foreign nations. There was little other official coöperation during this portion of the early period.

Middle Period, 1861–1912

The second or middle period of the development of official relations covered the fifty years from 1861 to 1912. It was characterized by enormous expansion in the structure and especially in the functions of government. The expansion in agriculture lay chiefly in the fields of education and investigation on the one hand, and regulation and control on the other. The trend also was toward a shifting of power from the lower to the higher levels of government, from city and county to State, and from State to Federal agencies.

In education and investigation.—At the very beginning of this period, in 1862, there were passed two Congressional acts of far-reaching significance to the development of Federal-State relations in agricultural education and investigation. The first was the Morrill (Land-Grant College) Act, granting lands from the public domain to aid the several States in establishing State colleges of agriculture and mechanic arts. The second was the act creating the United States Department of Agriculture. The development of these institutions and the State experiment stations (added by an act of 1887), and their enlarging relations with each other and with still other Federal and State agencies, are the basis for most of the coöperative history of this period.

In a summary of American agriculture, this fifty-year period is separated by the writer into two equal subperiods. The first, 1862 to 1887, was characterized by the development of Federal and

State official structures concerned with agriculture, the rise of investigations as a new function, and a very individualistic personnel outlook. The second subperiod, 1888 to 1912, was characterized primarily by the organization of numerous Federal and State structures into fewer and larger units. The investigational function was enormously expanded at both State and Federal levels. Regulation or control arose as a new but extensive function at all levels. Personnel perspective gradually changed from individualistic to organizational, the principal units of allegiance being the Division and the Bureau.

A distinctive feature of this period was the granting of Federal cash subsidies to the States to promote the general welfare through technical education and investigation. Such cash subsidy to the land-grant colleges of agriculture and mechanic arts began with the second Morrill Act of 1890, and was increased by the Nelson Amendment of 1907. The investigation of agricultural problems was subsidized by the Hatch Act of 1887, financing an agricultural experiment station in each State to the extent of $15,000 annually; and the Adams Act of 1906 increased the sum by another $15,000 annually. Further and larger increases are noted in the recent period. These acts established official relations on an increasing scale between the Federal Department of Agriculture which administered the funds and the State colleges of agriculture and experiment stations which received them. It also led to an increasing volume of coöperation between the technical divisions of the Federal Department and the corresponding divisions in the State colleges. The expansion of farming into semiarid and arid areas created problems which the frontier States were not equipped to solve, and thus led to larger Federal participation.

In many cases, the State departments of agriculture had undertaken investigations in various fields before the experiment stations were created, and continued to do so afterward. Considerable confusion and some difficulties arose from having two agencies within the State, generally separated geographically, undertaking many of the same functions. Similarly, questions arose about the relation of the U. S. Department of Agriculture to these two separate State agencies.

In regulation or control.—The second major development of this
period was the enactment of both Federal and State legislation,
and of municipal ordinances, for the regulation of various commercial practices. This was occasioned partly by the growing tendency
to organize larger and larger units of industrial development in
manufacture, commerce, transportation, and finance. Under the
rank individualism then prevailing, monopolistic tendencies developed rapidly, destructive competition was the rule, brazen frauds
were practiced, and the interests of the consuming public often
were ignored. Popular protest resulted in the beginning of that
long series of restrictive or control measures which characterizes
the period. The enforcement of these in turn led to increase of relation between many agencies at all levels.

Outstanding among the Federal laws were the Interstate Com-
merce Act of 1887 and its later amendments, the Sherman Anti-
Trust Act of 1890, the Meat Inspection Act of 1890, the Forest
Reserves Act of 1891, the Animal Quarantine Act of 1893, the
Lacey Wild-Life Conservation Act of 1900, the Grain Standards
Act of 1901, the Food and Drugs Act of 1906, the Plant Quarantine Act (Federal Horticultural Board) of 1912, and the Mi-
gratory Bird Act of the same year. A Federal Insecticide and
Fungicide Board was created in 1910. These are but samples of
the regulatory enactments, serving to show the wide scope of their
application in American life. Many of them were concerned with
fraud or discrimination in the manufacture or transportation of
agricultural products. Their enforcement required increasing collaboration between Federal agencies on the one hand and of these
agencies with official State agencies on the other.

Coincidently with the increasing volume of Federal legislation
exercising control over industry and interstate commerce, came
State legislation to the same ends. The Federal laws directly affecting agriculture are administered largely by the Federal Department of Agriculture, under rules and regulations prescribed by its
Secretary. At first, in certain States, the administration of laws
governing quality of seeds, feeding stuffs, fertilizers, and similar commodities, rested with the agricultural experiment stations.
Gradually, however, as the volume of such legislation increased
and the research activities of the stations became more and more

exacting, the enforcement of regulatory legislation was imposed upon or transferred to the State departments of agriculture—a process which is still going on. The Federal agencies coöperated with the State agency charged with enforcement.

Recent Period, 1913–1932

This recent period is characterized by the increasing expansion of the investigational and regulatory functions and the rise of a relatively new function, *agricultural extension,* to an equivalent position. Structurally it is characterized by the increasing coördination of these three functions and by a general trend towards operating each with a separate personnel and in separate units. The personnel outlook or perspective also has expanded from the scope of a division or bureau to that of the entire State institution or Federal department.

At first glance, there may seem to be no good reason for the separation of the middle and recent periods at the year 1913. Certain significant changes which had been taking place, however, became evident then and thus make the separation logical. These changes included a complete reversal of the historic position of the two great political parties on the question of enlarging the powers of the national government, the introduction of a new principle into the granting of Federal subsidies to the States, and a resulting enormous expansion of activities coöperative between the Federal and State governments. All of these antedated the entry of the United States into the World War, and the consequent period of stress which produced an enormous volume of official interrelations between international, Federal, Federal-State, and intrastate agencies.

The Democratic party, historic proponent of State rights and responsibilities, had completely reversed its position when it took over the Federal government in 1913. It became an outstanding proponent of enlarged Federal responsibility and participation, and the originator of new and large extensions of Federal operations in the States.

The new principle included in the granting of Federal money subsidies to the States was the so-called "50–50" plan, or the required matching of Federal grants, dollar for dollar, by State or local funds. It was applied in Federal legislation providing for agricultural extension, vocational education and rehabilitation, highway construction, forest protection from fire, and education in maternity hygiene and venereal diseases. The acts not only designated the purpose of the grant and required the matching of Federal funds, but also required the creation of a coöperating State agency, the preparation of a State program subject to Federal approval, and a final check of State performance by the Federal agency.

Similarly, there has been, recently, a large increase in Federal funds available to the State agricultural experiment stations. Beginning in 1925, the Federal contribution has risen gradually from $30,000 annually to $90,000 for each of the forty-eight States. The Purnell Act, like that of 1906, required Federal approval of projects financed thereby, as well as the customary annual report and auditing.

It must not be supposed that these transactions are financially one-sided. The various States have provided large sums for land, buildings, equipment, and personnel, totaling far more than the Federal subsidies, matched or unmatched. When the Federal legislation appropriating funds to be matched by the States was under discussion, fears were expressed that the States would make available only as much money for these activities as was required to obtain the maximum Federal grant. This fear has proved entirely groundless in the case of all the major coöperative activities, wherefor the State and intrastate contributions have become almost twice as large as the Federal grants.

Federal legislation in many cases has required Federal supervision of State activities. It has made joint Federal-State operation mandatory in some cases. So changed have become official attitudes that only coöperation instead of resentment or dissatisfaction has resulted from these legal requirements. Voluntary coöperation in nonmandatory activities also has been increasing very rapidly. While this is especially true of the strictly agricultural agencies, as will be shown conclusively in the several subject-matter chapters which follow, it is apparent in all fields of official activity.

Present Period, 1933–

A twenty-year recent period ended in 1932. A new period of unknown duration has begun. It is characterized by national planning for a regulated agricultural economy, including controlled production and land use. Investigation, regulation, and extension will continue to expand as basic functions, but planning will be the dominant function of the period. Development, organization, and coördination of agencies and functions will continue, but universal coöperation will be the dominant procedure. Personnel outlook or perspective also will expand from an institutional and departmental to a national scope.

3. PRINCIPLES AND ADVANTAGES OF COÖPERATION

FOR PRESENT PURPOSES, it is sufficient to summarize the progressive trend in the discussion of coöperation by those most intimately concerned with it in agricultural administration, teaching, research, and extension; to enumerate the general principles underlying the theory and practice of coöperation; and to present the advantages observed in its actual application.

STUDIES OF COÖPERATION AND PERSONNEL

In the past quarter of a century, increasing attention has been paid to the twin subjects of coöperation and personnel. While coöperation in fact is chiefly a matter of planned procedure, the development of the coöperative spirit and the initiation and maintenance of actual coöperation must rest with the personnel.

Discussions of Coöperation

Formulation and acceptance of principles and inauguration of practices come as the result of discussion and experience. This has been markedly true of progress in coöperation in agriculture. Discussions among workers and administrators, the presentation of papers before societies and organizations, and the recurring reports of committees charged with studying or effectuating relations, have kept the subject before the workers in agriculture and the related sciences. Experiments in coöperation have been scrutinized and their relative advantages and disadvantages presented and discussed. More and more heed has been given to procedure and personnel, as most profoundly influencing human relations.

The State colleges of agriculture and the U. S. Department of Agriculture are the principal public institutions having to do with the agriculture of this country. Both are represented in the Association of Land-Grant Colleges and Universities, which holds an annual convention for the presentation of papers, the hearing of committee reports, and the discussion of both. This Association has given large place to coöperation in its programs (2).* In the twenty-two years from 1912 to 1933, more than fifty papers discussing coöperation have been noted, besides the annual reports of the standing and special committees concerned with phases of Federal-State relations and often composed of both Federal and State representatives.

The authors of these papers have included the Secretary and other high officials of the Federal Department of Agriculture, and presidents, deans, and station directors from the land-grant institutions. Most of the writers have discussed both the pros and cons of coöperation, chiefly Federal-State, and have cited some or many of its advantages, which are summarized later in this subsection. Many of them have discussed both coöperation and personnel. Many papers not included in the fifty mentioned contain brief or incidental discussion of coöperation or of personnel and the problems they involve.

In 1925, a special conference of State and Federal officials concerned with agricultural research was held in preparation for the expanded research program to be financed by the Purnell Act. On request, a special discussion of the elements of successful coöperation in research was presented by the writer (4) as a Federal official of long experience. The discussion covered personnel, the principles and advantages of coöperation, and the attitudes and activities of the State stations and the Federal Department in coöperative research, both Federal-State and interstate.

Of the fifty or more papers alluded to above, eight dealt with the possibilities and advantages of coöperation among the State agricultural experiment stations themselves. Two papers presented

* Numbers in parentheses refer to the Literature Cited, at the end of the chapter.

in 1925 discussed the subject from both interstate and intrastate standpoints. The writer also reviewed interstate coöperation in the paper just now mentioned (4), and presented the standpoints of station directors during the preceding ten-year period (pp. 24–30).

Influence of technical organizations.—For substantially every subdivision of natural and economic science one or more societies or organizations of national or regional scope have been formed. Their membership comprises Federal, State, and local officials and private workers. Their program meetings promote the better acquaintance of workers, the discovery of mutual problems and interests, and the realization of the pleasure and profit of working together. These are the essence of coöperation. Symposium discussions and problem conferences held under their auspices have been potent in broadening perspective and in revealing the value of a combined attack on an overwhelming problem.

Almost all administrators and others who discuss coöperation and coördination in agricultural activities stress likewise the worth of conferences and other meetings of workers. Some of them point to the value of the annual meetings of the various national technical and scientific societies to which their workers belong. Some institutions assist workers to attend these official meetings. Many institutions allow them the official time required for such attendance.

Discussions of Personnel

Successful coöperation in agricultural activities depends largely on the attitude and reaction of the personnel involved. Attention to this phase of the problem, therefore, is amply justified. America's relative slowness in recognizing the personnel problem is owing, doubtless, to her strongly individualistic spirit. A corollary has been the habit of individual achievement for personal credit rather than of teamwork for the public welfare.

The last fifty years has seen a gradual but significant change in the American attitude toward matters of personnel. The passage of the Federal Civil Service Act in 1883 and the gradual extension of the idea to State and municipal government are concrete evidence of the change. The widespread attention to personnel problems by business organizations in late years shows how thoroughly the new idea has penetrated our national consciousness. Science and agriculture have not been behind, and in some ways have distinctly led the movement. Naturally, most attention given to the problem has been that of administrative bodies to the personnel making up their working force. In recent years, however, the rank and file of the personnel itself have been giving attention to the common problem.

Administrative and personnel viewpoints.—From the administrative standpoint, three somewhat distinct views have been developed. The first is that individuality is sacred, that the best work is done by the hermit in his secluded cell, without contact or interruption, and that, while coöperation may be desirable, it is practically impossible to achieve. The second view is that, however desirable coöperation may be, it must be wholly an individual concern and therefore cannot be planned for or required. If workers in different agencies wish to coöperate, all right. If they do not, nothing can or should be done about it. The third view, more recent and greatly increasing in acceptance, is that the methods and principles of coöperation can be taught, just as the principles of administration and the science of government can be taught, and that wise administrative action can bring about a much larger volume of coöperation than would otherwise come into being. Any discussion of personnel may be divided into a consideration of personnel as such and a consideration of standards or codes of ethics.

Substantially all papers which discuss coöperation in research give more or less attention to personnel. A few papers dealing especially with the personnel of research in agriculture are mentioned below. Two appearing in 1919 are worthy of mention; one is concerned with coöperation and individualism in scientific investigation (13), the other with democratic coördination of scientific efforts (25). These were followed in 1922 by an extensive and critical discussion of the scientist in the Federal service (6), which embodied a fine analysis of the individual worker and his opportunities and obligations, by a researcher and administrator of long experience. In the same year, before the Association of Land-Grant Colleges, an experiment-station director discussed the environment of the research worker as a human problem of station administration (2—36:165).

In 1925, a leader of agricultural extension presented before the

Association a paper on some aspects of a study of leadership (2—39:236) among extension workers. In 1926, the writer (3) presented an extensive discussion of personnel, personalities, and research, wherein the varying characteristics and attitudes of researchers were set forth.

The Federal Forest Service, which has widespread and intimate relation with other official agencies and with the general public, has given large attention to the training and the management of personnel. Region Five, covering California, considers these problems so important that it has issued a handbook on personnel management and procedure (23).

Codes or standards of ethics.—The Association of Land-Grant Colleges and Universities, as early as its convention of 1911, gave attention to the question of ethics in station work, which is largely a matter of personal attitudes. A series of three papers discussed such ethics as between individuals (2—25:151), as between the institution and the individual (2—25:146), and as between the institutions themselves (2—25:143). A further paper on institutional ethics was presented in 1919 (2—33:80).

In 1923, the Committee on Station Organization and Policy, of the Association, developed a tentative code of ethics for experiment station workers and presented it at the annual meeting (2—37:223). During 1924, the proposed code was referred to the directors of the fifty-five or more experiment stations with a request for submission to their station staffs. As a result, it was approved in principle by all except two, although nearly half of the directors suggested some modification and six thought that it was unnecessary to make a statement of principles. Their report, including the code as amended, was presented to the Association in that year (2—38:225).

In 1931, the Association of County Agricultural Inspectors of Kern County, California, published a code of ethics it had formulated (7).This was republished with discussion by the present writer (5). In 1933, a paper appeared on ethics among professors (8).

PRINCIPLES TENTATIVELY SUGGESTED

In all the voluminous writings on coöperation in the field of agriculture, briefly discussed above, little attempt seems to have been made to formulate its basic principles. Many writers have stated one or more of them, and have implied others. All that will be done here is to suggest those which appear desirable for consideration and then to proceed to a discussion of the more definitely recognized advantages. The tentative principles are as follows:

1. Coöperativeness is primarily a mental attitude and, as such, may be inspired and developed in individual persons.

2. Most persons are reasonable and therefore are willing to undertake coöperative activities if the advantages are recognized.

3. Coöperation is an additional means to effective progress under many conditions, but not a panacea for the solution of all problems.

4. Coöperation presupposes essential equality between the principals, rather than the relation of superior and subordinate. This principle does not require equal interest or contributions.

5. Coöperation, under proper conditions, has been observed to offer definite personal, technical, and financial advantages to the coöperating parties.

6. Coöperation is promoted (often unconsciously) by the mere fact of contact and conference by individuals, institutions, or organizations, on problems of common concern.

7. Coöperation is not universally desirable or expedient but only when advantages both to the principals and to their constituencies may be expected.

8. Coöperation, so far as it promotes personal harmony, increases individual efficiency, and avoids unnecessary competition, is an obligation upon the individual worker.

9. Coöperation, so far as it lowers costs and hastens effective progress toward planned objectives, is an obligation on the administrator.

10. Coöperation, to the extent that it increases individual efficiency, avoids unnecessary duplication, decreases costs, and hastens results to the constituency, is an obligation on organizations and institutions, especially those receiving public support.

From the preceding discussion, it is obvious that coöperation is a large potential factor of progress. Its importance warrants a fuller study of its principles, advantages, methods of promotion, and procedures.

ADVANTAGES RECOGNIZED

The principal advantages of coöperation have been shown to lie in three major fields, namely, (A) the promotion of better institutional and individual spirit, (B) the more effective advancement of knowledge, and (C) the definite saving of time, money, and materials. The distinctive ways in which coöperation accomplishes its objectives in each of these fields are listed immediately below.

A. Coöperation promotes better institutional and individual spirit and morale:

1. By avoiding a divided allegiance of constituencies within the area covered;
2. By obtaining better publicity, public sentiment, and appropriations;
3. By permitting better use of the talents of individual workers;
4. By stimulating workers through broader contacts and perspectives;
5. By itself begetting more coöperation.

B. Coöperation promotes a more effective advancement of knowledge:

6. By making possible a more rapid and comprehensive study of problems;
7. By manning projects more completely;
8. By preventing duplications and by standardizing methods to insure comparable results;
9. By reducing the time period necessary for obtaining results.

C. Coöperation conserves time, money, and materials:

10. By making data available promptly to all agencies concerned;
11. By requiring smaller expenditures from individual agencies;
12. By conserving and distributing material not locally usable.

The twelve advantages listed above are discussed briefly in the paragraphs which follow. Most of them have been presented at greater length in previous publications by the writer (2—35 :158; 4). In the second of these, references are made to other writers who have recognized the same advantages, though sometimes with more or different subdivisions. As Federal-State coöperation is the most common of the coöperative relations, most of the illustrations are drawn from that field.

1. Coöperation avoids the danger of a divided allegiance of the constituency within any State, such as might result if independent Federal operations were conducted or if two State agencies competed in the same or closely related fields. There is a real administrative danger in a divided allegiance within a State. Every official agency must depend on the good will of a benefited constituency for continued or amplified financial support. Where two State agencies compete for funds for essentially the same purpose, the rivalry takes on the aspects of a political campaign where the best advertising and not necessarily the best performance is likely to win. Funds for Federal activities are provided, of course, by the national representatives of State constituencies. If independent Federal activity within a State achieves beneficial results, it may obtain funds at the expense of a State agency, especially as Federal prestige often is higher than that of the more familiar State units.

Coöperation not only prevents rivalry for funds but, because of the advantages already mentioned, frequently commands a larger total endowment than the sum of those available to separate agencies.

2. Coöperation obtains better publicity for the results achieved, a better appreciation by appropriating bodies, and better financial support. Most official agencies are dependent on legislative bodies for their supporting funds. Legislators commonly are not specialists in agricultural activities. They must depend largely on technical information and public sentiment in determining the value of a given activity. Coöperative results have more news value, not only in the local press, but in the more widely circulated means of communication, and therefore are more likely to come under the eyes of those who influence support. The very fact that an enterprise is coöperative tends to give it greater prestige, and also provides it with more spokesmen. This favorable public sentiment, in turn, is likely to result in more favorable financial consideration.

3. Coöperation creates more opportunities for using the particular talents of a given worker to the best advantage. In the case of a complex problem, some workers are better fitted by training and preference for effective attack on one phase of the problem and others on other phases. A coöperative project, using several investigators, often is enabled to make a better distribution of work among the available personnel, from this standpoint, than otherwise could be done. This is advantageous through promoting more effective work and a better morale among the workers.

4. Coöperation tends to stimulate the associated workers. No station worker actually is isolated, unless on a small substation. He may be isolated, however, from much contact with other workers in his own particular field. If engaged in a coöperative problem with workers in other stations, the mutual operations, as well as occasional attendance on meetings and conferences, increase knowledge, quicken interest, strengthen appreciation, and enlarge production. This tends to keep the worker more keen, more alert, in better spirits, and in all ways better equipped for his work.

5. Coöperation begets more coöperation. There is a saying that nothing succeeds like success. In other words, success sells itself. Coöperation has the same power. A little of it often leavens an entire lump. Not infrequently, the establishment of coöperation be-

tween two agencies has resulted in increased coöperation among
the members of each. Fundamentally, coöperation still is more a
matter of individual psychology than of anything in the way of
organization, principles, policies, or financial necessities. Nevertheless, it has increasing attention from those charged with the conduct of local, national, and international affairs in every field of human activity. Everywhere, the spirit of coöperation is increasing,
with the growing realization of its advantages, technically, financially, and in terms of human satisfactions. Coöperation surely has
been justified of her children. Now she has come into her own.

6. Coöperation makes possible a broad and comprehensive survey
and a correspondingly comprehensive study of all the phases of
the problem, especially if of wide geographic scope. Few problems
are of interest to a single State. When one State attacks a problem
of interstate scope, however, it seldom has made a study of the
broader aspects of the problem. Such failure may be due to lack
of funds, to lack of opportunity for travel in other States, to hesi-
tancy on the part of workers to enter the territory of other workers,
or to concentration on the local phases of the problem. On the other
hand, a single State may not have the range of environing conditions, the personnel, the funds, or the equipment for the comprehensive attack on a given problem. In Federal-State or interstate
coöperation, these limitations are removed.

7. Coöperation frequently enables a better manning of an activity than otherwise is possible. Appropriated funds are expended
for personnel, buildings, equipment, traveling expenses, etc. The
buildings and equipment of State agencies frequently can serve a
larger personnel than is locally available. Coöperating Federal
agencies with funds at hand can furnish personnel to make use of
existing State facilities, thus expanding personnel with relatively
little other overhead expense and permitting a much more effective
attack on the given problem.

8. Coöperation avoids unnecessary duplication, and permits sufficient standardization of methods to make results comparable—
wherever obtained. The necessary amount of duplication to insure
validity of conclusion is determined. Unnecessary and therefore
wasteful duplication is prevented. Sufficient standardization is required to guarantee that results obtained by all the coöperating

agencies will be comparable. Separate investigations, however creditable individually, lose some or all of these advantages.

9. Coöperation reduces the time necessary for obtaining results. In much research the time element is important, as in the control of a spreading disease or destructive insect. A single agency may be obliged to spread its limited funds and efforts over a long period in order to cover all phases of the problem within its State. Many agencies, pooling resources and allocating portions of a regional problem to different units, may make a rapid advance that otherwise would be impossible.

10. Coöperation enables important advances in scientific knowledge made at one point to become immediately available to all coöperating workers. New leads are likely to develop steadily as the attack on a problem progresses. The newly discovered facts, whether positive or negative, may make changes in program and procedure advisable. Where agencies are working independently, these desirable adjustments cannot be made until after the publication of the new facts by the discovering agency, thus slowing down progress and entailing continued expenditures for a less effective procedure. Under these latter circumstances progress necessarily is slow, while publication of its results often is delayed long beyond the finding of isolated though important facts. Through coöperation, on the other hand, the successes of one unit are used to the immediate advantage of all others without in any way detracting from the credit or the responsibility of each. Credit goes to the discoverer, immediately in the appreciation of his associates and eventually in the published report.

11. Coöperation relieves each individual agency or State of the expense of financing the study of all phases of problems common to two or more of them. If each State should undertake to solve all phases of the original problem independently, it would require a large expenditure. Where a Federal agency coöperates with a State or States, there usually is a great saving in the overhead for buildings, land, and equipment, for only the State agencies need provide these. This avoids duplication of stations, equipment, and publications, and leaves larger funds free for the employment of personnel. The principle holds where several States coöperate on a regional problem. The largest saving should be possible where one

or more Federal agencies coöperate with a group of States on a common problem.

12. Coöperation aids in conserving material which might otherwise be wasted or less completely utilized. What is a by-product to one institution may be of major importance to the work of another. In plant-breeding operations, for instance, large quantities of hybrid material are produced at considerable labor and expense. Because of the varying adaptations of different kinds of plants, only a small part of the resulting material is likely to have characters adapting it to the conditions where it is produced. Parts of the remainder, however, may have characters especially adapting them to other sections. Only regional coöperation can insure the salvaging of such material. Its exchange may speed up results and reduce expenses. Likewise, plant or animal products produced under controlled conditions for certain purposes, but of no further interest to the producer, may have the highest value as material for additional research by another worker. This has been true notably of material needed for vitamin studies.

4. Scope and Nature of Official Relations

It is difficult to realize the enormous scope and the very diverse nature of the official relations actual or possible in the field of agriculture alone. A bird's-eye view of these interrelations is presented below.

Classified List of Official Relations

International relations
Federal interunit relations
  Interdepartmental relations
  Departmental interbureau relations
  Bureau interdivisional relations
Federal-State interrelations
  Independent Federal activities
  State facilities utilized
  Mandatory relations
    Federal supervision
    Mandatory coöperation
  Voluntary relations
Interstate relations
  Governors' conference
  Legislators' association
  Coöperation of technical agencies

Intrastate relations
  State interunit relations
  Interdepartmental relations
  Departmental interbureau relations
  Bureau interdivisional relations
  State-local relations
  State-county relations
  State-county-municipal relations
  State-municipal relations
  Local interrelations
  Intercounty relations
  County-municipal relations
  Intermunicipal relations
  Municipal interunit relations
Federal-local relations

It must be understood that the interrelations are not confined to the relatively simple network suggested above, but may, and do, crisscross in every direction from level to level and unit to unit. It must be remembered, also, that coöperation made mandatory by legislation and coöperation developed voluntarily, suggested above under Federal-State interrelations, are found also at several other levels of relationship. In the same way, interrelations of legislative representatives are by no means confined to interstate affairs. Likewise, the subject-matter extent of coöperative relations presents an enormous diversity, and the nature of the coöperative relation itself varies widely.

The brief discussion which follows is arranged in the order of the items in the classified list. As indicated above, it is not intended to present a complete picture of the scope or nature of the relationships, but rather to illustrate each of the different fields.

INTERNATIONAL RELATIONS

National interrelations with respect to agriculture have not been especially numerous. They have developed farther in this field, however, than in many others, probably because agricultural products are prime necessities. It must be remembered that in general the nations are organized on a basis of competition rather than of coöperation. They compete for markets, for land areas and their natural resources, and for dynastic aggrandizement. It is not surprising that international coöperation is no farther advanced.

International relations in agriculture and the sciences contributing thereto have been developed to some extent in three separate fields, namely, meteorology, statistics, and exchange of plant and animal material. These are discussed more fully in the chapters on Climate, Agricultural Economics, and Plant Industry. The International Institute of Agriculture, at Rome, financed and directed coöperatively by many nations, including the United States, is an outstanding example.

FEDERAL INTERUNIT RELATIONS

The relations in this category may occur at any one of three levels— interdepartmental, departmental interbureau, or bureau interdivisional. Interdepartmental is used in a broad sense, including not only the ten executive departments of the Federal government but also the numerous independent executive establishments and the legislative and the judicial branches of the Federal government. The term departmental interbureau refers to relations between the major units of an executive department or comparable independent establishment. Similarly the term interdivisional refers to relations between the divisions or offices which comprise a bureau or comparable administrative unit.

Interdepartmental relations may be either mandatory under an act of Congress or wholly voluntary. They are likely to be most numerous in a period of national emergency such as that of the World War or the present economic depression. They may vary from the creation and operation of an interdepartmental committee to a minor coöperation on a special method of procedure or piece of apparatus.

Interbureau relations are more simple. They generally result from a common interest in a broad problem and may take the form of an interbureau Committee. On the other hand, they may be merely a temporary and informal arrangement for handling one part of a bureau problem which falls within the scope of another bureau.

Interdivisional relations within a bureau are of the same nature as interbureau relations but naturally on a somewhat smaller and more intimate scale. They may take the form of committees for the formulation and correlation of an attack on a broad problem, or of direct coöperation between two or more divisions on two different phases of a limited problem, or of assistance rendered by one unit to another in some minor outreach of a divisional problem.

There is no organization of Federal agencies comparable to the Association of Land-Grant Colleges and Universities and therefore no meeting of such agencies, nor is there any similar meeting of the units composing the U. S. Department of Agriculture.

FEDERAL-STATE INTERRELATIONS

The development and scope of Federal-State relations involve much of the philosophy and history as well as the practice of coöperation. They deserve and require a much more extended discussion than can be given logically in this cursory survey of interrelations of government at all levels, and will be treated, therefore, rather extensively in the succeeding sections of this chapter. It is sufficient, here, that they are the most extensive, the most carefully planned and documented, and the most abundantly financed of all of the official relationships in the domain of agriculture. In origin they are both mandatory and voluntary. It must not be suspected, however, that the relations originating in mandatory legislation are any less satisfactory, harmonious, or truly coöperative than those that have been developed voluntarily.

The major Federal-State relations are those between the Federal Department of Agriculture and the State colleges of agriculture in the interest of research and of extension, and between the Federal Department of Agriculture and the State departments or boards of agriculture in the interest of regulation. Many of the activities in extension and regulation reach down through the State official agencies to those of the counties also. Another extensive field of coöperation lies between the Office of Education in the Department of the Interior and the State colleges of agriculture and State universities, and between the Federal Board of Vocational Education, now a part of the Office of Education, and the colleges and high schools of the various States.

INTERSTATE RELATIONS

Interstate relations in general have about the same scope and nature as are found in the Federal-State relations, but on a more limited geographical scale. A few outstanding illustrations are given here.

In 1887, the directors of the State Agricultural Experiment Stations of New England, New York, and New Jersey held a conference on a problem common to their stations, that is, on the valuation of fertilizers. The conference was continued annually, with the discussion confined at first to the one subject. Later, the subject-matter scope was extended to cover the major problems common to the region, and the regional scope was stretched to take in Pennsylvania, Maryland, and Delaware. These conferences have resulted in the gradual formation of a research program which coordinates the activities of the stations in these eleven States and allocates certain problems or phases of problems to each.

The Association of Land-Grant Colleges and Universities, which meets annually in a three-day convention, is really a gigantic interstate coöperation in agriculture. Through program papers and discussions in its three sections on Agriculture (with three subsections—resident teaching, experiment-station work, and extension work), on Engineering, and on Home Economics; through its standing committees on organization and policy, reporting to the extension and experiment-station subsections respectively; through the Joint Committee on Projects and Correlation of Research, reporting to the Association's subsection on experiment-station work—through all these and in yet other ways it discusses and develops the principles and practice of coöperation among the stations as well as with the Federal agencies.

In a similar way, the National Conference of Commissioners on Uniform State Laws (1892), Governors' Conference (1908), National Association of Secretaries and Departments of Agriculture, American Legislators' Association (1925), Council of State Governments (1933), and many others, harmonize State viewpoints, discuss State problems, and engender the spirit of working together where coöperative action is desired. In the agricultural field there is much room for such interstate relations in the enforcement of quarantine regulations, control and eradication campaigns, and regional conservation programs, and more recently in the correlated national, regional, and State planning boards and their programs of coördinated development and rehabilitation.

INTRASTATE RELATIONS

The discussion of these interrelations can be disposed of so briefly that it seems scarcely necessary to separate the categories given in the tabular presentation.

State Interunit Relations

The relations which may develop between the departments and other establishments of State government, between the bureaus in any one of these departments, and between the divisions of a given bureau, are exactly comparable to the relations which develop between comparable Federal units. The discussion already given for the Federal setup, therefore, is equally applicable here.

State-Local Relations

The relations which develop between the State agencies and those of counties and municipalities are comparable to those which develop between Federal and State agencies. There may be mandatory relations, such as those between the State department of agriculture and the county agricultural commissioners, in California and elsewhere, or the extensive voluntary coöperation authorized by law and developed between State and county agencies in the Agricultural Extension Service.

Local Interrelations

In agriculture, the relations between counties, between counties and municipalities, or between municipalities themselves, are relatively very few. The interrelations of counties in agricultural quarantines, for instance, are developed mostly through State or Federal agencies, or both, rather than by direct action between counties. Between counties and municipalities, about the only agricultural relation lies in coöperation in fire protection for grain fields and other rural properties. In California, this relation between municipal and unincorporated territories has been developed fairly widely. While many relations exist between municipalities themselves, they naturally lie outside of agriculture.

FEDERAL-LOCAL RELATIONS

In general, Federal relations within the States touch local government agencies only through the intermediation of State agencies. In some cases, however, there are direct relations between a Federal agency and a county or city, though few concern agriculture and these mostly the control of local outbreaks of some pest, such as rats or termites.

5. Analysis of Federal-State Relations

FEDERAL-STATE RELATIONS have been of major importance since the beginning of the Republic. In fact, they were the chief cause of the break with the British Government. They loomed large in the conduct of the Revolutionary War, in the debates on the Articles of Confederation, and in the framing of the Constitution. They were the subject of acrimonious debate and of vigorous political campaign in the years that followed, and were one important cause of the Civil War. Federal-State relations still are important, for that matter, as discussions of New Deal legislation abundantly reveal. In the meantime, however, great progress has been made and Federal activities once controverted now are accepted as matter of course.

Federal-State relations may be classified roughly into four major groups, as shown below:

1. Federal activities, within the States, wholly independent of State agencies.

   a) Competitive or paralleling activities, such as surveys or researches within a State but wholly independent of State agencies, and sometimes without their knowledge. The establishment of independent Federal field experiment stations is a good example.

   b) Noncompetitive activities, such as Federal meat inspection, etc., or operations on the public domain.

2. Federal use of State-owned facilities (laboratories, stations, etc.) for intrastate work, without actual coöperation in the similar State activities conducted therein or administered therefrom.

3. Federal supervision, in some degree, of State standards, activities, and expenditures, mandatory under Federal law as a condition of Federal support.

   a) Supervision more or less nominal, as of the land-grant colleges of agriculture and mechanic arts, and the State agricultural experiment stations under the Hatch Act of 1887.

   b) Supervision mandatory and Federal approval of State projects and expenditures required, as of the Federal Adams (1906) and Purnell (1925) funds appropriated to the State agricultural experiment stations, although the resulting State research may be wholly independent.

   c) Coöperation mandatory in certain activities, and projects and expenditures requiring Federal approval, as in the Agricultural Extension Act, the Vocational Education Act, and the Federal Highway Act.

   d) Funds appropriated to the Department rather than to the States, but coöperation in activities mandatory, as in certain sections of the Clarke-McNary Forestry Act.

4. Federal-State coöperation in activities wholly voluntary. In this subdivision are included the great majority of the coöperative activities of the Federal and State agencies, supported by funds appropriated independently to the two coöperating parties, and inaugurated voluntarily because of the recognized advantages of coöperative procedure in those particular cases.

   a) Regional programs involving few to many States and usually two or more Federal bureaus.

   b) State programs separate for each State but similar in two or more States and correlated by the Federal agency.

   c) State programs having no particular relation to any other State, the Federal agency merely coöperating.

INDEPENDENT FEDERAL ACTIVITIES WITHIN THE STATES

Aside from its offices and laboratories in (or close to) the District of Columbia, which represent its exclusive field of action, the Federal government operates only in the States and Territories, where obviously there is the possibility of its coming into competition with the agencies of State and county governments. Agricultural activities conducted by Federal agencies within the several States but wholly independent of State agencies are of two classes, those paralleling normal State activities and therefore competitive with them, and those which do not parallel any usual State activity and therefore are noncompetitive. Both classes need discussion.

Federal legislation created the State colleges of agriculture and mechanic arts and the State agricultural experiment stations, and gave them continuing subsidies. More and more Federal supervision has been required under acts of Congress. In view of these facts, coöperation by Federal agencies in all competitive Federal activities within the States would have seemed natural. This, however, has not always been the case. The neglect to coöperate seems the more illogical in view of the mandatory coöperation in agricultural extension, highway building, etc., under recent legislation.

Competitive or Paralleling Activities

During the past forty or fifty years, the Federal government has inaugurated numerous activities within the States. Some of these have been undertaken not only without coöperation with State agencies but even without consultation, and sometimes without even the courtesy of a notice that such action was contemplated or had been begun. These activities have varied all the way from surveys to determine existing conditions, through the establishment of small field offices and laboratories, to the location of large and well-equipped experiment farms, comparable to State experiment substations and sometimes reaching almost the proportions of a State experiment station itself.

A few Federal experiment farms have been established through direct act of Congress, at the request of one or another local constituency which ignored the State station and sought Federal assistance on its local problem. Commonly, however, Federal activities have been located in States on the direct responsibility of some unit of the Federal Department of Agriculture. Such procedure by Federal agencies naturally has given rise to dissatisfaction and occasionally to open protest. The attitudes of the two groups of agencies concerned, namely, the State colleges of agriculture and the Federal Department, should be noted.

Viewpoint of the States.—Curiously enough, the forty-eight State colleges of agriculture, though independent and widely scattered, make a more coherent body than the Federal Department of Agriculture. This is largely because the Association of Land-Grant Colleges and Universities, formed in 1887, holds annual conventions for discussion of administrative and technical problems, and thus tends to bring about in its membership a greater cohesion, a more widespread appreciation of situations and problems, and a closer approach to uniformity of sentiment. Also, under Federal invasion of State areas through independent action, the State institution is the aggrieved party and therefore most likely to have pronounced opinions and to give expression to them.

The annual convention of the Association of Land-Grant Colleges and Universities has given much attention to this problem of independent Federal activities in the States. Its Joint Committee on Projects and Correlation of Research, which includes Department men also, has discussed this in many of its annual reports. Many station directors, also, have included it in the papers already referred to in the discussion on coöperation and personnel. The station attitudes regarding such Federal action have varied all the way from the feeling that it was not a matter of State concern, on through the desire that State officers be notified before or when such action was undertaken, to an increasing belief that all such activities should be coöperative with State agencies, even though no State funds are contributed directly to the projects.

In the survey of land-grant colleges and universities, made by the Department of the Interior in 1928, a brief discussion was given (24—2:592) of independent research by the Federal Department of Agriculture within the States. Of forty States reporting, twenty-four listed a total of fifty-one Federal stations maintained independently, these evidently being the data used by the committee later. Much other research than that connected with field stations was conducted independently by the Federal Department, but thirty-four States reported that no such action had been taken within the past five years without the knowledge of the State college and station, while only five reported that such action had occurred.

Report of Association committee.—Because the situation persisted, the Association in 1930 appointed a "Committee on Federal-State Relations in Research" which discussed all phases of this problem in its report (2—45 :514–22). It refers to the independent Federal field stations as "one of the most embarrassing features of Federal-State relations in agricultural research" (p.516). There were said to be fifty-one such field stations in 1928, located in twenty-four States, one State having as many as five and another four. Of these twenty-four States, fourteen reported that the research of these Federal field stations in their States was not correlated with the research program of the State station, four that it was partially correlated, and six that it was fully correlated. The stations were virtually unanimous in their belief that the Department, as far as possible, should avoid establishing field stations and that when their establishment was necessary they should be administered in coöperation with the State stations. Regarding all independent Federal research within States, most of the stations held to the view that while the consent of the State station director should not be a prerequisite, the director always should be informed, and should be kept acquainted with progress, but that no memorandum of agreement should be required.

The committee referred also to the still more numerous independently maintained Federal field offices and field laboratories located throughout the United States. These are small units, either without land area attached or with very small tracts to accommodate greenhouses, gardens, etc. The total number of these was not stated, but fifty-one were reported for California alone.

The final recommendations of the committee on Federal-State relations were four in number. First, that the Federal Department establish field stations or laboratories in any State only in definite coöperation, with memorandum of agreement and joint responsibility in planning and procedure and joint publication of results, irrespective of whether the work is maintained with Federal funds only or Federal and State funds jointly. Second, that the Federal Department inform a given experiment station of any Federal research either conducted or proposed in its State, whether maintained by Federal funds alone or by Federal and State funds jointly, and that it furnish an outline of the objectives and proposed procedure and keep the station acquainted with progress and the resulting information. It was recommended also that in such cases the station offer suggestions for adapting projects to local conditions and offer such facilities as are available. Third, that the Federal Department recognize the State experiment stations as coöperators and not merely as contributors, when it undertakes to formulate and conduct projects of wide scope in which station coöperation would be desirable; and that it therefore propose to the interested station a joint responsibility in planning a project, adapting it to local needs, and interpreting and publishing the results. Fourth, that the Department consider whether present somewhat divergent policies in the several Bureaus regarding coöperative relations with the State stations could not advantageously be unified by designating some agency such as the Office of Experiment Stations to represent all the groups in Federal-State relations in research.

Viewpoints of the Federal Department.—Officially, the U. S. Department of Agriculture may be considered favorable to the principle of coöperation. Various Secretaries of Agriculture and other high officials, in addressing the Association of Land-Grant Colleges and Universities through the years, have expressed themselves as being heartily in favor of the most complete collaboration between the Federal and the State agencies. Many members of the staff of the Department, in publishing papers delivered before the Association and elsewhere, have approved coöperation in the States in principle and practice. An increasing number of Bureaus and Divisions within the Department have conducted their field work within the States with a steadily growing percentage of coöperative relations. Certain other facts, however, need mention.

The Department of Agriculture itself has no annual or regular meeting of any kind, let alone a meeting comparable in scope and purpose to that of the land-grant college Association. At such meetings as are held there is little in the way of assigned and prepared

programs. It has created no effective way of achieving unity of
opinion or consistency of procedure through discussion of problems and methods. Very few Federal administrators or researchers
regularly attend the meetings of the Association and therefore the
majority do not hear the recurring discussions or sense the dissatisfaction felt by State agencies.

It seems a fair assumption that if such an annual meeting were
held, for presentation and discussion of administrative problems,
it would go far toward developing a singleness of purpose and procedure on the part of Departmental units in their relations with
State agencies.

Secretaries of Agriculture usually have a short tenure of office,
much shorter than the average for a station director. Partly because of this limited tenure and partly because of the large size
and complex problems of the Department, the Secretary seldom,
if ever, has the same personal and influential relations in the Department which the director usually bears to the staff and activities of his station. On the other hand, Bureau chiefs are relatively
permanent and relatively independent of the Secretary as compared to a station department chief in relation to his director.
Until recently, many of the Federal Bureau chiefs were elderly
men who attained to administrative position before collaboration
had been widely developed. Some of these men never developed the
coöperative spirit which alone can produce just and harmonious
relations with State agencies. The new group of younger men, now
succeeding them, mostly have had a wider experience in coöperative action.

The consequence is that the Department itself, apparently, has
never officially adopted the principle of coöperation or recognized
an obligation to eliminate competition and insure more harmonious
and effective relations with the States. Members of the Department
staff who are coöperatively inclined have developed coöperation
extensively, but those who are not so inclined have felt no obligation to do so. Because of replacements of administrative personnel,
the growing spirit of coöperation, and the increasing number and
complexity of Federal-State interrelations owing to emergency
activities, progress is being made. It now seems probable that the
Federal Department soon will adopt coöperation as its official prin-

ciple and working practice in all possible activities conducted within the States.*

Noncompetitive Activities

Numerous agricultural activities of the Federal government within the States do not directly touch the fields normally occupied by State agencies and therefore are noncompetitive and not looked upon with disfavor. Among these are the Federal meat inspection, operated in all requesting plants which ship in interstate commerce; certain other regulatory activities located at the larger marketing centers, such as the enforcement of the Packers' and Stockyards Act, the Cotton Futures and Grain Futures Acts, and similar types of legislation; the construction of irrigation enterprises by the Federal Bureau of Reclamation; the agricultural operations of the Indian Service of the Department of the Interior on Indian reservations, and the grazing activities of the Federal Forest Service within the national forests.

FEDERAL USE OF STATE FACILITIES WITHOUT COÖPERATION

Federal use of State facilities may be obtained for activities which are noncompetitive, as in the case of quarters and equipment furnished the Federal census supervisors in some States. These cases need no discussion.

When a Federal agency makes permanent or long-continued use of quarters or other facilities of a State agency while conducting activities closely paralleling those of the State agency, new questions necessarily are raised. Should acknowledgment of the facilities furnished, printed on local letterheads and in resulting publications, be sufficient? Or should true coöperation be established and thereafter acknowledged in the usual ways? Certain interesting examples of this Federal-State relation come to mind.

One marked instance is that of the California Forest and Range Experiment Station, a unit of the Federal Forest Service, which occupies a suite of twenty-six rooms in Giannini Hall, one of the College of Agriculture buildings at the University of California.

---

* In 1935 the Secretary of Agriculture, in approving and putting into effect the recommendations of a Departmental committee on principles and procedures for the newly organized Soil Conservation Service, virtually made Federal-State coöperation a basic principle in their activities.

This Federal station is given not only quarters but also water, heat, light, and janitor service without charge by the University. On another floor of the same building is located the College of Agriculture Division of Forestry, which also conducts forestry research. The two units are not coöperating in their research programs, although engaged in similar and competitive activities within the State of California. The Forest and Range Experiment Station in its publications makes no mention of the above-named facilities furnished by the State, amounting annually to several thousands of dollars in actual value.*

The Citrus Experiment Station at Riverside, a branch of the University of California Agricultural Experiment Station at Berkeley, provides office room and other facilities of the station, including its experimental orchards, to the workers of certain units in the Federal Bureau of Plant Industry. Since 1909, the present Federal Division of Horticultural Crops and Diseases has used these facilities in its study of the improvement of citrus fruits through bud selection. In 1928, the Division of Western Irrigation and Agriculture was accorded similar facilities to study the boron content of irrigation water and the soil solution, and the tolerance of boron by different kinds of orchard crops. The Bureau of Plant Industry regards these activities as coöperative with the Citrus Experiment Station and so lists them and others in its *Directory of Field Activities* (16—129). The director of the station, however, does not regard these relations as truly coöperative, because the work, though done partly or wholly on the station property, is conducted entirely independently. As the station has no part in the planning of the projects, in the manner of their execution, in the interpretation of results, or in their publication, he regards the relation merely as a case of friendly courtesy in providing services.

MANDATORY FEDERAL RELATIONS TO STATE ACTIVITIES

The varying degrees of mandatory relations have been tabulated at the beginning of this section and illustrative instances cited. As those germane to agricultural education, research, and extension

---

* Since the above was written, a single instance of the Federal recognition of this coöperation has been noted, namely in *Technical Bulletin* No. 408 of the U. S. Department of Agriculture, issued in 1934.

have been discussed in full in the chapter on Agricultural Education, only a summary need be given at this point.

In general, it may be said that while the relation may be mandatory, the spirit of the Federal supervising agency is that of participation rather than administration. For the most part, therefore, these relations have resulted in practically as complete coöperation as exists where the relation is wholly voluntary. This is a tribute to the administrative personnel. It is the testimony of many States, also, that the mandatory programs and procedures are more definite and therefore more effective than many of those developed under voluntary activities. These points have been developed in reports of the Committee on Experiment Station Organization and Policy and the Joint Committee on Projects and Correlation of Research, as well as in many individual papers presented at the annual meetings of the Association of Land-Grant Colleges and Universities. These types of relationship were discussed in the *Survey of Land-Grant Colleges and Universities,* in the chapters concerned with control and administrative organization, agriculture, military education, extension service, and research. They were treated also in the two-volume report of the National Advisory Committee on Education, *Federal Relations to Education* (10). They likewise were considered in the report of the Association's Committee on Federal-State Relations, under such headings as the Function of the U. S. Department of Agriculture in Research, National Programs in Research, Over-organization of Research, and Nationalization of Agricultural Research. These committees are discussed more fully in the next section, under the topic, Creation of Coöperative Committees.

Mandatory Reports and Advisory Relations

The original Morrill Act of 1862 required each land-grant college to make an annual report to the Secretary of the Interior. The Second Morrill Act of 1890 provided that such an annual report be made to the Secretary of Agriculture as well. The Hatch Act of 1887, creating the State experiment stations, made it the duty of the U. S. Commissioner of Agriculture to furnish advice and assistance to the stations, to indicate from time to time such lines of inquiry as seemed to him most important, and to furnish forms, where practicable, for the tabulation of results of investigations. The stations, in turn, were required to make a detailed annual report to the Governor of the State and to furnish a copy of it to the Federal Commissioner of Agriculture and to the Secretary of the Treasury. In a special instance, nutrition investigations, the Secretary of Agriculture was authorized in 1894 to require that all stations report to him the results of their independent investigations.

Mandatory Federal Approval and Supervision

In 1893, the Secretary of Agriculture pointed out to Congress that no national officer was authorized to direct, limit, control, or audit the itemized expenditure of Federal appropriations to the State experiment stations. In 1894, the Congress stipulated that the Secretary should prescribe the form of the previously required annual financial statement, ascertain if expenditures were in accordance with the original act, and report thereon to Congress. The stations approved heartily, feeling that this action would protect them from irresponsible charges of misuse of Federal funds and would strengthen the relation between the Federal and the State agencies.

The Adams Act of 1906, appropriating additional Federal funds to State agricultural experiment stations, specified that the money should be expended only for original research and experiments bearing directly on the agricultural industry, required an annual report from the stations to the Secretary of Agriculture, charged him with proper administration of the law, and required him to withhold moneys if the stations did not comply with the law. These restrictions necessitated station submission of projects for Federal approval before expenditures were begun. The Purnell Act of 1925, still further enlarging Federal appropriations to State stations, specified funds for certain lines of research, placed on the Secretary of Agriculture the same responsibility for administration, and thereby entailed the same procedures.

Mandatory Federal Supervision and Coöperation

In 1914, the Federal Congress established a new principle, the so-called "50-50" or fund-matching plan, in appropriating funds for activities within the States. It required that each Federal dollar appropriated for a given activity be matched by the State or local governments. The laws specified that a State agency should be designated or created, that the activities should be coöperative between the Federal and the State agencies, that the Federal agency should be responsible for State compliance with the requirements of the legislation, and that the State agency should report annually in detail. These acts again necessitated that the Federal agency should consider and approve projects before funds were expended, and that it supervise State activities sufficiently to be able to certify that the requirements of the law had been met. The most important pieces of legislation of this type were the Smith-Lever Act of 1914 establishing coöperative agricultural extension, the Federal Highway Act of 1916, the Smith-Hughes Act of 1917 providing for coöperative vocational education, the Civilian Rehabilitation Act of 1920, and the forestry extension section of the Clarke-McNary Forestry Act of 1924.

Mandatory Coöperation but Funds Appropriated Only to Federal Agency

The Clarke-McNary Forest Extension Act of 1924 illustrates mandatory coöperation in activities financed by funds appropriated directly to the Federal Department of Agriculture without provision for State matching or for allocation of funds to States. The Secretary is authorized and directed to coöperate with the various States in the procurement, production, and distribution of forest tree seeds and plants for the purpose of establishing windbreaks, shelter belts, and farm wood lots upon denuded or nonforested lands within such coöperating States.

VOLUNTARY FEDERAL-STATE COÖPERATION

This division includes a great range of coöperative activities financed from funds appropriated by Congress directly to the Department and by Congress or legislatures directly to the State agencies, without any mandatory requirements as to coöperation in their expenditure. In the outline of classified relationships at the beginning of this section, three types of wholly voluntary coöperative programs were indicated, namely, regional programs, correlated State programs, and individual State programs.

Regional projects generally are conducted under a committee

composed of Federal and State representatives. The six regional Purnell Act projects were carried on by five regional committees created by the Association of Land-Grant Colleges and the Department of Agriculture. Other similar projects, such as the extensive study of the economics of the combined harvester-thresher, and the control of the corn borer, are arranged by Departmental inter-bureau committees through personal contact with corresponding State experiment station workers.

Examples of projects coöperative between a Federal agency and individual States but correlated into a regional program through the medium of the Federal agency are relatively numerous. The Plant Industry Division of Cereal Investigations in its study of dry-land cereal production coöperated with the State stations in the Great Basin and Pacific Coast areas, but so correlated the experiments that it was possible to publish a joint bulletin covering contributions from two or more of the States (15). Somewhat similar relations occur in its maize-breeding program. The Division of Dry-Land Agriculture has a series of rotation and tillage experiment stations, conducted partly in coöperation with individual States of the Great Plains, but correlated to a regional attack on the problem.

6. PRACTICE OF FEDERAL-STATE COÖPERATION

AN ANALYSIS of the actual and potential scope of Federal-State relations has just been made. The actual practice in this most important field of government interrelations deserves illustration.

The practice of coöperation is evidenced by the creation of coöperating committees, the development of coöperative agreements, and the recognition given in publications to the fact of coöperation, as well as by the increasing number of coöperative projects.

CREATION OF COÖPERATING COMMITTEES

One of the evidences of increasing Federal-State coöperation in agriculture has been the growing number of committees representing both sets of agencies. Substantially all such joint or coöperating committees have been created since 1913, the year which marked the beginning of what was designated above as the recent period in the historical development of coöperation.

Many of these committees are the joint products of the Association of Land-Grant Colleges and Universities and the U. S. Department of Agriculture. Others represent coöperation between one of these and some other agency. A third group has arisen through the promotion of definite coöperation between different Federal agencies in the solving of specific problems, while a fourth group represents similar relations between groups of States. To these might be added the many committees created to promote effective coöperation between two or more Bureaus of the Department of Agriculture or some other Federal Department, between the different departments or institutions of a State government, or between the component units of a Federal Bureau or a State department or institution.

This significant development may be illustrated by a discussion of the creation, objectives, and duration of committees representing the more important classes listed above.

The Land-Grant College Association and the Federal Department of Agriculture

Many coöperating or joint committees have been created by or through the Association of Land-Grant Colleges and Universities. Some have been appointed by the Federal Department of Agriculture with the assistance of the Association. Others have been created by the two agencies jointly.

The Association itself maintains three groups of committees: standing committees, joint committees, and special committees. Representatives of the Federal Department of Agriculture appear in some of the committees of all groups and in all of the joint committees comprising the second group.

Standing committees.—Among the standing committees, eight or nine in number in recent years, are two on which Federal members serve regularly. These are the Committee on Instruction in Agriculture, Home Economics, and Mechanic Arts (1896), and the Committee on Experiment Station Organization and Policy (1906). The latter committee at first was composed entirely of station officials but, in 1911, a member of the staff of the Federal Office of Experiment Stations was included as one of the six members, while in recent years the number of Federal members has been increased to two. The annual reports of these committees are published in the *Proceedings* of the Association (2).

Joint committees.—Three permanent committees subsequently known as joint committees were created by the Association of Land-Grant Colleges and Experiment Stations at its meeting held in 1913, as noted above, to represent the Association in certain of its relations with the U. S. Department of Agriculture.

The first was a general committee on relations. By vote of the Association, the Executive Committee itself was empowered to act as Committee on Relations with the Federal Department of Agriculture, in conjunction with such committee as the Department might designate. For several years this committee was listed in the annual volume of *Proceedings* merely as the executive committee, but from 1920 to 1922 the entry read: "The Executive Committee of the Association and the Committee on State Relations of the U. S. Department of Agriculture." After 1922, this latter committee disappears from the record altogether.

The second of the joint committees was the Committee on Projects and Correlation of Research, which passes on coöperative research projects and problems. It consists of six members, three from the Association and three from the Federal Department of Agriculture, each agency selecting its own representatives. This committee continues.

The third was the Committee on Publication of Research, which is responsible for the *Journal of Agricultural Research* (9), containing papers originating in both agencies but financed by the Federal Department of Agriculture. It is constituted like the preceding committee, and has been continued.

At first the Association published annually, in its *Proceedings,* only its own membership on these two last-named joint committees, but from 1920 onward it has included the Department members.

Special committees.—The Association of Land-Grant Colleges and Universities has created many special committees in recent years. Several of these have used members of the staff of the Federal Department of Agriculture either as active members or as advisors. Most of these committees have been created since the great expansion of State experiment station research beginning in 1925.

Agricultural terminology: In the *Proceedings* (2—29) of the meeting of 1915, a "Special Committee on Agricultural Terminology" is listed, with two members from the Federal Office of Experiment Stations and three from the Association. This committee last appears in the *Proceedings* for 1918, but no reports of its activities have been found.

Radio problem: A "Special Committee on the Radio Problem" was created at the meeting of the Association in 1925 and reported at the meeting in 1926 (2—40:407). Originally there were no Federal representatives on this committee, but two officers of the U. S. Department of Agriculture were asked to act as advisory members in connection with legislation pending before Congress in the spring of 1926. The original committee was discharged, but in 1927 the Executive Committee appointed a new "Special Committee to Give Attention to the Radio Problem." This committee worked in close coöperation with officials of the Federal Department of Agriculture on pending legislation. After reporting in that year (2—41:431), it was established as one of the standing committees of the Association.

Special Research Committees: The Purnell Act of 1925 provided increased Federal funds for research by the State agricultural experiment stations and specifically authorized investigations to cover home economics, agricultural economics, and rural sociology. In order to formulate programs and coördinate the research in these new fields, several "Special Purnell Committees" were created by the Association. From 1929, they were called Special Research Committees. Each of them contained at least one Federal representative drawn from the field of its subject matter.

The five committees were as follows: on Vitamin Content of Food in Relation to Human Nutrition; on Factors which Influence the Quality and Palatability of Meat; on Distribution and Marketing of Farm Products and on the Problem of Surpluses of Farm Products; on Rural Social Organizations and Agencies Essential to a Permanent and Effective Agriculture; and on Rural Home Management Studies. From 1925 to 1930, the committees on vitamin research and rural home management reported annually to the Section on Home Economics. From 1927 to 1930, these five committees were listed in the roster published annually.

Committee on land utilization: In 1929, the question of holding a national conference on land utilization was referred to the Executive Committee of the Association with power to act. In 1931, a land-utilization conference was called jointly by the Secretary of Agriculture and the Executive Committee of the Association, to follow immediately the sessions of the Association. The conference created two national committees. The first, known as the National Land-Use Planning Committee, was composed of five representatives of the Federal Department of Agriculture, five representatives of other Federal agencies, and five representatives of the Association of Land-Grant Colleges and Universities. This Association committee, listed in the *Proceedings* for 1932, held nine meetings during 1932 and 1933, and its report was published in 1933 in the *Proceedings* (2—47:48). It recommended that the Association appoint a new committee, to coöperate with the Department of Agriculture and other Federal agencies concerned, and this was approved.

Committee on relations with the Department of Agriculture: At the Association meeting in 1930, the subsection on experiment station work suggested that a committee be appointed to study coöperation between the Federal Department of Agriculture and the State agricultural experiment stations. The committee appointed reported in the following year (2—45:514) and again in 1933 (2—47:159), but it is not listed in any of the *Proceedings* and was not, in fact, a coöperating committee. Its findings have been presented under Analysis of Federal-State Relations (see p. 28, above).

The Land-Grant College Association and Other Federal Agencies

Committee relations similar to those between the Association of Land-Grant Colleges and Universities and the Department of Agriculture have developed between the Association and other Federal agencies. Other types of coöperating committees likewise have been created by Federal and State units of government.

Coöperation with the Department of the Interior.—There are certain mandatory relations between the land-grant colleges and the Office of Education in the Federal Department of the Interior. Apart from these, certain coöperative committee relations have developed between the two agencies.

Committee on statistics of higher education: At the meeting of the Association in 1915, a staff member of the Federal Office (then Bureau) of Education presented by invitation a paper on the relations of the Bureau to the agricultural colleges (2—29:140). In this paper he outlined a "committee on higher educational statistics" which the Bureau was organizing from representatives of various associations of institutions concerned with higher education and invited the Association of Land-Grant Colleges and Experiment Stations to appoint one representative to this committee and to take part in its proposed activities.

Coöperation with the Federal Office of Education and National Advisory Committee: For several years before 1926, the executives of the land-grant colleges had been discussing the desirability of a comprehensive survey of the history, objectives, and accomplishments of those institutions. Early in 1926, the Association, with the advice of the Secretary of Agriculture, invited the Federal Office of Education to coöperate in such a survey. The invitation was accepted with the provision that the Office should direct the work and publish the results. A special appropriation was made by Congress and a "National Advisory Committee" set up under the chairmanship of the Secretary of the Interior, including the Secretary of Agriculture and representatives of State universities, agricultural colleges, technical colleges, agricultural experiment stations, home economics departments, and State departments of public instruction. One member directly represented the Association of Land-Grant Colleges and Universities. In addition, fifteen special advisory committees representing subject-matter departments and groups were created, largely from the staffs of the land-grant colleges and universities. Furthermore, each such institution arranged for a local coöperating committee within the institution. The survey staff itself included a large number of specialists from these institutions, loaned for different periods of time to review the findings and write portions of the resulting manuscript, which was published in two large volumes (24).

This piece of coöperation is to be distinguished from the Association's lesser concern with quite another "national advisory committee," next to be considered.

Coöperation with the national advisory committee on education: In 1929, the Association appointed a committee of seven as a "Committee to Coöperate with the National Advisory Committee on Education." This was the result of a recommendation from the Director of the American Council on Education, who was chairman of the advisory committee as appointed by the Secretary of the Interior. The Association's committee was listed among its other special committees from 1929 to 1932. In 1931 and again in 1932, it presented reports regarding legislation proposed and enacted in the interest of vocational education and a national Department of Education (2—46:484). At the meeting in 1933, the committee was discharged, for the National Advisory Committee on Education had published (10) a two-volume report and ended its labors.

Coöperation with Federal Farm Board.—In 1929, the Association, after considerable discussion, authorized its executive committee to add five members to its number for the purpose of acting as a "Committee to Coöperate with the Federal Farm Board." It was listed with other committees from 1929 onward. This was not in any sense a joint committee, and apparently there was no comparable committee established by the Federal Farm Board itself. Its reports were made to the Executive Body of the Association and appear in the *Proceedings* from 1930 to 1932, after which the committee was dissolved because the Federal Farm Board had been abolished and its functions largely absorbed by the Farm Credit Administration.

Coöperation with the Tennessee Valley Authority.—After considerable discussion of the increasing coöperative activities within the Tennessee Valley area, the Association, in 1933, appointed a committee of three members to confer with the Tennessee Valley Authority and ascertain whether it would be desirable for the Association to create a committee to confer and advise with the Authority in regard to such features of its work as might fall within the province of the institutional members of the Association. The committee was appointed and reported that, after conference with officers of the Authority, it was understood that communications from the Association would be welcomed, but that apparently the Authority did not feel any need of a definite committee of coöperation.*

The Land-Grant Colleges and State or Scientific Organizations

The Association of Land-Grant Colleges and Universities has created committees from time to time to promote relations with State agencies and scientific organizations. These are mentioned briefly.

Committee on affiliation with scientific societies.—In 1909, the Association of Agricultural Colleges and Experiment Stations created a "Committee on Affiliation" to consider the possibility of holding its meetings and those of various national scientific organizations during the same time and at the same place. The committee recommended inviting such societies to meet on the day before the meeting of the Association. It made a further report in 1910.

Coöperation with State boards of agriculture.—In 1917, the Committee on Field Work, of the National Association of Commissioners of Agriculture, submitted to the land-grant college Association a report outlining the proposed fields of work of the State departments of agriculture. It recommended the transfer of their educational and extension activities to the State colleges of agriculture and the transfer of all regulatory functions from these institutions to the State departments. These proposals were approved by the latter Association. In 1925, the matter was discussed again in the land-grant college Association because of the enlarged functions of both groups of institutions and because of some confusion of thought and violation of accepted procedure which had developed. In 1927, the Association authorized a special committee to take necessary action. In 1928, this committee reviewed the history of the matter (2—42:465) and recommended that a thorough study of the relation then existing should be made. This investigation was made through correspondence and the entire subject given an extensive review at the meeting in 1929 (2—43:451). The Association then reaffirmed its approval of the generally understood line of division between the two sets of institutions.

---

* Since 1934 the Authority has been coöperating heartily with a regional group of land-grant colleges, and with Federal agencies, in their far-reaching program of research·and extension on agricultural problems in the Tennessee Valley area. More recently it has developed widespread coöperative activities with these colleges in States outside this area.

Committee to confer with the National Association of State Universities.—In 1927, the executive committee of the Association of Land-Grant Colleges and Universities was authorized to negotiate with the National Association of State Universities, either directly or through a special committee, in order to bring about closer working relations between the two organizations. In 1929, the land-grant college Association appointed a committee to negotiate with a similar committee from the university Association on a more satisfactory arrangement of time and dates for meetings of the two organizations in order that individual members of both bodies might be able to attend both sessions. The two committees reached an agreement which was approved by the two associations.

At the convention of the land-grant college Association in 1930, the committee on radio problems was ordered to coöperate with the similar committee of the National Association of State Universities. A member directly representing the Executive Body of the former Association was added to its radio committee.

FORMULATION OF COÖPERATIVE AGREEMENTS

There is the widest possible variation in the types of agreements under which coöperative enterprises are carried forward. Within limits, this is natural and desirable. There is an extremely wide range of conditions and degrees of relationship in coöperative undertakings. Agreements may be grouped roughly as informal and formal. Informal agreements may represent merely a verbal understanding between two agencies or may result from a written proposal and a subsequent written acceptance of the proposal as a basis for operation.

Formal agreements may include the details of operation or they may set forth only the objectives and the principles under which procedure takes place. In each case, they may be so written as either to require annual renewal or to continue in force until terminated. In general, the trend has been from the detailed formal agreement, renewable annually, to that which sets forth merely the objectives, together with the principles governing the conduct and termination of operations, the publication of results, etc., and continues until terminated by official action.

In the various discussions of coöperation and personnel to which reference has been made, it was pointed out by many writers that while agreements are desirable and sometimes necessary, they are only as good as the personnel that enforces them or operates under them. In other words, the terms of a perfectly satisfactory agreement may be jeopardized by a forgetful or noncoöperative administrator or worker. On the other hand, a true coöperative spirit among officers and workers makes a formal agreement practically a forgotten document.

Coöperative agreements between Federal and State agencies occur in all the three major fields of agricultural activity : research, extension, and regulation. In the case of research, the coöperative agreement is between the Federal Bureau and a State experiment station, and is signed by the Chief and the Director, respectively. In the case of extension, it is between the Federal Department of Agriculture and the State college of agriculture, and is signed by the Secretary of the one and the President of the other. In regulatory activities, coöperation is between the Federal Bureau and the State agency, usually the State department of agriculture.

Coöperative Research Agreements

There has been a greater diversity of practice regarding coöperative agreements in research than elsewhere. This is because coöperation in research activities developed rather earlier than in the other two fields, and because little administrative attention was paid to coöperative relations in the earlier years. In recent years, the complexity of problems, the enormous increase in projects, and the requirement of Federal approval of certain types of State station projects, all have combined to focus administrative attention on the scope and nature of coöperative agreements. This has resulted in greater uniformity and considerable simplification. The tendency now is to specify only the major principles governing the mutual activity, including the objectives sought, the general responsibilities of each agency, the provision for publication of results, and finally, the method of terminating the agreement if and when desirable.

Such a blanket agreement often covers several very definite projects. For instance, work under an agreement to conduct coöperative experiments in the improvement, production, and protection of

cereal crops might start with a project on improvement of wheat
and gradually extend in the course of years to similar projects on a
half dozen other cereals and the control of their diseases, without
requiring any change in the coöperative agreement. The text of
such a standardized agreement is reproduced herewith, on pages
47–49.

MEMORANDUM OF UNDERSTANDING
<small>BETWEEN</small>
THE ——— AGRICULTURAL EXPERIMENT STATION
<small>AND</small>
THE BUREAU OF PLANT INDUSTRY
UNITED STATES DEPARTMENT OF AGRICULTURE
<small>RELATIVE TO</small>
THE PRODUCTION, IMPROVEMENT, AND DISEASES OF CEREAL CROPS,
PARTICULARLY CORN, OATS, WHEAT, AND BARLEY
Effective April 1, 1935

The ——— Agricultural Experiment Station ——— and the Bureau of
Plant Industry recognize that coöperation is a matter of working together
to a common end, rather than one of financing, each agency contributing what
it can to the planning, conduct, and interpretation of the experiments as a
whole, and furnishing such facilities and funds for particular experiments as
is practicable. To this end it is mutually agreed that all investigations on the
production and improvement of cereals and the control of cereal diseases undertaken by either agency in the State of ——— will be deemed to be coöperative.
Nothing in this broad understanding is to be construed as interfering with
the basic responsibilities of either party, and it is recognized that successful
operation can be only through mutual helpfulness.

The specific object of these coöperative investigations is to improve the
status of cereal production through (1) developing better cultural practices,
(2) producing varieties superior in yield and quality and more resistant to
disease and other factors adversely influencing production, (3) studying the
diseases of cereals and determining methods for their control, (4) developing and applying methods for utilizing and maintaining quality seed stocks,
and (5) determining the underlying principles concerned in the biology of
cereal plants, including research in genetics, cytology, and physiology.

It is understood that both the ——— Agricultural Experiment Station and
the Bureau of Plant Industry are interested in fundamental research, the Bureau of Plant Industry being concerned primarily with the results having
regional application, and the ——— Agricultural Experiment Station with
the results having local application.

A. The ——— *Agricultural Experiment Station agrees:*

1. To furnish suitable land for the coöperative work.

2. To furnish all necessary tools, machinery, and other farm equipment
unless otherwise mutually agreed upon.

3. To furnish necessary office and laboratory space, and such heat, light,
water, and gas for these as may be needed and available; and to furnish heat,
light, and water for such building or buildings as may be erected by the Bureau of Plant Industry at ——— for housing in part the coöperative work
on cereals.

4. To furnish such portion of labor and team or tractor work as may be
mutually agreed upon.

B. The Bureau of Plant Industry agrees:

1. To assign to these investigations, temporarily or permanently, such members of the Division of Cereal Crops and Diseases as may be necessary to assist in properly planning and conducting the work, and to pay their salaries and travel expenses or such portion as may be mutually agreed upon.

2. To provide, as far as possible, such cereal seeds or other plant material as may be of value in conducting the investigations.

3. To furnish supplies and such additional labor and team or tractor work as may be mutually agreed upon.

C. It is mutually agreed that:

1. The details of the coöperative work shall be planned and executed jointly by the ———— Agricultural Experiment Station through its Farm Crops and Soils, Botany, and Genetics Sections (and such other sections as may later be able to contribute to solution of the problems), and the Bureau of Plant Industry through its Division of Cereal Crops and Diseases. Project outlines covering the work and methods of procedure shall be prepared jointly, subject to revision by joint action as progress of the work justifies. Copies of these projects will be filed with the Director of the ———— Agricultural Experiment Station, the Heads of the Coöperating Sections or Subsections, and the Division of Cereal Crops and Diseases, Bureau of Plant Industry.

2. A complete report of the results of the experiments shall be submitted each year by the individual in direct charge of the coöperative work, one copy to be furnished to the ———— Agricultural Experiment Station and one copy to the Division of Cereal Crops and Diseases, Bureau of Plant Industry, such report to be delivered as soon after the close of the crop season as is practicable.

3. Either party to this agreement shall be free to use any of the results obtained in the coöperation in official correspondence, giving due credit to the other agency. It is understood that neither party will publish any results without consulting the other. Publication may be joint or independent as may be agreed upon, always giving due credit to the coöperation and recognizing within proper limits the rights of the individuals doing the work. In case of failure to agree as to manner of publication or interpretation of results, either party may publish data after due notice and submission of the proposed manuscript to the other. In such instances the party publishing the data will give due credit to the coöperation, but will assume full responsibility for any statements on which there is difference of opinion.

4. Either party shall be free to install such equipment as may be needed and otherwise unavailable. Equipment purchased from Federal funds shall remain the property of the United States Department of Agriculture, subject to removal or other disposition upon termination of this agreement. Equipment purchased from State funds shall remain the property of the ———— Agricultural Experiment Station, subject to its disposition.

5. New varieties or strains found through the coöperation shall be distributed for commercial growing within the State, as and when mutually agreed upon. A part of the seed of all new material developed during the coöperation

shall be available to either party for use in investigational work elsewhere. Surplus crops produced in the coöperation, not needed for experimental purposes, or not specifically covered by coöperative undertakings with other agencies, shall be the property of the ——— Agricultural Experiment Station, which agrees to make to the Bureau of Plant Industry such reports of sale of surplus as may be agreed upon.

6. The obligations of the Bureau of Plant Industry and the ——— Agricultural Experiment Station are contingent upon the action of Congress and the State Legislature, respectively, in appropriating funds from which expenditures legally may be made.

7. All Government funds expended in connection with these investigations shall be disbursed in accordance with the fiscal regulations of the United States Department of Agriculture, and all State funds shall be disbursed according to the fiscal regulations of the ——— Agricultural Experiment Station.

8. The parties to this agreement will expend on this coöperative work for the fiscal years indicated, approximately the amounts given below. These figures are inclusive of both cash expenditures and estimated values of facilities furnished:

	Fiscal year	
	1935	1936
Bureau of Plant Industry	$13,160	$14,520
——— Agricultural Experiment Station	14,000	14,000

Expenditures will continue approximately as indicated for the fiscal year 1936. Changes in amount may be made in advance of any fiscal year, provided that expenditures by the Bureau of Plant Industry shall not exceed $16,000 in any one fiscal year.

9. This memorandum shall become effective April 1, 1935, and shall continue to June 30, 1935, subject to renewal from year to year thereafter by mutual consent of the coöperating parties. Requests for termination or any major changes shall be submitted to the other party for consideration not less than ninety days in advance of the effective date desired.

(Date)   Director,
  ——— Agricultural Experiment Station

Head, Farm Crops and Soils Section

Head, Farm Crops Subsection

Head, Botany and Plant Pathology Section

Head, Genetics Section

(Date)   Chief, Bureau of Plant Industry

Approved..
   (Date)

Chief, Office of Experiment Stations

Coöperative Extension Agreements

In the field of extension, covering agriculture and home economics, the coöperative relations between Federal and State agencies, which began in about 1902, were covered by agreements of different types, depending upon the respective agencies and problems involved. After the passage of the Agricultural Extension (Smith-Lever) Act of 1914 and the unification and coördination of all the extension activities of the Federal Department of Agriculture, a standard type of coöperative agreement was adopted.

After these memorandums of agreement had been enforced for some two years, the Committee on Extension Organization and Policy of the land-grant college Association made a questionnaire survey to determine if operations were conducted satisfactorily thereunder. The committee considered the replies and the specific charges of violation of the agreements which were presented. The entire matter was then discussed at a joint conference of this committee, the Executive Committee of the Association, and representatives of the States Relations Service. At this conference, agreements were reached on all points of procedure under the memorandum of agreement. These points were reported by the committee to the Association at its meeting in 1916, and were published, together with a copy of the standard memorandum of understanding, in the *Proceedings* of that year (2—30 :134).

At first the standard agreement covered all phases of agricultural extension. Later a separate agreement was adopted for each major project or phase of the work, such as administration; the employment of county agents (advisors), assistant county agents, and home demonstration agents in the various counties of the State; and each of a series of subject-matter specialties such as agronomy, forestry, marketing, etc. These agreements are continuous until modified or terminated. A general annual agreement listing these project agreements is signed each year in connection with the annual budget.

Coöperative Regulatory Agreements

Regulatory activities are conducted on an extensive scale by three different Bureaus of the Federal Department of Agriculture, namely, Agricultural Economics, Animal Industry, and Entomology and Plant Quarantine. While coöperative agreements in the Federal Department of Agriculture have not been completely standardized, there is much more uniformity now than existed a few years ago. In most of these activities the coöperating agency is the State department of agriculture or some board or commission separate from the college of agriculture.

The Bureau of Agricultural Economics administers the Grain Standards Act, the Cotton Standards Act, the Standard Containers Act, the Federal Warehouse Act, and others. The Bureau of Animal Industry is charged with the enforcement of the various Acts covering animal quarantine and disease control or eradication campaigns, those governing the manufacture of viruses, serums, etc., and the Packers and Stockyards Act. The Bureau of Entomology and Plant Quarantine, formerly the Bureau of Plant Quarantine, administers the various domestic and foreign plant quarantines designed to prevent the introduction and spread of noxious insects and plant diseases.

PUBLICATION OF COÖPERATIVE RESULTS

In coöperation between a unit of the Federal Department of Agriculture and a State agricultural experiment station, especially in the research field, the results may be published by either agency. Most frequently they are printed in one of the series of publications of the Federal agency, or in the coöperatively managed and Federally printed *Journal of Agricultural Research* (9). There are several reasons for this, among them the following:

1. The Federal agency usually enters into coöperation on problems or those phases of problems which have at least regional, if not national, interest. Federal publication makes the results more readily available to interested persons in other States than the one coöperating.

2. Often the Federal agency has arranged coöperation with two or more State stations on different phases of the same regional problem. All agencies may decide to combine the coöperative re-

sults from all the States in a single publication. This is more logically issued from the Federal source than from any single one of
the States involved.

3. Many manuscripts reporting coöperative results are written at
the Federal headquarters, where joint employees often spend a
part of the winter season in making contacts with other workers,
using the library, writing reports, and preparing manuscripts. It
perhaps is only natural that a large percentage of such manuscripts
should be published by the Federal agency.

There are several ways in which Federal and State agencies
issue coöperative publications jointly, rather than as a publication
by one agency only. These are:

1. By inserting in the *Journal of Agricultural Research,* which
is published under the direction of an editorial board (Joint Committee) composed of three members of the U. S. Department of
Agriculture and three representing the Association of Land-Grant
Colleges and Universities.

2. By publishing in one of the series of Department Bulletins and
printing on the cover a statement that the publication also is a
designated number in the bulletin series of the coöperating State.
Thus *Department Bulletin No. 1091* of the U. S. Department of
Agriculture is stated on the cover to be *Technical Bulletin No. 1*
of the Arizona station, also.

3. By publishing in one of the series of the Department publications, the coöperating station at the same time purchasing a supply of the publication, without covers, and attaching a printed
State cover before distribution within the State.

4. By publishing in a single Federal publication data on a given
subject prepared on a national basis and similar data prepared
on a State-wide basis by one or more coöperating States, each
contribution occupying a separate section of the publication. The
interested States then purchase reprints of their own State contributions and distribute them within their borders, either with
or without a printed State cover. An example of such coöperative
action is *Department Circular 341,* covering recommendations to
farmers on increasing flax acreage in 1925 and containing the Federal recommendations and those of Minnesota, Montana, North
Dakota, and South Dakota.

To plan for coöperative activities, or to enter into coöperation as activities proceed, is relatively simple. To remember to acknowledge that coöperation during the pressure of preparing a manuscript is not so easy. The possibilities of acknowledgment in a publication, in ascending order, are about as follows:

No mention whatever at any point.

Footnote statement on first or early text page.

Textual statement placed in
  Letter of Transmittal;
  Preface or Introduction;
  Opening paragraphs of text;
  Paragraph of acknowledgment at end of text.

Cover and/or title-page statement, placed
  On outside of front cover, with or without a box;
  On inside of front cover, with or without a box;
  In authors' titles, showing institutional affiliation;
  Below authors' names and titles, as a separate paragraph.

Combinations of any two or more of the above possibilities.

It is impossible, within the limits of this volume, to indicate the nature of the acknowledgment in the thousands of publications containing the results of coöperative effort. Only a few outstanding instances of desirable practice, or illustrations of different methods, can be given. Some are from Federal and some from State sources.

Federal Acknowledgments

The U. S. Department of Agriculture is by far the largest Federal coöperator in agricultural activities. It issues both administrative and technical publications in various series and these offer a broad opportunity for studying acknowledgments of coöperation.

In administrative publications.—Among the administrative publications are the annual reports of the Secretary (14), the annual reports of the chiefs of the numerous Bureaus (see Literature Cited in subject-matter chapters), the annual *List of Technical Workers* (22), and the occasional *Directory of Field Activities* of the different Bureaus (see subject-matter chapters).

The Secretary and the Bureau chiefs, in discussing the activities of their respective organizations, frequently but not consistently mention coöperating agencies. They supply indications of coöperation but not complete records. The personnel list and directories show the geographic location of projects as well as personnel, and sometimes indicate that a project is coöperative. The field directories are especially helpful. Recent issues of the personnel list have omitted most of the previously printed indications of coöperation.

In technical publications.—The acknowledgment of coöperation in the technical publications of the Department may be considered from two standpoints. There are long-continued and consistent acknowledgments in a series of publications covering results from a single project or constituting a single series, and there are acknowledgments in single unrelated publications.

The Bureaus of Animal Industry and Chemistry and the Office of Experiment Stations of the U. S. Department of Agriculture afford instances of consistent and long-continued prominent acknowledgment of State coöperation.

Animal Industry: For more than a quarter of a century, from 1896 onward, the Federal Bureau of Animal Industry conducted a critical study of animal nutrition in formal coöperation with Pennsylvania State College. This resulted in at least twenty papers published by one or the other of the offical agencies. The series is remarkable not only for its number and duration but also for the uniformly prominent display of the coöperative relation. From 1903 to 1912, nine papers were published as bulletins of the Bureau (18—51, 74, 94, 101, 108, 124, 128, 139, and 143). Two others were published as bulletins of the Pennsylvania Station (12—84 and 105) in 1907 and 1910. Eight additional papers appeared in the *Journal of Agricultural Research* during the years from 1915 to 1921, and a final paper in 1925, after the coöperation was terminated and the State collaborator had died.

In the nine Bureau bulletins, the coöperation is shown plainly and prominently on the cover page and the title page. In six cases it is in prominent capital letters in the center of the page. In the other three the author, Dr. Armsby, carries both Bureau and Station titles in italics, below his name. In all of the nine bulletins the coöperation is mentioned in the Bureau Letter of Transmittal, and in the six bulletins previously noted it appears also in the Pennsylvania Station Letter of Submittal. On the two State bulletins the coöperation is plainly stated on the covers. In the series of papers in the *Journal of Agricultural Research* (9) from 1915 to 1921 the words "Coöperative investigations between the Bureau of Animal Industry, United States Department of Agriculture, and the Institute of Animal Nutrition of the Pennsylvania State College," are printed in capital letters just below the scientific titles of the authors. In the later papers the order of the two institutions was reversed. In the final paper the relation is shown only by a footnote on the first page.

Chemistry: The Federal Bureau of Chemistry furnishes an early and gratifying illustration of unusually prominent and frequent acknowledgment of coöperative relations in the published results of coöperative activities. From 1900 to 1904, it conducted experiments on the effect of environment on the chemical composition of the sugarbeet, in coöperation with other Federal units and State agricultural experiment stations. The results were published annually in its bulletins (19—64, 74, 78, 95, and 96).

Coöperation was indicated plainly and with unusual frequency in this series of publications. On the front cover, and again on the title page, of each bulletin appear the words, printed in small capitals, "In collaboration with the Weather Bureau and the Agricultural Experiment Stations of ———— ———— [names of the States]." This probably is the earliest instance of this plain and prominent statement of coöperation on the covers and title pages of publications. The coöperation of the Weather Bureau and the State stations was acknowledged again in the Letter of Transmittal of the bulletins. The coöperating State stations were named in the introductory paragraphs. The Table of Contents showed the coöperation plainly by the entry, "Experiments conducted by ———— [State] Station," and this was repeated, or at least the name of the station was, as a boldface center heading in the text, under which the State data appeared. The collaboration of the Coast and Geodetic Survey and the Naval Observatory was acknowledged in the Letter of Transmittal in three of the five bulletins, and as footnotes to the tables in two of them.

Office of Experiment Stations: In 1895, the Department of Agriculture was authorized to coöperate with the States in studies of foods and dietaries. Results obtained in coöperation with both State and private institutions appeared in some sixty of the bulletins of the Office of Experiment Stations. The official relationships usually were indicated on the cover page, in the Letter of Transmittal, and in the text.

Plant Industry: There also are outstanding examples of painstaking acknowledgment of coöperation in individual publications. Five bulletins prepared by the Division of Cereal Crops and Diseases in the Federal Bureau of Plant Industry are representative. They contain compilations of all available official records of the yields of certain cereal crops. Two are concerned with Marquis (15—400) and durum (15—618) wheats, respectively, and were issued in 1916 and 1918. Three others included still more extensive compilations of barley yields. The first of these (15—1334) contains barley data from all except one of the forty-eight State experiment stations in the United States and from the Dominion stations and substations in Canada, from the beginning of such tests down to 1921. The second (17—96) contains similar data from all States and from both Dominion and Provincial stations in Canada for the five years from 1922 to 1926, inclusive, and had international joint authorship. The third (17—446) is a similar treatment for the years 1927–31, with similar authorship.

All of these bulletins contain both published and previously unpublished official records. In both cases, some had been obtained through coöperative experiments and some had been obtained independently by Federal or State agencies, including Dominion and Provincial agencies in Canada. In all the bulletins the coöperation in experiments, or the coöperative courtesy in furnishing independent data, was acknowledged in three separate places. A summarized statement of the existing relations was given in the introductory paragraphs of text in each bulletin. The relationship for each State or Canadian station was shown again in the text devoted to that station. Thirdly, the relationship was shown again in the headings of the table containing the data for each individual station. By this means, the reader was informed of the coöperative relations whether he read the text of the entire publication or merely that portion concerning some station or substation in which he was interested.

State Acknowledgments

Opportunities for the State agricultural experiment stations to acknowledge coöperation with the Federal Department are found in administrative publications issued by or for the stations and in the series of technical publications they issue.

In administrative publications.—The administrative publications of the stations are of two classes : First, the annual reports of the director and other special publications descriptive of the station activities or summarizing the contents of its recent publications, and, secondly, annual compilations of personnel and project data furnished by the stations for publication by the Federal Department.

In the annual reports of the various stations some mention is made of those projects which are coöperative with the Federal Department of Agriculture or are parts of regional projects in which several States and the Federal Department of Agriculture coöperate. Such mention, however, apparently is not so frequent or prominent as in the comparable annual reports of the chiefs of the various Federal Bureaus.

The Federal Department publishes annually a list of workers, in subjects pertaining to agriculture, in State agricultural colleges and experiment stations (20). For each State the personnel is arranged by subject-matter groups or divisions, and after the names of those employed on coöperative projects it is customary to insert the parenthetic expression, "(Coöp. U.S.D.A.)." The experiment stations usually list their own field stations at the end of these divisional lists, and coöperation on such field stations is indicated by the same statement after the names of the coöperating personnel.

The Federal Department occasionally publishes lists of the research projects conducted by the various stations (21). The station officers furnishing such lists indicate which of the individual projects are conducted in coöperation with Federal or other State agencies. The Department has not included this information regarding coöperation in its compilations except in the single year 1930, although it usually makes known the number of projects which are coöperative and the percentage they form in the total.

In technical publications.—There is no greater uniformity in place or method of acknowledging coöperation in State station publications than in those issued by the Federal Department. When the coöperation is acknowledged on the cover of a State bulletin, the State is more likely to set the name of the coöperating agency in prominent type than is the Federal Department under similar circumstances. The probable reason for so doing is that there is much less uniformity in the cover typography of the bulletins of a single State than in a similar series of Federal publications. The Federal rules for typographic expression are relatively standardized. It is the Federal practice uniformly to set the name of the coöperating State agencies in smaller type than that employed for the name of the Department or Bureau itself. On the other hand, the States are less likely to indicate coöperation on the cover of a publication than is the Federal Department. This may be caused in part by the fact that stations are more likely to use an illustrated cover on which there is relatively little room for lettering.

For many years, while the staffs of various stations were comparatively small, it was not uncommon to print the names of the entire research staff on the inside of the front cover of the station bulletin. While the practice lasted, it gave the stations the same opportunity to indicate employees engaged on coöperative projects which they still have in the annual list of their workers published by the Federal Department. Certain States began to indicate coöperation in this way at a relatively early date.

The Arizona Experiment Station lists its staff in its bulletins (1) in the manner just noted. Since 1925, the list has contained the name of one coöperating Federal employee located at the station. The coöperative relation is indicated by a footnote reading, "In coöperation with U. S. Department of Agriculture, Bureau of Plant Industry," dropped from his name. In State bulletins authored by this joint employee, no other acknowledgment of coöperation is given than this footnote.

The bulletins (11) of the North Carolina station, beginning in 1914 with No. 224, bear on the cover the words, "North Carolina Agricultural Experiment Station, conducted jointly by the State Department of Agriculture and the College of Agriculture and

Mechanic Arts," in display type. Beginning with *Bulletin 224* also, and continuing thereafter, a more nearly complete list of the station staff is printed on the inside of the front cover, and includes men located at the station for coöperative investigations by the different Bureaus of the U. S. Department of Agriculture. This first list includes eleven such coöperative workers, with their personal designations or lines of work and their Federal Bureau affiliations shown (substantially *verbatim*) as follows:

Bureau of Animal Industry
  1 Dairy farming
  1 Poultry clubs

Office of Experiment Stations
  1 Drainage engineer

Bureau of Soils
  1 Soils expert

Bureau of Plant Industry
  1 Farm demonstrations
  1 Farm management
  1 Boys' clubs
  2 Girls' clubs
  1 Tobacco investigations
  1 Tobacco investigations (also Assistant Director of Branch Farm)

Federal-State Extension Service Acknowledgment

When the Agricultural Extension Service was created in 1914, coöperation between the Federal Department of Agriculture and the State colleges of agriculture was made mandatory under the terms of the act. In the Federal Department that unit of the Extension Service which is charged with the administration of the Smith-Lever Act is the Office of Coöperative Extension Work, and its annual reports are entitled *Coöperative Extension Work*. This Office also publishes a series of extension service circulars, each of which bears at the top of the first page the phrase, "Coöperative Extension Work in Agriculture and Home Economics." In this case, no reference is made to the State agency coöperating.

Most of the State colleges publish series of extension bulletins or circulars, or both. Usually the Federal-State relation is shown in the following language appearing on the cover: "Coöperative Extension Work in Agriculture and Home Economics, College of Agriculture, University of [State], and U. S. Department of Agriculture coöperating. Distributed in furtherance of the Acts of Congress of May 8 and June 30, 1914." Less formal series of extension publications, such as the various leaflets containing suggestions for the programs of boys' and girls' clubs, etc., usually show the coöperation in simpler language. For example, in California the phrase reads either, "Division of Agricultural Extension, University of California College of Agriculture and U. S. Department of Agriculture coöperating," or "Agricultural Extension Service, U. S. Department of Agriculture and University of California."

7. Prevalence of Coöperation

AMERICA IS STATISTICS-CONSCIOUS and is becoming coöperation-conscious. If there are compilable statistics on coöperation, they should obtain favorable attention. There are two methods of determining the statistical prevalence of coöperation and the trend of that prevalence. One is by a study of projects to determine the percentage which are coöperatively conducted. The other is by a study of publications to determine the percentage which contain results obtained coöperatively. Both methods have been used within limited fields for the present purpose.

It is difficult to obtain complete data by either of these methods. In the first place, it is necessary to distinguish between actual coöperation in activities and the rendering of mere friendly assistance by one agency to another. No definite standards have been erected against which official agencies or the writer can measure the degree of interrelation. In the second place, there is diversity of opinion and practice as to what constitutes a project. In the third place, most official agencies publish results of their activities in many different series of publications, and it is quite impossible to review them all in a study like the present one. For these reasons, therefore, the data which follow and the trends which they seem to indicate should not be taken as complete or final, but merely as indicative within the limits of the fractional fields they cover.

PROPORTION OF COÖPERATIVE PROJECTS

Successive surveys of the total number of projects conducted by a given official agency, and the determination of the proportion of these which are coöperative, should reveal both facts and trends. Both the Federal Department of Agriculture and the State agricultural experiment stations have organized their activities on a project basis for many years. The provisions of the Adams Act of 1906, increasing Federal financial contributions to the State stations, required Federal approval of State research programs financed thereunder. This made necessary the formulation of definite projects for many new activities, and gradually led to a similar procedure for the projects previously in operation. The Federal Department of Agriculture introduced a project system on a very comprehensive scale at approximately the same time. It was developed to a point, however, where the subdivisions of activities into projects became too minute to be logical and the time required to make reports was excessive. The recent Federal tendency has been the reverse of this procedure, and major divisional activities have come to be regarded as the equivalent of projects.

Data on only the State experiment station projects can be discussed here. All station projects have been tabulated frequently in recent years by the Federal Office of Experiment Stations, whereas no such tabulation is published for projects of the Department. Among the stations, however, there is no universal agreement as to what constitutes a project. One official agency may regard a broad line of investigation as a single project, even though numerous subdivisions are recognized administratively. Another agency may regard each such subdivision as a separate project. These differences, however, should not materially affect the statistical results.

State Station Projects

At the meeting of the Association of Land-Grant Colleges in 1916, the Joint Committee on Projects and Correlation of Research reported about 1200 station research projects and about 750 similar projects conducted by the Federal Department of Agriculture. Beginning with the fiscal year 1919, the Federal Office of Experiment Stations has published at intervals a classified list of projects carried on by the State agricultural experiment stations in a given year (21). Some have covered fiscal years and some calendar years, while some years have been skipped entirely. There are discrepancies in the figures, but they serve to indicate trends.

In 1919, there were approximately 3750 projects, and in 1920 there were 4064 research projects. For the year 1925, the number had risen to 5484. The year 1926 showed a large increase, the total number being 6652. This was the first year in which the increased funds provided by the Purnell Act had been available and 600 of these projects were carried on that fund. By 1930, the total number of research projects was 7019, of which 1221 were carried on Purnell Act funds, then available in their maximum amount. The numbers of projects given above are exclusive of station projects concerned with administration and control, and of the projects maintained by the insular experiment station. The increase in the ten-year period was nearly 3000 projects and, as noted, nearly half of these had been started on Purnell Act funds.

Data on the number and percentage of these station research projects which are coöperative with Federal agencies or with other State agencies would be exceedingly valuable, but are difficult to obtain. Not until 1926 did the Office of Experiment Stations publish these figures and then (and even now) they are given in round numbers only. Admitting these discrepancies, the figures still show tendencies. In 1926, the coöperative projects numbered 500 out of 6652, or 7.5 per cent of the total. This number represented only those covered by formal agreements. Many were conducted under informal arrangements. In 1927, those formally coöperative numbered 630 out of 6186, or 10 per cent; in 1928, about 900 in a total of 6600, or 13.6 per cent; in 1929, about 1100 from approximately 7000, or 15.7 per cent. In 1930, coöperative projects numbered 1196 out of 7019, or 17 per cent of the total. This growth of coöperation from 7.5 per cent in 1926 to 17 per cent in 1930 is a striking confirmation of the generally observed trend. Very probably the increase was not as rapid as indicated here, for it is likely that not all the projects conducted coöperatively in 1926 were reported as such when the tabulation was first started.

Purnell Act projects, or those financed under the increased Federal appropriations for State stations, effective in fiscal year 1926, have increased from 600 or more in 1926 to approximately 1300 in 1930, and more than 1400 in 1933. The percentage of these which were coöperative has been published for only the years 1929 and 1930, when it was 12.5 and 14 per cent respectively.

This rapid increase in number and percentage of coöperative projects since 1925 is the result of at least two separate forces. In part it is due to the accelerating growth in the spirit of coöperation. In part, also, it arises from the encouragement given by the Purnell Act to research in agricultural economics and rural sociology, two fields in which the Federal Department of Agriculture had a more experienced organization and better perspective than had most of the States, and therefore was able to act as a leader in establishing research projects.

Since 1930, the total number of projects has been somewhat decreased, in part because of reduced financial support, in part because of reorganization of the research program to meet emergency conditions. While data are not available, there is no reason to believe that the percentage of coöperation has diminished.

Data on the distribution of coöperative projects by agencies involved would be helpful but are not available. The comprehensive survey of land-grant colleges and universities made by the Federal Office of Education in 1928 gave a brief discussion of coöperative and noncoöperative State station projects (24—2:591–606), with some facts on distribution. Complete data on coöperative projects cannot be derived from their statements because coöperating State field stations, each of which may comprise many projects, were not given in terms of the total number of projects involved but merely by total numbers of such stations. In addition to these stations, however, 321 other projects were carried on in coöperation with the Federal Department of Agriculture, an unnamed number in coöperation with other Federal agencies, 94 in coöperation with other States, and 42 in coöperation with other official State agencies.

Figures on the distribution of coöperative State projects by Bureaus of the Federal Department of Agriculture are available for 1930. In that year, the Joint Committee on Projects and Correlation of Research, reporting to the Association of Land-Grant Colleges and Universities, indicated, as noted previously, that nearly 1200 of the more than 7000 station projects were conducted coöperatively by stations or groups of stations and the Department of Agriculture. "Of these, 398 involved coöperation mainly with the Bureau of Plant Industry, 311 with the Bureau of Agricultural Economics, 134 with the Bureau of Animal Industry, 88 with the Bureau of Chemistry and Soils, 86 with the Bureau of Entomology, 68 with the Bureau of Public Roads, 50 with the Bureau of Dairy Industry, 25 with the Forest Service, 10 with the Bureau of Home Economics, and 6 with the Weather Bureau."

Every State experiment station was represented in the above

total—California, Washington, and North Carolina leading, with 53, 49, and 48 projects, respectively. The committee stated that there also were about 21 major regional projects under way, involving the coöperation of groups of stations varying from three to thirty and including from one to three Bureaus of the Department. In 1931, the California Agricultural Experiment Station reported that it had 224 active projects, of which 57 or 25.4 per cent were coöperative with the U. S. Department of Agriculture.

Federal Projects

No data are available on either the total number of Federal research projects or the percentage conducted coöperatively, whether within the Department, with other Federal agencies, or with the States. It is obvious, of course, that most of the 1200 coöperative State projects represent Department projects also. They do not represent as many Department projects, however, because several States may report separately their coöperation on what would be a single project in the Department. It is certain and natural that a much larger percentage of the total Federal projects are coöperative than of the State projects, because the Federal government conducts most of its agricultural activities within the States.

PROPORTION OF COÖPERATIVE PUBLICATIONS

Determining the true prevalence of coöperation by the proportion of coöperative publications is difficult because most official agencies issue or contribute to many different series of publications. A State agricultural experiment station not only issues two or three separate series of its own publications, but it also publishes its papers, especially those that are coöperative in origin, in certain Federal publications and also in numerous private technical journals. It was impossible to search all of these various series for the present study. Of the different series issued by a given station, some are devoted largely to results from those activities in which coöperation can take place readily, whereas others contain many papers covering fields not susceptible of coöperative activity. A series must be included or omitted in its entirety, but either course results in discrepancies or inaccuracies.

In the present paper, determination of the extent of coöperation has been ascertained by discovering the proportion of coöperative publications appearing in the bulletins and certain equivalent publications of the various State agricultural experiment stations and in some of the series issued by the U. S. Department of Agriculture, as noted below.

It is especially difficult to determine just what constitutes coöperation and what is more properly regarded as the rendering of friendly assistance by one agency to another. The difficulty is increased by the varying ways in which acknowledgment is made of these interrelations, as has been discussed already in a separate subsection. The distinction in the mind of the author between assistance and coöperation is indicated roughly in the definition of terms at the end of this chapter, and, in general, published results have been classified on that basis.

For all the reasons stated, the data given below should not be regarded as exact pictures of the percentage of coöperation obtaining, but rather as valuable indications of its proportions.

State Agricultural Experiment Station Bulletins

The publications listed include bulletins (all States), *Hilgardia* (California), memoirs (New York–Cornell), research bulletins (Idaho, Iowa, Missouri, Nebraska, Wisconsin), special bulletins (Michigan), and technical bulletins (Arizona, Colorado, Michigan, Minnesota, Mississippi, New Hampshire, New York–Geneva, North Carolina, Virginia). No circular or popular bulletin series were used. The numerous station papers contributed to private journals also are omitted. The period covered is the fifteen years from 1920 to 1934, although the latter year was not concluded at the time the facts were determined.

For convenience, the data are arranged in two tables. In Table 1, the percentages of coöperative State publications are separated into somewhat unequal groups, and the States falling in each group are arranged alphabetically. The different publication series are lumped to determine the percentages, and the two Connecticut and two New York Stations are considered as one, in each case. In Table 2, the entire series of States is arranged alphabetically, the numbers and percentages of coöperative bulletins are shown, and the numbers then are distributed according to the character and scope of the coöperation. The publication series and the pairs of stations are entered separately.

It must be remembered that the percentage scope of the columns in Table 1 is not always the same. The first column has a range of 10 per cent, the second and third a range of only 5 per cent each, the fourth a range of 10 per cent, and the fifth a range of more than 20 per cent.

TABLE 1

STATES ARRANGED IN PERCENTAGE GROUPS BY PROPORTION OF EXPERIMENT
STATION BULLETINS CONTAINING COÖPERATIVE RESULTS IN THE 15-YEAR
PERIOD FROM 1920 TO 1934, INCLUSIVE.

PERCENTAGE GROUPS									
0 to 10		10+ to 15		15+ to 20		20+ to 30		30+	
State	Per cent	State	Per cent	State	Per cent	State	Per cent	State	Per cent
Ark.	6.2	Ala.	12.1	Iowa	19.6	Colo.	26.7	Calif.	31.5
Conn.[a]	6.4	Ariz.	12.6	Ky.	15.7	Ga.	27.1	Kan.	39.7
Del.	4.7	Fla.	15.0	N. H.	16.8	Idaho	20.2	Mont.	43.6
Md.	5.9	Ill.	11.6	Okla.	17.0	Ind.	20.5	Neb.[c]	46.6
Mass.	6.0	Me.	12.9	Ore.	15.5	La.	27.5	Nev.[d]	51.3
Mo.	6.9	Mich.	12.5	S. C.	19.8	Minn.	26.6	Utah	35.4
N. J.	9.3	Miss.	13.4	Wis.	19.9	N. M.	20.8		
N. Y.[b]	6.3	Ohio	12.5	Wyo.	19.0	N. C.	23.0		
R. I.	0	Pa.	13.6			N. D.	29.9		
Tenn.	6.7	Tex.	14.2			S. D.	22.2		
Vt.	8.8					Va.	26.9		
W. Va.	9.1					Wash.	26.9		

[a] New Haven and Storrs Stations combined.
[b] Cornell and Geneva Stations combined.
[c] Includes 10 annual tractor bulletins involving mandatory coöperation.
[d] Only 20 bulletins involved, of which 8 represent interdivisional coöperation.

It will be noted that the twelve States with low percentages of coöperative bulletins are all eastern or central in location, that the thirty States with mid-low to mid-high percentages are widely distributed geographically, and that the six States with high percentages are all west central or western. This suggests, not different attitudes toward coöperation in different regions, but rather a greater urgency in western problems.

The twelve States, or 25 per cent of the total, having less than 10 per cent of their bulletins coöperative in the period covered, are well distributed in the percentage range. If the Connecticut

(Storrs) Station and the New York (Cornell) Station are taken each from its companion station in the same State, they would pass to the next column with 11.2 per cent each. In the two columns covering the range from 10 to 20 per cent are found eighteen States, or 37.5 per cent of the total, well distributed through the percentage range and fairly equally distributed in the two 5-per-cent ranges. In the range from 20 to 30 per cent of coöperative publications, twelve States or 25 per cent again are found, well distributed in the percentage scale. The remaining six States, or 12.5 per cent of the total, cover the wide range of 31.5 to 51.3 per cent.

It will be remembered that coöperative results from these same States may be published also in the *Journal of Agricultural Research* (9), in one or another of the series of Department publications, and in private technical journals. The data given, therefore, must be understood to represent only that coöperation shown by the series of publications included in this particular table.

Table 2 presents the detailed data on the prevalence of coöperation as revealed by the various series of bulletins published by the State agricultural experiment stations. The data show a total of 7166 such bulletins issued between 1920 and 1934, inclusive. Of this number, 1230, or 17.2 per cent, were found to contain results obtained in coöperation. Of these, 884, or 12.3 per cent, represented Federal-State coöperation. Another 30, or .4 per cent, represented interstate coöperation, and 319, or 4.5 per cent, represented intrastate coöperation. All the above represent primary coöperation and are mutually exclusive and nonduplicating. The last item can be further subdivided into inter-institutional coöperation, represented by 163 bulletins, or 2.3 per cent, and coöperation among the units of a single institution, represented by 156 bulletins, or 2.2 per cent.

In all categories, there was some secondary coöperation, as indicated by the five columns designated "B." This is secondary to the primary coöperation shown in the "A" columns and, of course, represents part of the same bulletins. All told there are 228 bulletins which show secondary coöperation, but the different columns making this total are not mutually exclusive, for more than one degree of secondary coöperation may be present in one bulletin.

For the interinstitutional subdivision of interstate coöperation, there are 156 bulletins showing secondary coöperation, which is nearly as many as those showing primary coöperation.

It is interesting, though not statistically significant, that the percentage (17.2%) of coöperative bulletins in these series published by the States for a period ending in 1934 is substantially identical with the percentage (17%) of coöperative projects in the State agricultural experiment stations for the year 1930.

U. S. Department of Agriculture Technical Publications

Many of the old series of Bureau bulletins contained coöperative papers in large numbers. For instance, the Federal Bureau of Animal Industry issued 167 Bureau bulletins (18) between 1893 and 1913. Of these 62, or 37 per cent, were coöperative to some extent.

Three series of the Federal Department's recent technical publications have been checked to determine the proportion of their issues which are of coöperative origin and also the official scope of the coöperation. These series are the *Department Bulletins* (1500 numbers), the *Technical Bulletins* (461 numbers), and the *Journal of Agricultural Research* (2562 separate papers). Among them they cover more than twenty-one years, from July, 1913, to late 1934.

Omitting 400 Department bulletins which were not examined, there remain 4123 papers from which data were taken. The results are presented in Tables 3 and 4. These tables show that a grand total of 942 papers or 22.8 per cent were the results of coöperative activity or of assistance rendered. Omitting the relatively small number representing assistance rendered, there were 862, or 20.9 per cent, which resulted from definite coöperative activities.

An analysis of the *Department Bulletins* and the *Technical Bulletins* with reference to the degree and the scope of the relations has been made, as will be noted in Table 3. Two degrees of relationship are distinguished, namely, definite coöperation in the planning and conduct of the investigations, and informal assistance received during the course of these procedures. From the standpoint of the scope of relationship four levels are distinguished, namely, Federal-State, Federal interunit, international, and interstate. Coöperation, in turn, is separated into primary or major

TABLE 2

ALPHABETICAL LIST OF STATES, THE NUMBERS OF EXPERIMENT STATION BULLETINS AND EQUIVALENT PUBLICATIONS (*Memoirs, Research Bulletins, Special Bulletins, Technical Bulletins, Hilgardia*) ISSUED 1920 TO (LAST ISSUE CONSULTED IN) 1934, THE NUMBER AND PERCENTAGE COÖPERATIVE, AND THEIR DISTRIBUTION BY OFFICIAL SCOPE OF THE PRIMARY (A) AND SECONDARY (B) COÖPERATION INVOLVED.

Note that the "A" columns, showing the primary or major coöperative relations, contain no duplicates and their totals equal the total numbers of coöperative bulletins. The "B" columns show secondary or minor coöperation existing in addition to the primary (A) coöperation and therefore duplicate part of those in the "A" or primary columns.

STATE	PUBLICATION SERIES	ISSUE NUMBERS			COÖPERATIVE		FEDERAL			Interstate		INTRASTATE Inter-institution		INTRASTATE Interdepartment or Interdivision	
		First in 1920	Last consulted	Total	Number	Per cent	Federal-State A	Inter-bureau B	Inter-division B	A	B	A	B	A	B
Ala.	Bulletin	209	211	33	4	12.1	4								
Ariz.	Bulletin	91	147	57	2	3.5	2				2		1		2
	Tech.Bul.	0	54	54	12	22.2	12								
	Both			111	14	12.6									
Ark.	Bulletin	165	309	145	9	6.2	9								
Cal.	Bulletin	317	584	268	108	40.3	72	3	1	2	6	25	28	9	
	Hilgardia	0	138	138	20	14.5	18					1	2	1	
	Both			406	128	31.5									
Colo.	Bulletin	253	409	157	43	27.4	32	4		1	2	3	6	8	
	Tech.Bul.	0	8	8	1	12.5	1								
	Both			165	44	26.7									

TABLE 2—*Continued*

BULLETINS AND JOURNAL ISSUES IN PERIOD

STATE	PUBLICATION SERIES	ISSUE NUMBERS			COÖPERATIVE		SCOPE OF COÖPERATION								
							FEDERAL			Interstate		INTRASTATE			
							Federal-State	Inter-bureau	Inter-division			Inter-institution		Interdepartment or Interdivision	
		First in 1920	Last consulted	Total	Number	Per cent	A	B	B	A	B	A	B	A	B
Conn. (New Haven)	Bulletin	220	363	144	5	3.5	4					1		2	1
(Storrs)	Bulletin	105	193	89	10	11.2	3			1		4	1		
	Both			233	15	6.4									
Del.	Bulletin	126	189	64	3	4.7	2			1		1		1	
Fla.	Bulletin	156	268	113	17	15.0	9					6	3	6	
Ga.	Bulletin	136	183	48	13	27.1	7						1		
Idaho	Bulletin	119	206	88	19	21.6	12	1		2		2	1	3	1
	Res. Bul.	0	11	11	1	9.1	1				1				
	Both			99	20	20.2									
Ill.	Bulletin	225	405	181	21	11.6	13	2				8	5	6	
Ind.	Bulletin	235	395	161	33	20.5	27	1					2	7	
Ia.	Bulletin	193	320	128	27	21.1	17					3	2	14	1
	Res. Bul.	57	173	117	21	17.9	7				1				
	Both			245	48	19.6									

TABLE 2—*Continued*

State	Pub.					%									
Kan.	Bulletin	223	268	46	19	41.3	13	1	2			3	2	3	1
	Tech. Bul.	6	37	32	12	37.5	4							8	
	Both			78	31	39.7									
Ky.	Bulletin	225	345	121	19	15.7	16	1	1			2	1	1	
La.	Bulletin	169	245	80	22	27.5	17	2				3		2	
Me.	Bulletin	285	369	85	11	12.9	7			1		4			
Md.	Bulletin	234	351	118	7	5.9	6				1	1			1
Mass.	Spec. Bul.	195	310	116	7	6.0	4				2	1	1		
Mich.	Bulletin	100	247	148	16	10.8	9					4		3	2
	Tech. Bul.	48	139	92	14	15.2	5			1			1	9	
	Both			240	30	12.5									
Minn.	Bulletin	188	300	113	35	31.0	18	1		4		8	2	9	
	Tech. Bul.	0	94	94	20	21.3	15						1	5	
	Both			207	55	26.6									
Miss.	Bulletin	187	300	114	12	10.5	10	2				2	1		
	Tech. Bul.	9	21	13	5	38.5	1						3		
	Both			127	17	13.4									
Mo.	Bulletin	167	339	173	9	5.2	6			1	2		2	2	1
	Res. Bul.	36	210	175	15	8.6	11			2				2	
	Both			348	24	6.9									
Mont.	Bulletin	134	289	156	68	43.6	54	5		2		7	6	5	
Neb.	Bulletin	175	284	110	40	36.4	26	1				10		4	1
	Res. Bul.	16	70	55	13	23.6	7	1				1		5	
	Both			165	53	32.1									

TABLE 2—*Continued*

BULLETINS AND JOURNAL ISSUES IN PERIOD

State	Publication Series	Issue Numbers: First in 1920	Last consulted	Total	Coöperative: Number	Per cent	Federal: Federal-State A	Inter-bureau B	Inter-division B	Interstate A	Interstate B	Intrastate: Inter-institution A	Inter-institution B	Interdepartment or Interdivision A	Interdepartment or Interdivision B
Nev.	Bulletin	98	136	39	20	51.3	10			1		1	1	9	
N. H.	Bulletin	195	280	86	13	15.1	9			2		1	1	2	
	Tech.Bul.	15	59	45	9	20.0	3							4	
	Both			131	22	16.8									
N. J.	Bulletin	341	576	236	22	9.3	16	3			2	5	9	1	
N. Mex.	Bulletin	122	222	101	21	20.8	20					1	5		
N. Y. (Geneva)	Bulletin	471	644	174	0	0				2		2			
	Tech.Bul.	75	223	149	4	2.7									
	Both			323	4	1.2									
(Cornell)	Bulletin	400	606	207	36	17.4	30					5	5	1	1
	Memoirs	30	162	133	2	1.5	2								
	Both			340	38	11.2									
N. C.	Bulletin	242	293	52	14	26.9	12	3				1		1	
	Tech.Bul.	19	40	22	3	13.6	3					1	2		
	Both			74	17	23.0									

TABLE 2—*Concluded*

	Type														
N. D.	Bulletin	134	277	144	43	29.9	39	8		1	2	1	5	2	1
Ohio	Bulletin	339	538	200	25	12.5	16	1		1	1	4	2	4	2
Okla.	Bulletin	130	217	88	15	17.0	13	2	2				2	2	2
Ore.	Bulletin	161	321	161	25	15.5	19	3				5	1	1	1
Penn.	Bulletin	202	246	147	20	13.6	18				1	2	3		1
R. I.	Bulletin	202	297	45	2	4.4									
S. C.	Bulletin	188	286	96	19	19.8	18	2	1	2	2	1	2	4	
S. D.	Bulletin	123	152	99	22	22.2	18	1					4	1	1
Tenn.	Bulletin	259	490	30	2	6.7	1					1	1		
Tex.	Bulletin	171	249	232	33	14.2	29	5	1	2		2	4	2	
Utah	Bulletin	216	375	79	28	35.4	22	2		2		2	3	2	
Vt.	Bulletin	224	293	160	14	8.7	10				5	2	4	1	1
Va.	Bulletin	20	53	70	20	28.6	14	1			1	5	6	1	1
	Tech. Bul.			34	8	23.5	6					1	2		
	Both			104	28	26.9						12			
Wash.	Bulletin	155	288	134	36	26.9	21	1	1		3	6	5	3	5
W. Va.	Bulletin	173	260	88	8	9.1	8				1	1			
Wis.	Bulletin	310	427	118	18	15.3	12	2					5		5
	Res. Bul.	47	119	73	20	27.4	20						7		
	Both			191	38	19.9									
Wyo.	Bulletin	124	202	79	15	19.0	14			1	1				1
Totals				7166	1230		884	59	11	30	33	163	156	156	29
Percentages					17.2%		12.3%	.8%	.2%	.4%	.5%	2.3%	2.2%	2.2%	.4%

coöperation (A), and secondary or minor coöperation (B). For instance, if a project coöperative between Federal and State agencies developed also minor coöperation between two Federal agencies or two State agencies, these latter would be regarded as secondary coöperations and listed in the "B" column.

Department Bulletins.—Exactly 1500 numbers were comprised in the series of *Department Bulletins* (15) begun in July, 1913, and discontinued in 1927. A few delayed numbers actually appeared in 1928 and 1929. Of the 1500 numbers issued, only 1100 were examined for indications of coöperation. These were Nos. 1 to 200, issued from 1913 to 1915, and Nos. 601 to 1500, issued from 1917 to 1927. Table 3 contains the tabulated data obtained, as well as similar data for the series of *Technical Bulletins* (17).

The 1100 bulletins were analyzed for degree and scope of coöperation. Of them, 260, or 23.6 per cent, were coöperative, and 17 of these represented secondary coöperation also. Of the 260 coöperative bulletins, 167 represented Federal-State relations, 89 represented Federal interunit relations, and 4 represented international relations. In addition, 35 bulletins, or 3.2 per cent, represented assistance rendered. Two thirds of these were at the Federal interunit level. Six of the 35 showed secondary assistance also. A grand total of 295 bulletins, or 26.8 per cent of the total, represented either coöperation or the relation of assistance. For convenience, the Federal interunit coöperation is broken down into interdepartmental, Departmental interbureau, and Bureau interdivisional coöperation. The same subdivisions are made for assistance rendered.

Technical Bulletins.—Begun in 1927, the series of *Technical Bulletins* (17) had reached 461 numbers by the end of 1934. An analysis of these with respect to degree and scope of relation has been made. From Table 3 it will be noted that 170 numbers, or 36.9 per cent, of these bulletins were the result of coöperation, and that 45, or almost 10 per cent more, showed definite assistance rendered by one agency to another. The total for both coöperation and assistance is 215 bulletins, or 46.7 per cent of the gross number.

Naturally, the greater part of the coöperation, represented by 133 bulletins, or nearly 29 per cent out of the total 37 per cent, was between Federal and State agencies, and most of the remainder between Federal units, chiefly in the U. S. Department of Agriculture. The same facts hold true for assistance rendered.

Besides the primary coöperation (A), or that of major importance, many of these bulletins show that secondary coöperation (B), or that of lesser importance, was present also in some of the research already classified under primary coöperation. Data for this secondary coöperation are given in the right-hand, "B," columns of the table. The data show that 37 bulletins, or 8 per cent of the total number of coöperative bulletins, have secondary coöperation between other agencies than those of the primary coöperation. Most of these were Federal interunit relations, secondary to primary Federal-State interrelations. In the same way, 22 bulletins, or 4.8 per cent of the total, contain records of assistance as a secondary relation. In these cases, the primary relation may have been coöperation, or it may have been assistance at some other level of official agencies.

The combined number showing either coöperation or assistance as a secondary relation was 59, or 12.8 per cent of the grand total. This is slightly more than one fourth of the number resulting from primary coöperation or assistance.

A survey of the occurrence of joint authorship by different agencies in these *Technical Bulletins* recorded in Table 3 as resulting from coöperation is revealing. Of the 133 bulletins representing Federal-State coöperation, 37 were of joint Federal-State authorship, and 4 of these had Department of Agriculture interbureau authorship also. Of the 30 bulletins in the Federal interunit class, 21 had interunit joint authorship. Of the 22 based on Department of Agriculture interbureau coöperation, 16 had interbureau joint authorship, of which number 2 had interdivisional authorship also. Of the 5 representing primary interdivisional coöperation, all had interdivisional joint authorship.

Journal of Agricultural Research.—The *Journal of Agricultural Research* (9) has been published since October, 1913. It is a coöperative journal of the U. S. Department of Agriculture and the State agricultural experiment stations. The volumes vary greatly in their size, duration of the period covered, and number of papers included, as will be noted in Table 4. In the first ten-year period, to the end of 1923, covered by volumes 1 to 26, inclusive,

TABLE 3

DEPARTMENT BULLETINS AND TECHNICAL BULLETINS CONTAINING RESULTS OBTAINED BY COÖPERATION OR ASSISTANCE, SHOWING, FOR EACH TYPE OF RELATION AND EACH LEVEL OF AGENCY, THE NUMBER AND PERCENTAGE OF BULLETINS REPRESENTING PRIMARY (A) OR SECONDARY (B) DEGREES OF SUCH RELATIONSHIPS.

COÖPERATION AND ASSISTANCE IN RESEARCH

Scope and Nature of Relations	1100 Department Bulletins								461 Technical Bulletins							
	Primary Coöperation (A) and Assistance				Secondary Coöperation (B) and Assistance				Primary Coöperation (A) and Assistance				Secondary Coöperation (B) and Assistance			
	All Levels		Federal Interunit		All Levels		Federal Interunit		All Levels		Federal Interunit		All Levels		Federal Interunit	
	Number	Per cent	Number	Per cent	Number	Per cent	Number	Per cent	Number	Per cent	Number	Per cent	Number	Per cent	Number	Per cent
A. Coöperation involved																
1. Federal-State	167	15.2			5	0.4			133	28.9			1	0.2		
2. Federal Interunit	89	8.0			5	0.5			30	6.5			33	7.2		
Interdepartmental			7	0.6			0	0.0			3	0.6			2	0.4
Departmental Interbureau			67	6.1			3	0.3			22	4.8			27	5.9
Bureau Interdivisional			15	1.3			2	0.2			5	1.1			4	0.8
3. International	4	0.4			5	0.4			7	1.5			2	0.4		
4. Interstate	0	0.0			2	0.2			0	0.0			1	0.2		
TOTALS	260	23.6			17	1.5			170	36.9			37	8.0		

TABLE 3—*Concluded*

Scope and Nature of Relations	1100 DEPARTMENT BULLETINS								461 TECHNICAL BULLETINS							
	Primary Coöperation (A) and Assistance				Secondary Coöperation (B) and Assistance				Primary Coöperation (A) and Assistance				Secondary Coöperation (B) and Assistance			
	All Levels		Federal Interunit		All Levels		Federal Interunit		All Levels		Federal Interunit		All Levels		Federal Interunit	
	Number	Per cent	Number	Per cent	Number	Per cent	Number	Per cent	Number	Per cent	Number	Per cent	Number	Per cent	Number	Per cent
B. Assistance received																
1. Federal-State	9	0.8			2	0.2			28	6.1			7	1.5		
2. Federal Interunit	24	2.2			4	0.4			16	3.5			15	3.3		
Interdepartmental			3	0.3			1	0.1			3	0.6			2	0.4
Departmental Interbureau			20	1.8			3	0.3			11	2.4			11	2.4
Bureau Interdivisional			1	0.1			0	0.0			2	0.4			2	0.4
3. International	2	0.2			0	0.0			1	0.2			0	0.0		
4. Interstate	0	0.0			0	0.0			0	0.0			0	0.0		
TOTALS	35	3.2			6	0.6			45	9.8			22	4.8		
GRAND TOTALS, COÖP AND ASS'T	295	26.8			23	2.1			215	46.7			59	12.8		

TABLE 4

VOLUMES OF THE *Journal of Agricultural Research*, SHOWING YEAR OF PUBLICATION, TOTAL NUMBER OF PAPERS CONTAINED, AND THE NUMBER AND PERCENTAGE OF PAPERS OF COÖPERATIVE ORIGIN, WITH AVERAGES FOR SELECTED PERIODS

VOLUME	YEARS	PAPERS INCLUDED		
		Total Number	Coöperative Number	Coöperative Per cent
1	1913–14	29	3	10.3
2	1914	29	6	20.7
3	1914–15	31	4	12.9
4	1915	38	5	13.2
5	1915–16	75	6	8.0
6	1916	67	4	6.0
7	1916	30	5	16.7
8	1917	25	0	0.0
9	1917	23	6	26.1
10	1917	36	3	8.3
11	1917	38	4	10.5
12	1918	33	1	3.0
13	1918	40	11	27.5
14	1918	38	9	23.7
15	1918	32	8	25.0
16	1919	22	3	13.6
17	1919	17	3	17.6
18	1919–20	38	3	7.9
19	1920	31	14	45.2
20	1920–21	57	6	10.5
21	1921	58	11	19.0
22	1921	35	3	8.6
23	1923	58	16	27.6
24	1923	58	14	24.1
25	1923	32	5	15.6
26	1923	52	7	13.5
1–26	1913–23	1022	160	15.6
27	1924	53	9	17.0
28	1924	95	19	20.0
29	1924	46	6	13.0
30	1925	80	13	16.3
31	1925	82	7	8.5
32	1926	67	14	20.9
33	1926	81	13	16.0
34	1927	85	4	4.7
35	1927	72	8	11.1
36	1928	63	7	11.1
37	1928	45	11	24.4
27–37	1924–28	769	111	14.4
38	1929	43	6	14.0
39	1929	55	6	10.9
40	1930	72	14	19.4
41	1930	64	8	12.5
42	1931	60	11	18.3
43	1931	75	14	18.7
44	1932	65	9	13.8
45	1932	49	7	14.3
46	1933	86	19	22.1
47	1933	75	23	30.7
38–47	1929–33	644	117	18.2
27–47	1924–33	1413	228	16.1
48	1934	75	23	30.7
49	1934 8 Nos.	52	21	40.4
48–49		127	44	34.6

there were published 1022 papers, of which 160, or 15.6 per cent, were coöperative in origin. The percentage ranged from 0 per cent in one volume of 1917 to 45 per cent in one volume of 1920. In the second ten-year period, 1924 to 1933, inclusive, covered by volumes 27 to 47, there were published 1413 papers, of which 228, or 16.1 per cent, were the result of coöperation. The range of percentage in this second decade was from 2 per cent in one volume of 1924 to 30.7 per cent in the last volume of 1933.

There is virtually no gain in percentage of coöperative papers in the second ten-year period as compared with the first. This is true in spite of the fact that there was a slow but steady increase in the percentage of the total number of projects which were conducted coöperatively. The probable explanation for the lack of a corresponding increase in percentage of coöperative papers published in the second decade is that the stations, at the beginning of the publication of the *Journal,* may have singled out papers resulting from Federal-State coöperation to be sent to the *Journal.* Then later, as they came to regard the *Journal* as an official organ of the State also, they sent to it an increasing proportion of papers of noncoöperative origin, a practice which would mask the fact of increasing coöperation.

If the second decade is broken down into two periods of five years each, the first period, 1924 to 1928, inclusive, provided 769 published papers, of which 111, or 14.4 per cent, were coöperative. The second five-year period, 1929 to 1933, inclusive, was represented by 644 papers, of which 117, or 18.2 per cent, were coöperative. This shows an appreciable gain in the second five-year period, somewhat comparable to the gain in proportion of coöperative projects.

Of volumes 48 and 49, published in 1934, the first 20 issues contained 127 papers, of which 44, or 34.6 per cent, represented coöperative investigations. The percentage in volume 48 was 30.7 per cent and in the first 8 issues of volume 49, it was 40.4 per cent. Volume 47, published during the last half of 1933, also contained 30.7 per cent of coöperative papers. The reason for these increased percentages of coöperative papers in the last year and a half is not clear. Whether they are due to an increased proportion of coöperative projects, or to a better survival of such projects with decreasing financial support during the depression, or to a conscious preference for coöperative papers when more papers were offered than could be printed, or to these and other causes, is not known.

In the 21 coöperative papers published in the first 8 issues of the last volume, the degree of coöperation represented was as follows: 2 Federal interdepartmental, 3 Federal interbureau, 13 Federal-State, 1 interstate, and 2 intrastate. Of these two, one was interinstitutional and one interdivisional.

8. DEFINITIONS OF TERMS

SOME OF THE GENERAL TERMS used throughout this volume should be defined, as to the sense in which they are employed, in order that the reader may make the correct interpretations of the text.

Activity: A procedure or procedures or line or lines of work conducted in the exercise of a given official function. For instance, the conduct of a station farm is an activity of the State agricultural experiment station. So also the testing of wheat varieties or milking machines or plowing methods at such a station would be an activity. An activity may consist of multiple or single lines of work.

Agency: Any official unit or institution of government, whether international, Federal, State, district, county, or municipal. It is applied without regard to the size or relation of these units. In one instance, it may refer to an entire executive department in the Federal government, in another, to a single bureau of that department, in a third, to a division of that or another bureau, and in a fourth, to a subordinate unit of that division. In the same way, it may refer to some department of State or municipal government, or to a subdivision of such department. Its use is not confined by any means to units of executive departments of government, for it may refer to judicial or legislative bodies, to boards, commissions, and authorities of all kinds, and to governmentally subsidized educational institutions. At times, the term unit is used with the same meaning.

Assistance: Acts of friendly courtesy in supplying information, loaning temporary facilities, or helping briefly on special phases of a problem. See Coöperation.

Coöperation: Working together. It is used in the present discussion for every degree and kind of such mutual operations, from jointly planned and executed long-period research projects to minor collaboration on some special phase of a project, such as chemical analyses of the products of crop or livestock investigations. From the standpoint of formality, it covers everything from a jointly signed agreement of coöperation to operations under a verbal arrangement. There is no hard and fast line between assistance rendered and coöperation undertaken.

Coördination: Harmonious adjustment of relations in functions and activities. Not regimentation.

Function: A broad, inherent, or designated official duty, requirement, or calling of an agency. For instance, crop and livestock improvement and protection are functions of the Federal Department of Agriculture.

9. LITERATURE CITED

1. Arizona Agricultural Experiment Station. Bulletins 1–, 1890–.

2. Association of Land-Grant Colleges and Universities. Proceedings of the ——th Annual Convention of the Association of Land-Grant Colleges and Universities. 24th (1910)–, 1911–.

For previous proceedings, see U. S. Department of Agriculture, Office of Experiment Stations, *Miscellaneous Bulletins,* and *Bulletins.*

The name of the Association has varied. Before 1920, it was the Association of American Agricultural Colleges and Experiment Stations. From 1920 to 1926 it was the Association of Land-Grant Colleges.

3. Ball, Carleton R. Personnel, personalities, and research. Sci. Mo. 23:33–45, July, 1926. Reprinted.

4. Ball, Carleton R. Some elements of successful coöperation in research. U. S. Dept. Agric., Bur. Pl. Ind., Cereal Invest., 43 p., mim., letter size, 1925.

5. Ball, Carleton R. Code of ethics suggested for public employees. Calif. State Employee 1 (2):5–6, December, 1931.

6. Brooks, Alfred H. The scientist in the federal service. Jour. Wash. Acad. Sci. 12:73–116, February 19, 1922.

7. California, Kern County. Association of County Agricultural Inspectors. Code of ethics for county agricultural inspectors. Calif. State Dept. Agric., Mo. Bul. 20:479–80, July, 1931.

8. Conrad, Henry S. Ethics among professors. Amer. Assoc. Univ. Professors, Bul. 19:144–48, February, 1933.

9. Journal of Agricultural Research. 1–, 1913–.

Published by the U. S. Department of Agriculture, under the direction of a joint committee representing the Department and the Association of Land-Grant Colleges and Universities.

10. National Advisory Committee on Education. Federal relations to education. Report of the National Advisory Committee on Education. Part I: Committee findings and recommendations. Part II: Basic findings. 1:i–viii, 1–140; 2:i–xvi, 1–448, figs. 1–17. (744 Jackson Place, Washington, D. C., 1931.)

11. North Carolina Agricultural Experiment Station. Bulletins 1–, 1877–.

Numbers were first applied to No. 57, and lists vary slightly as to the publications comprised in the first 56 numbers.

12. Pennsylvania Agricultural Experiment Station. Bulletins 1–, 1887–.

13. Shear, C. L. Coöperation and individualism in scientific investigation. Sci. Mo. 9:342–48, October, 1919. Reprinted.

14: U. S. Department of Agriculture. Report of the Secretary of Agriculture for the year ———. 1862–.

Report of the Commissioner, 1862–88; Report of the Secretary, 1889–. From 1862 to 1920, inclusive, and for 1922 and 1923, the reports of Chiefs of Offices, Divisions, and Bureaus are included with the report of the Secretary in a consecutively paged volume. For 1921 and 1924 to date, all these reports are issued separately each year, with separate paging.

15. U. S. Department of Agriculture. Department Bulletins 1–1500, 1913–29.

All Bureau series of publications were discontinued on June 30, 1913, and various Departmental series inaugurated on July 1. This series of *Department Bulletins* was succeeded by *Technical Bulletins* and *Miscellaneous Publications*, the issuance of which, however, began in 1927. The Department bulletins were designated simply *Bulletins* until after No. 1100, when the word *Department* was inserted.

16. U. S. Department of Agriculture. Miscellaneous Publications 1–, 1927–.

The different publications in this series range in size from 16mo or smaller up through 12mo, 8vo, and 4to, which means that bound sets rarely are complete. This series should not be confused with the concurrent series of *Miscellaneous Circulars*.

17. U. S. Department of Agriculture. Technical Bulletins 1–, 1927–.

18. U. S. Department of Agriculture, Bureau of Animal Industry. Bulletins 1–167, 1893–1913.

19. U. S. Department of Agriculture, Bureau of Chemistry. Bulletins 1–166, 1883–1913.

From Division of Chemistry, 1883–1901, and Bureau of Chemistry, 1901–13. Thereafter its bulletins were included in the various Departmental series.

20. U. S. Department of Agriculture, Office of Experiment Stations. List of workers in subjects pertaining to agriculture in state agricultural colleges and experiment stations, 19 . .–19 . . U. S. Dept. Agric., Misc. Publ. 12, 43, 67, 100, 134, 154, 214, for the years 1925–35.

21. U. S. Department of Agriculture, Office of Experiment Stations. A classified list of projects carried on by the agricultural experiment stations, 19–.

Unnumbered mimeographed publications, letter size, of 200 to 400 pages each. Those for 1919 to 1921 covered calendar years, while 1923 and 1925 to 1927 were for fiscal years. The list for 1930 was printed as *Miscellaneous Publication 89.*

22. U. S. Department of Agriculture, Office of Personnel and Business Administration. List of technical workers in the Department of Agriculture and outline of Department functions. U. S. Dept. Agric., Misc. Publ. 5, 32, 63, 93, 123, 177, for the years 1927–33 (excluding 1932).

23. U. S. Department of Agriculture, Forest Service, Region Five. Handbook on personnel management and procedure. Part 1. U. S. Dept. Agric., unnumbered publ., 67 p., 1932.

24. U. S. Department of the Interior, Office of Education. Survey of landgrant colleges and universities. U. S. Dept. Int., Off. Educ., Bul. 1930 (9, vol. 1):i–xxviii, 1–998; (9, vol. 2):i–iv, 1–921, 1930.

25. Whetzel, H. H. Democratic coördination of scientific efforts. Science 50: 51–55, July 18, 1919.

Chapter II : CLIMATE

[Because each chapter covers a different subject and therefore will be used chiefly by a different constituency, it seems desirable to make each one complete and self-contained. For this reason, among others, a complete table of chapter contents is placed at the beginning of each chapter, rather than at the front of the volume. A list of all literature cited in the chapter will be found at the end of the chapter and the numbers in parentheses in the text refer the reader to the corresponding entries in the list. All entry numbers occurring in each major section of a chapter are also listed in numerical sequence at the end of that section, thus forming what is in effect a section list of literature cited. These features all should prove of great convenience to readers.]

CHAPTER CONTENTS

Chapter II

CLIMATE

1. INTRODUCTION

CLIMATE PROPERLY may be classed as a natural resource. It is discussed in this volume, first, because of the great and fundamental importance of meteorological information to agricultural production and distribution; second, because—seeing that the separation of agriculture and natural resources had to be made rather arbitrarily—the inclusion of climate here makes for a better balance in size between the two volumes.

2. SCOPE AND AGENCIES

BECAUSE THE SUBJECT is less familiar to both administrators and laymen than are many lines of official activity, it seems desirable to give more attention to the definition and scope of its content than ordinarily would be done. For the same reason, the interrelation of climate and the subject matter of other volumes than that on agriculture is set forth rather fully.

DEFINITION AND SCOPE

Climate is the characteristic long-time condition of the atmosphere of a place or region, the persisting result of several aerographical factors. Weather, on the other hand, is the temporary and sometimes local manifestation of aerographical or meteorological processes. Climate changes with exceeding slowness, measured in units of geologic time. Weather changes rapidly and frequently, measured in hours and days. Both vary with the seasons.

Climatology is the science dealing with climates. Meteorology is the name commonly applied to the body of physical laws and data concerning weather. It is an old but rather unfortunate name (for meteors have nothing to do with weather) and might well be replaced by such preferable terms as aerography and aerographics, or aerology and aerologics. The term aerology, however, has been used by aerographers in the rather restricted sense of applying only to the upper air.

[87]

It is customary to define both climate and weather in terms of their relation to the development of plants and animals, and especially to the comfort of humans (see dictionaries), but obviously this is an unwarranted limitation. Climate and weather exist where humankind are absent and animals and plants are virtually negligible in numbers. There also is much confusion of thought as to the relative geographic scope of climate and weather, but again it is obvious that climate, as well as weather, must be both regional and local. Some appear inclined to regard weather as embracing phenomena within land and water surfaces, as well as of the atmosphere. There can be no doubt, however, that the conditions within the land and water bodies of the earth's surface are an effect of weather, rather than a part of it. The chief exception to this is the local effect of hot springs, geyser basins, etc., on temperature, humidity, etc.

Climate, in itself, usually is a great natural resource. At the same time, it has a profound influence on agriculture and also on certain other natural resources, such as soil, water, forests, and parks, not to mention the formation of petroleum and its products.

The chief factor of climate is temperature. Solar radiation is the principal source of heat, and as it therefore is the principal influence on temperature it is the basis of climate. As water covers about three fourths of the surface of the earth, the heat absorbed by water is tremendously important. Air in turn is warmed by radiation of heat from the earth (land and water), from various structures, and from water and other materials in the air.

Air and water, being fluid, move readily under the impulse of gravity. The gravity of air and water changes with their temperature, both being lighter and tending to rise when warmer, both being heavier and tending to sink when colder. Warm waters, heated in the more tropical parts of the world, tend to flow in great ocean-surface rivers or ocean currents toward the colder polar areas, displacing the colder waters, which sink beneath them. When either warm or cold currents approach or impinge on the shores of land masses, definite climatic effects are produced. In the same way, bodies of heated air rise and are replaced by the inflow of colder, heavier air beneath them. These movements of bodies of air normally are called winds, and in their extreme forms are known as gales, hurricanes, tornadoes, typhoons, etc. This continued circulation of air and water, caused by solar radiation and modified by the rotation of the earth and by its topography, is the chief cause of climate and of the temporary manifestations which we call weather.

Next to temperature, the most important factor of climate is moisture, and this because it is antecedently a factor of temperature. Heating of water surfaces causes the evaporation of moisture into the superimposed stratums of warm air. The circulation of this moisture-laden air, and the condensation or precipitation of the moisture when the air becomes cooled, produce the different forms of moisture known as halo, fog, cloud, mist, rain, snow, sleet, hail, frost, and dew.

Solar radiation, together with the circulation of air and water, the evaporation, condensation, and precipitation of moisture, and the variations in temperature and moisture—all of these, influenced by latitude and longitude and by the physiographic features of the earth's surface, make up the complex we call climate. The local fluctuations of these variable forces from day to day are the phenomenons we call weather.

AGENCIES AND INTERRELATIONS

The three chief factors of climate, as noted above, are solar radiation, ocean temperature and flow, and atmospheric temperature and movement. Solar radiation as such exerts its chief direct influence on agriculture, so far as known now, although it may directly affect health also. Ocean temperature and consequent current movement profoundly affect navigation. Meteorologic processes affect almost every human activity, although others perhaps are not so extensively or profoundly affected as those of agriculture.

Only two Federal agencies, the Astrophysical Laboratory of the Smithsonian Institution and the Weather Bureau of the U. S. Department of Agriculture, are concerned with solar radiation. Three Federal agencies and one State agency in California have present responsibility for studies of ocean temperatures and currents. These are the Hydrographic Office of the Navy Department, the Coast and Geodetic Survey of the Department of Commerce, and the Weather Bureau of the Department of Agriculture in the Federal government; and the Scripps Institution of Oceanography, of the University of California, as a State agency. Considerable international coöperation exists in obtaining data on ocean temperatures and current flows.

The Weather Bureau is the one Federal unit concerned primarily with climate and weather. In this responsibility it is the successor of the Medical Department (Surgeon-General's Office) of the War Department, the General Land Office and the Patent Office (then) of the Interior Department, the Smithsonian Institution, the Division of Statistics of the Department of Agriculture, and, finally, the Signal Service (Office, Corps) of the War Department.

Within its field the Weather Bureau has wide and varied activities, as will be shown. Not nearly all of its work relates merely to climate discussed here as basic to agriculture, or to weather discussed here in relation to agricultural operations and products. Climate and weather affect not only agriculture, but also commerce, industry, labor, education and recreation, public health, social welfare, public works, transportation, and national defense, not forgetting public finance. It is evident, therefore, that the work of the Weather Bureau concerns virtually every one of the group activities which are to be considered in this comprehensive survey of the Federal, State, and local governmental relations in human affairs.

Studies of the relations of climate and weather to plants and animals, as well as the regular forecasts and special forecasts of storms, cold waves, frosts, harvest weather, fruit-drying weather, etc., are discussed in the chapters on Plant Industries and Animal Industries, in this volume on Agriculture, so far as such studies relate to the protection of those industries from unfavorable climatic influences. The forecasting of weather favorable to the development of forest fires, and the hourly forecasts on going fires, will be treated in the section on Forest Protection in the chapters on Forests and Parks, in the volume on Natural Resources.

The river and flood service of the Weather Bureau, with coöperation from the Forest Service, the Geological Survey, the Reclamation Bureau, the Army Engineer Corps, and other Federal, State, and municipal agencies—a service which includes river gaging throughout the year and flood forecasts and warnings as needed when floods threaten or occur—, relates to the chapter on Water Resources in the volume on Natural Resources, as well as to the volumes on Transportation, Public Works, etc.

That portion of the work of the Weather Bureau which serves to protect shipping from damage or loss by storms on oceans, lakes, or rivers, will relate to the volumes on Transportation and on Commerce. So also will its forecasts for the protection of perishable products in storage and during shipment.

The aerological observations and reports of the Weather Bureau, as well as its aviation forecasts and warnings, and its commercial airways service, will require some treatment in connection with the airways division of the study on Transportation; and they also are important to National Defense.

The recording and interpreting of aerographical data, done by the Weather Bureau and covering both meteorological conditions in the air and their influence on conditions upon the earth, are of large importance to the studies on Public Health, Public Welfare, Education and Recreation, and National Defense, and therefore must receive mention in the volumes that are devoted to those subjects.

3. Research Fundamental to Weather Service

From the introductory discussion it is seen that there are three lines of research fundamental to knowledge of climate and weather and to ability to forecast weather. These are solar radiation, ocean temperatures and current movements, and aerography itself, or meteorological manifestations and processes.

SOLAR RADIATION

Studies in solar radiation are conducted by two separate Federal agencies, the Astrophysical Observatory of the Smithsonian Institution (142),* and the Weather Bureau (150; 151) of the U. S. Department of Agriculture. Studies of sun-spot numbers and intensities are conducted by the Naval Observatory of the Navy Department (174).

---

* Numbers in parentheses refer to the Literature Cited, at the end of the Chapter.

Astrophysical Observatory

The Smithsonian Institution, one of the independent establishments of the Federal government, not connected with any executive department, has been conducting research on solar radiation in California during most of the years since 1905 (142). The Carnegie Institution established an observatory for solar research on Mount Wilson, in Los Angeles County, about 1905. Upon invitation of George E. Hale, then director on Mount Wilson, the Smithsonian Institution built its Astrophysical Observatory there, and Dr. Charles G. Abbot, director of the Astrophysical Observatory, transferred from Washington, D. C., with certain of his staff, to Mount Wilson during the summers. The work was continued there from 1905 to 1920. During 1909 and 1910, a temporary coöperating station of the Carnegie Institution was occupied on Mount Whitney.

At the request of the Astrophysical Observatory, in 1919, the Weather Bureau coöperated fully in helping to find a mountain peak more favorable than Mount Wilson in respect of freedom from cloudiness and atmospheric dust. Several peaks were investigated in Arizona, Nevada, and southeastern California. Old Dads Mountain near Bagdad, and Kessler Peak near Cima, both in San Bernardino County, California, and Mount Harqua Hala, several miles from Wenden, Arizona, were tentatively selected by the two agencies. Thereafter the Weather Bureau made daily observations on all three peaks from December, 1919, to December, 1920. Mount Harqua Hala finally was selected and the observatory moved there from Mount Wilson (11).

In November, 1925, the observatory was returned to California from Arizona, and set up on Table Mountain, near Swartout, California. This location is in the Los Angeles County Park, on the edge of the Mojave Desert, thirty miles northeast of the former location on Mount Wilson. The park supervisors coöperated in giving the observatory the right of occupancy, and built an automobile road to the site. Here the altitude of 7500 feet insures excellent conditions for the reception of radiation. Observations of night seeing, made at the request of the California Institute of Technology, show that the location is exceptionally fine in this particular.

The research conducted covers the intensity of solar radiation, the distribution of radiation over the sun's disk, the radiation of the earth outward, the scattered radiation of the sky, the reflecting power of clouds, etc. All of these are problems which relate directly to meteorology. A permanent field director, Mr. A. F. Moore, resides on Table Mountain, and observations are made daily throughout the year, whereas on Mount Wilson they were made through the summer.

While the work was being conducted at Mount Wilson, the practicability of using solar heat for cooking purposes was demonstrated (12). In 1929 the agricultural engineering division in the California Agricultural Experiment Station contributed a bulletin on the solar heater (50) in which the coöperation of various Weather Bureau stations in California and Arizona was acknowledged (p. 30).

In 1918, the Astrophysical Observatory established an observing station at Calama, near Montezuma, Chile, for the purpose of determining solar radiation under more favorable atmospheric conditions. In 1920, the station was moved to Montezuma. Since December, 1919, daily reports of the records of radiation at this station in Chile have been telegraphed to the Weather Service of Argentina, for use in forecasting. Both the Argentine and the Chilean Governments were helpful in starting the enterprise. The government of Argentina now publishes a forecast of the weather for one week in advance, based largely on these Chilean records of solar radiation made by the Smithsonian Institution.

A mathematical analysis of the accumulated observations has yielded some results of large potential importance to the study of climate and weather (9; 10). Determinations of the departures from the solar radiation constant of 1.940 calories per minute per square centimeter indicate several different periodicities, varying from five months to thirty-three years. Comparison of these determined departures with recorded weather data indicates direct connection, with some promise for long-range weather forecasting. Apparent periodicities had been detected by the Smithsonian observers in the United States, but the less favorable observing conditions had made the results of doubtful significance.

There has been occasional coöperation between the Office of Solar Radiation Investigations in the Weather Bureau and the Astrophysical Observatory in obtaining data on radiation. In July and August, 1913, the Weather Bureau joined with the Smithsonian Institution and the Carnegie Institution observatory at Mount Wilson, California, in an expedition to Mount Whitney in the southern Sierra Nevada, with balloon observations at other points. Self-recording pyrheliometers of the Smithsonian observatory were carried in the balloon soundings conducted by the Weather Bureau in free air at Santa Catalina Island, Mount Whitney, and Lone Pine. The results were published by the Astrophysical Observatory (5; 6) and the Weather Bureau (24).

In 1914, three pyrheliometers were furnished by the Smithsonian Institution and carried by the sounding balloons of the Weather Bureau in measurements of solar radiation in free air at great elevations over Fort Omaha, Nebraska, where the Signal Corps of the Army also collaborated in the experimentation.

Weather Bureau

Preliminary experiments were made in the field of solar radiation while the weather service still was in the Signal Corps of the Army. In 1883, an expedition to Mount Whitney, California, was organized to study the absorption of solar heat by the earth's atmosphere. The Signal Corps had the coöperation of the Ordnance and Infantry Departments of the Army in manning the expedition, of commercial agencies in its financing, and of astronomical observatories in its research personnel (98).

The solar radiation studies of the Weather Bureau are carried on in conjunction with related studies of other radiation, including that of the stars, the sky, and the earth. They were begun many years ago and are conducted now at four stations. They consist in measuring this radiation from both sun and stars, as received at the earth's surface. They include the rate at which heat is received during the day by radiation from the sun and from the sky, the rate at which it is lost at night by radiation from the earth, and the relation of these radiations to atmospheric conditions. From these measurements are compiled the daily and annual variations in intensity with reference to geographical position, and the effects produced by latitude, altitude, and the vapor content of the atmosphere. Correlated studies determine sky brightness, or the intensity of natural lighting, in different parts of the country, under the different conditions occurring at different times in the day or in the season, or under the different conditions of the atmosphere.

Coöperation with the University of Nebraska was begun in June, 1915, when two types of pyrheliometers were installed on the buildings of the State agricultural experiment station at Lincoln, the results to be used by both agencies (150—1915:75, and 1916:66).

In 1918, the Office of Solar-Radiation Investigations of the Weather Bureau, then located at American University, Washington, D. C., coöperated fully with the Chemical Warfare Service of the War Department (formerly the experiment station of the Bureau of Mines) in determining meteorological conditions during experiments in the open air (150—1918:68).

In the designing and construction of an improved thermoelectric recording pyrheliometer, the Weather Bureau and the Bureau of Standards of the Department of Commerce coöperated extensively in 1923 (93). One of these instruments was furnished to the Chemical Warfare Service for use in its research at the Edgewood Arsenal in Maryland (150—1923:129).

The International Meteorological Organization maintains various commissions, including a Commission on Radiation Researches (112). Both the Weather Bureau and the Astrophysical Observatory have been represented on this international committee of coöperation.

While, as noted previously, there is only occasional direct coöperation between the Astrophysical Observatory and the Weather Bureau in making their studies of solar radiation, there is large coöperation in the use and publication of results. In 1919, at the request of the Bureau, the Smithsonian Institution (7) began the transmission of its observations in Chile to the Bureau, and these were published in the *Monthly Weather Review* from February, 1919, to January, 1923, inclusive. They then were discontinued temporarily because of instrument difficulties at the observatory. In the meantime a study of the Smithsonian solar-constant values was begun by the Weather Bureau, with reference to the effect on weather conditions in the United States. In 1926, at the further request of the Bureau, the Smithsonian Institution allowed the transcription of all its Chilean records from 1920 to 1926, inclusive, and these were published by the Bureau, for the information of scientists, with an introductory statement by the Astrophysical Observatory (8). Recently the Bureau has made a popular presentation of the relation of solar radiation to agriculture (92).

A study closely related to the determinations of solar radiation is that of the interceptive or shading effect of screening constructions, such as wire insect cages, lath or fabric screens or covers for growing plants, and clothing worn by humans, and the influence of such interception on the organisms shaded. Another very similar study, even more directly related to the physical problems of radiation, is concerned with the interceptive values of various foreign substances, such as smoke and dust, in the air. Research in the shading effects on plants and insects belongs to the chapter on Plant Industries, as it chiefly concerns the protection of plants. Studies in the radiation of artificial heat by different types of orchard heaters belong also to plant protection. The studies of smoke and dust are more pertinent to this chapter on Climate, although smoke studies have been made with direct reference to orchard protection.

The combustion of ordinary materials for the purpose of creating smoke screens or covers produces higher temperatures as well. In order to test the interceptive values of such screens, apart from increased temperatures, the Weather Bureau and the Chemical Warfare Service of the Army coöperated in critical experiments with white phosphorus smoke covers at the Edgewood Arsenal in 1923 (94).

In 1922 plans were made by the Weather Bureau to take part in an international investigation of the dust content of the atmosphere, under the direction of the International Geodetic and Geophysical Union. The Bureau received one of the twelve Owens dust-counters distributed by the Meteorological Section (C) of the Union, and the study was begun in 1923. Through coöperation by the Air Service of the Army the research was carried into the upper atmosphere to an altitude of 12,000 feet (150—1922 :97, and 1923 :130).

Naval Observatory

The Naval Observatory, at Washington, D. C., a unit of the U. S. Department of the Navy, makes daily determinations of the number, area, and position of sun spots. The work was begun in 1897 and now is part of an international coöperation, with participation by several other American observatories, including the Table Mountain Observatory of the Smithsonian Institution, in Los Angeles County, in establishing which the county coöperated. Sunspot intensities may have direct influence on weather through changes caused in the quantity of solar radiation and in magnetic condition on the earth. Since January, 1927, the Weather Bureau has had the coöperation of the Naval Observatory in furnishing these daily records by months for publication in the *Monthly Weather Review* (174—1931 :17).

The publications in the Literature Cited at the end of the chapter (pp. 152 ff.) which have been cited in this section on Solar Radiation are Nos. 5, 6, 7, 8, 9, 10, 11, 12, 24, 50, 92, 93, 94, 98, 112, 142, 150, 151, and 174.

OCEAN TEMPERATURES AND CURRENTS

The heating of oceanic waters by solar radiation, and their circulation under the influence of unequal heating and the earth's rotation, are among the major factors in the production of both climate and weather, as is pointed out in the introductory discussion of climate. On the other hand, the barometric pressure and the winds exert a direct influence on the velocity and direction of currents (17; 72; 197).

Systematic collection and study of records of ocean temperatures and current movements are activities of at least three separate Federal agencies, namely, the Division of Marine Meteorology of the Hydrographic Office of the Navy Department, the Division of Tides and Currents in the Coast and Geodetic Survey of the Department of Commerce, and the section on Marine Meteorology of the Weather Bureau of the Department of Agriculture. The Engineer Corps of the War Department, rather than the Coast and Geodetic Survey, has jurisdiction over the Great Lakes and any similar studies made there. Fluctuation of water level in the Great

Lakes is of large importance to shipping, engineering, and other commercial interests. The relation of wind velocity and direction to changes in the water level has been made the subject of coöperative study by the Weather Bureau and the Engineer Corps (77). For a time, at least, some Signal Service weather observers obtained water temperatures in rivers and harbors in coöperation with the U. S. Fish Commission (1).

Hydrographic Office

The hydrographic work of the Navy Department was first definitely established in 1842, when Congress created a Depot of Charts and Instruments. From 1844 to 1861, this depot was under charge of Lieutenant, subsequently Commander, Matthew F. Maury. He organized an extensive system of collecting hydrographic information from the logs of men-of-war and merchant vessels in all parts of the world. The reports covered ocean currents, wind movement, water temperature, and air pressure and temperature, besides preserving other meteorological data. During this eighteen-year period, *Wind and Current Charts* were published in six separate series. Series D, *Thermal Charts,* showed the surface temperatures of the oceans. The work covered first the Atlantic and later the Pacific and Indian Oceans. After 1853, the work became broadly international, through the agreement of a conference held in Belgium in that year, as a result of Commander Maury's interest in hydrographic research. The conference prepared two forms of international abstract logbooks, one for naval vessels and one for commercial vessels. Another gratifying result was the establishment of meteorological observations throughout most of the world on a uniform basis, both on land and at sea.

Numerous publications, official and private, present the history of this organization and its work (18; 19; 36; 39; 57; 86; 143; 172; 173; 190; 195; 196; 198).

The present Hydrographic Office was created in 1866 by separation of three units to be known thereafter as the Depot of Charts and Instruments, the Hydrographic Office, and the Naval Observatory. The obtaining of oceanic and aerographic data from naval and merchant vessels, which had been interrupted by the Civil War, was resumed by the Office in 1873 and has been continued and expanded since that time. In 1884, six branch offices were established by the Hydrographic Office, including one at San Francisco, California. The number now is eighteen.

From the organization of the meteorological branch of the Signal Service of the War Department in 1870, there was some duplication in the work on ocean meteorology done in this field by this unit and its successor, the Weather Bureau of the Department of Agriculture (1891), on the one hand, and the work of the Hydrographic Office on the other. This continued until 1904, when an interdepartmental board defined the scope and duties of each. In 1913, a further agreement between the two units was made. In both cases, it was provided that the reporting of meteorological data by ocean vessels should be made directly to the Weather Bureau, which, in turn, should furnish to the Hydrographic Office all meteorological data needed for its pilot charts, on which due credit to the Weather Bureau was to be printed.

Since 1904, the data of climatic value received directly by the Hydrographic Office from ocean-going vessels are confined to the direction, velocity, and temperature of ocean currents, and the direction and velocity of the wind. By 1930, more than 13,000 such reports were being received annually. The work of collating this extensive mass of information regarding ocean waters was begun systematically in 1923, before which time the Section of Ocean Currents had been combined with the Section of Pilot Charts. Under the new method the ocean is divided into areas each five degrees square. For each square are recorded the reported set and drift of currents, the wind direction and force, the surface-water temperatures, salinity, gravity, etc. The resultant data have been used in publications since 1923. The work was about three-fourths completed in 1930 and it was hoped to finish it by 1932. Data collected along the coast are not included in the above collation, but the compilation of these will begin when the assembling of the oceanic records is completed.

Some additional data on current movements are obtained through calculation of the records of bottle drifts. In this study bottles containing record sheets supplied by the Hydrographic Office are dropped from vessels into the ocean at recorded locations, with a contained request that the finder report to the U. S. Hydrographic

Office. Several hundred such reports are received each year, through international coöperation, the number amounting to nearly 1200 in 1930.

On the initiative of the Hydrographic Office, the Secretary of the Navy called a conference of representatives of all departments and scientific organizations of the government to consider a proposed naval expedition for research in oceanography. The conference lasted from July 1 to October 2, 1924, and submitted an exhaustive report outlining the reasons, objectives, and geographic areas of such a research (172—1924:32–35). The Hydrographer subsequently was made permanent chairman of an Advisory Committee on Oceanography.

The Hydrographic Office has been in coöperation with the Scripps Institution of Oceanography, of the University of California, for several years, in gathering data on temperatures, ocean currents, and circulation of oceanic waters in the Pacific. In the most recent phase of this coöperation, the Scripps Institution has furnished special equipment to two vessels of the Hydrographic Office which will operate off the west coast of Central America and especially in the vicinity of the Panama Canal. Temperature at various depths to 1200 meters, or nearly three fourths of a mile, will be obtained.

At the Fifth Pan-Pacific Science Congress, in 1929, resolutions were adopted providing for collection of oceanographic data and making the Hydrographic Office the international custodian of the resulting collections, which indeed it long had been already (172—1932:29).

United States Coast and Geodetic Survey

The Coast Survey, now the United States Coast and Geodetic Survey, in the Department of Commerce, was created in 1816. Many different publications contain accounts of its history and activities (114; 146; 163; 164; 167; 189) and of its publications (165; 166). Only the most important recent ones are cited.

The Survey has been engaged on hydrographic surveys of the shores of California since 1849. The measurement of the direction, depth, velocity, and temperatures of currents, especially those that occur along shore lines, is an important part of its work. In ear-

lier years, both before and after the Civil War, it made extensive
studies of the Gulf Stream (127). While current studies are carried on primarily as an aid to navigation, the facts accumulated
have an important bearing on the understanding of climatic factors, as has been shown. Three classes of currents, tidal, continuous, and accidental, are studied, but only the continuous currents
have particular climatic influence. The observations on continuous
currents must cover long periods of time in order to be able to
measure the effects of varying temporary and seasonal weather
conditions on the currents, and the counter effects of the currents
on the weather factors.

Where major ocean currents impinge on the land, as the Japan
Current does on the coast of Alaska, marked influences are exerted
on climate. The returning portion of that current which moves
southward along the Pacific Coast of America influences temperatures and fog production along the California coast (90). So also
do various onshore currents, as well as the upwellings of cold water
from the ocean depths, like those which occur near Cape Mendocino and at other points along the California shore. In 1920 a
Division of Tides and Currents was organized from a previous section of the Hydrographic Division of the Survey. At about the same
time, coöperation was begun with the Bureau of Lighthouses of
the Department of Commerce in making observations on currents
and on meteorological factors. The anchored lightships were used
as stations, the Pacific Coast studies starting on five such vessels
in the fiscal year 1921 (169).

The Coast and Geodetic Survey has a wide range of coöperation
in many of its hydrographic studies, in addition to that with the
Bureau of Lighthouses. It exchanges survey information with the
governments of Canada, Great Britain, France, and other countries (163—1927, et seq.). It maintains many tide stations, a considerable proportion of them in coöperation with other official
agencies. At many of the coöperative stations the Survey furnishes
only the instruments and bears no other expense than that of assembling the obtained data. Records of water temperatures and den-
sity are taken at all primary tide stations, such as San Francisco,
Los Angeles, La Jolla, and San Diego. Among coöperating official
agencies at tide stations are the Navy Department, at San Diego;

the Engineer Corps of the Army, at Monterey and in San Francisco Bay (153 current stations in 1932); county officials at Oakland, Alameda County, and Santa Ana, Orange County; municipal officers at Los Angeles and Newport Beach, California; and Port Authority, at Marshfield, Coos Bay, Oregon. Observations on continuous currents are made at some of these tide stations.

Several recent publications contain data on Pacific Coast coastal and harbor currents (168; 170), in addition to the one previously cited (169). *Pacific Coast Current Tables* have been issued for some years, but the *Annual Combined Tidal-Current Tables* are new, that for New York Harbor dating from 1928, Massachusetts Bay from 1929, and San Francisco Bay from 1930. *Combined Tidal-Current Charts* are still more recent, that for New York dating from 1929, and those for Massachusetts and San Francisco Bays from 1931 (163—1931:36).

The publications in the list of Literature Cited at the end of the chapter which have been cited in this section on Ocean Temperatures and Currents are Nos. 1, 17, 18, 19, 36, 39, 57, 72, 77, 86, 90, 114, 127, 143, 146, 163, 164, 165, 166, 167, 168, 169, 170, 172, 173, 189, 190, 195, 196, 197, and 198.

AEROGRAPHIC OR METEOROLOGICAL RESEARCH

Aerography, aerographics, aerology, or meteorology, as it is variously called, is the study of those phenomenons of the air which in the aggregate comprise weather and climate. The primary ones are temperature, which in turn induces two others, evaporation (causing humidity), and movement (called wind), from which, under the influence of temperature, are produced cloudiness and precipitation (rain, snow, frost), and barometric pressure. Aerography is concerned with data of the air over land masses (terrestrial aerography, or meteorology), over the oceans and seas (marine aerography or meteorology), and in the heights (free air) above the land and water surfaces. The term meteorology has been commonly used for aerographics but, as meteors have no known or probable relation to weather or climate, this term seems rather absurd as well as misleading to the layman, and preferably would be replaced by one or another of the informing names for this branch of knowledge.

Naturally, the studies of terrestrial aerographics are of much earlier origin and have produced much more extensive information than those of marine air phenomenons. Observing stations on land are easily established, fixed in location, and accessible for information—conditions not true of vessels at sea, except of the anchored lightships which really are auxiliary offshore land stations. And yet, because the oceans cover some two-thirds of the surface of the earth, the happenings in the air above them are tremendously important to a knowledge of land weather and climate.

Historical Development of Aerography, 1814–70

Much attention has been given in recent years to the historical development of studies in aerography or meteorology in the United States, especially to the work of official agencies. A few papers have covered the whole field or special portions of it (43; 76; 78; 101; 117; 155). Others have described the important contributions made by outstanding individuals (100A; 118; 119; 123; 199). Most of them, however, are concerned with the work of a single agency, and will be mentioned in the discussion of that agency. The work of the present Weather Bureau probably is as well known to the average citizen as that of any Federal organization, but the fact that a succession of Federal agencies has been actively engaged in the collection and compilation of aerographic data over a period of nearly a century and a quarter is little known to others than the professional meteorologists. The extensive accumulations of data, by which their present successor profits, and the volume of national and international coöperation they developed, are worthy of brief mention as a background for the present setup.

Medical Department (Surgeon General's Office), U. S. Army.— Most historical writers in this field have stated that the first official order to Army surgeons to keep a record of weather observations at their posts and report them to the Surgeon General was issued in 1818 and that the first records on file date from January, 1819. Major Smart (139) shows, however, that the first order was sent out as of May 2, 1814, during the War of 1812, and that the first record filed in response is dated July, 1816. He lists the various volumes in which the accumulating data were published, both alone and as supplementary to statistical reports on mortality and sickness in the Army, but overlooks (*op. cit.*, p. 214) one of the major compilations, covering twelve years (38), and also the annual publication of the data for 1820 and 1821. The entire series covered the forty years from 1819 to the end of 1859. These data were included also in the great compilations of meteorological data by the Smithsonian Institution, mentioned below. Outstanding names were those of Forry and Espy, as well as Coolidge, the later compiler. Espy enlisted the coöperation of naval and lighthouse stations, as well as of colleges. Myer, who later became Chief Signal Officer and organized the weather service, was a Medical Department surgeon before the Civil War, and presumably had made meteorological reports in that capacity.

The Medical Department continued to make and report observations until about 1873, when such of the surgeons as were willing became voluntary observers of the newly established meteorological service of the Signal Service of the Army, as did the observers of the Smithsonian Institution at the end of 1873.

General Land Office, Treasury Department.—In 1817, Josiah Meigs, then Commissioner of the General Land Office, asked Congress to require the keeping of meteorological records at land offices (76). Congress took no action, but Meigs asked the registers of the then twenty offices to make such observations and include them with their regular monthly reports, as evidently was done at least until 1819. It is possible that his enthusiasm helped to encourage the increased activity of the Medical Department of the Army along this line in 1818 and 1819.

The Smithsonian Institution.—In December, 1847, Joseph Henry, the first secretary of the newly created Smithsonian Institution, in his "Programme of Organization" proposed to the Board of Regents a "System of extended meteorological observations for solving the problem of American storms." The plan was approved, and in 1848 the coöperation of the existing systems in the Medical Department of the Army, and in the States of New York and Pennsylvania, was obtained (20; 99). While the Medical Department chiefly had in mind the relation of weather to health, Henry desired to solve the problem relating to weather. By 1849, he was receiving brief telegraphic reports of the weather from the operators of the telegraph companies. By 1850, he was constructing a daily weather map from his telegraphed reports, posting it in the Institution, and indicating the weather prospects by signals displayed on the tower of the building.

Probably the most important contribution of the Smithsonian Institution was in its three great series of volumes of aerographical data, in which many other government units coöperated. Professor Arnold Guyot was asked to compile available meteorological data in tabular form and first published the volume known as *Guyot's* (meteorological and physical) *Tables,* in 1852, with enlarged revised editions in 1857 and 1859 and a fourth in 1884. Based on the Guyot tables was a later series known as *Smithsonian Meteorological Tables* (42). The original publication was in 1893, the second (revised) edition in 1897, and the third (revised) in 1907. Coöperation with the Coast and Geodetic Survey, the Signal Corps of the Army, and the Weather Bureau of the Department of Agriculture was acknowledged in the prefaces. The fourth (revised) edition was compiled and interpreted by Professor Charles F. Marvin, assisted by H. H. Kimball, both of the U. S. Department of Agriculture's Weather Bureau (111; 155—37). Coöperation of the U. S. Bureau of Standards and the Coast and Geodetic Survey in furnishing certain formulas is acknowledged. In the meantime, these two series of general compilations had been supplemented by special compilations of all available data on precipitation, temperature, etc. (135; 136). These included all the data accumulated by the Medical Department and the Lake Survey of the Army Engineer Corps, the Patent Office, the Smithsonian Institution, the Coast Survey of the Treasury Department, the Signal Corps of the Army, the Division of Statistics of the U. S. Department of Agriculture, New York University, and other agencies. Under mutual arrangement, the compilation was done by Charles A. Schott of the Coast Survey.

The tabulations not only covered the United States but included data from stations in Canada and Mexico, and in Central and South America as well. When the work was established by Congress in the Signal Service of the United States Army in 1870, therefore, extensive aerographic records covering a period of more than fifty years were already assembled and tabulated and available to the workers in published form. The importance of these publications, and the extensive coöperation that made them possible, should not be overlooked.

Hydrographic Office, Navy Department.—The chief work of the Hydrographic Office which relates to climatology already has been mentioned under Ocean Currents. Commander Maury inaugurated an extensive international coöperation in supplying oceanographic information from the logs of naval and commercial vessels of all nations. This included data on air temperatures and pressures, wind direction and velocity, and other factors, as well as water temperatures. Most important also were Maury's vigorous and persistent efforts to promote the organization of "a uniform system of meteorological observations for the land as well as for the sea" (29; 173). These efforts, begun in 1851, were continued until the outbreak of the Civil War. He contemplated especially a service for agriculture, and his appeals were made to farmers, to agricultural societies, and to Congress. In 1871 and 1872 he resumed his efforts to have a nation-wide weather service provided, as the meteorological work of the Signal Service, which had been established in 1870, was organized primarily as an aid to shipping.

Patent Office, Departments of the Treasury and the Interior.— The Patent Office was officially invested with certain agricultural duties (seed collection and distribution, and statistics) as early as 1839, while still in the Treasury Department. Later, under the Interior Department, it was charged with the publication of meteorological information as part of the agricultural statistics (37 :p. iv). An immense quantity of meteorological data, collected by the Patent Office and the Smithsonian Institution for the years 1854 to 1859, inclusive, was compiled at the joint expense of the two institutions and published as a Senate Document in 1861 (37). The agricultural work at the Patent Office was transferred to the Department of Agriculture on its creation in 1862. Coöperation of that Department with the Smithsonian Institution in financing the compilation of the joint information was continued until about 1873 (*Smithsonian Institution Report*, 1874 :286).

The publications in the list of Literature Cited at the end of the chapter which have been cited in this section on Historical Development are Nos. 20, 29, 37, 38, 42, 43, 76, 78, 99, 100A, 101, 111, 117, 118, 119, 123, 135, 136, 139, 155—37, 173, and 199.

Signal Service Period, 1870–91

Chiefly in response to a commercial demand for storm warnings for shipping on the Great Lakes, the Congress in 1870 established a national weather service in the War Department, as a function of the Signal Service of the Army. Colonel Myer, then its head, had been an Army surgeon before the Civil War and was familiar with the weather observations made by the officers of the Medical Department. The act (16 U.S. Stat. L, 369) provided for meteorological observations and for storm warnings on the lakes and seacoasts. Administration and observations were in the hands of officers and enlisted men of the Signal Service who were trained for these new duties by reading courses and special schools at Fort Whipple (now Fort Myer) and elsewhere. For the purposes of interpretation of data and forecasts of probable weather, however, the Service was obliged to obtain qualified civilian scientists from the first. Prominent among these were Professor Cleveland Abbe from the Mitchell Astronomical Observatory at Cincinnati, and Professor I. A. Lapham of Milwaukee, the former remaining permanently in the service. They were largely instrumental in developing the program of aerographic research, as a foundation for more accurate forecasting. The Signal Service has a record for extensive coöperation, both domestic and international, from the very beginning.

Several publications contain briefer or more extensive accounts of the history of the Signal Service (designated as Signal Corps in 1880, and also called Signal Office) during the twenty-one-year period when it was charged with the aerographic work of the United States government (1; 175; 178; 179; 180; 182; 183; 184; 188). The last three list some or all of its publications. The Signal Service also started two series of publications of its own. In July, 1872, it founded the quarto *Monthly Weather Review* (176), which has been continued by the Weather Bureau to the present time. In 1881 it started a series of *Professional Papers* (177), to contain longer contributions, of which numbers 1 to 18 were issued in the period from 1881 to 1885.

Official coöperation in the United States.—In 1872 the Signal Service was obliged to collect reliable data on the elevation of all its stations and their instruments in order to be able to reduce data of observations to mean sea-level barometric pressure. The official agencies which coöperated in this extensive task included the Topographic Office of the Post Office Department, with 300 railroad levels and 14 canal levels from their records; the General Land Office of the Interior Department with 12 western survey and 7 railroad survey levels; the Army Engineer Corps of the War Department, with 7 river and lake survey levels; the U. S. Coast Survey in the Treasury Department, which furnished the height and range of tides at all important ports of the United States; State engineers, who furnished 43 complete lists of State surveys; and city engineers, who furnished 46 levels of railroad crossing surveys (175—1872 :86).

As the Signal Service began equipping its numerous observing stations with delicate instruments, the problem of safe transmission immediately arose. By direct coöperation and order of the Postmaster General, the interest of postal employees was enlisted and continued effectively throughout the twenty-year period (175—1871 and 1890).

By act of June 10, 1872, the Congress extended the benefits of the weather-forecasting service to the agricultural areas of the country. The Signal Service immediately asked the coöperation of State agricultural societies and other agricultural organizations in obtaining additional observers and in the appointment of committees to make suggestions for the establishing and betterment of the service (175—1872 :83). A good response was obtained.

At the end of 1873 the Smithsonian Institution transferred its 283 voluntary observers to the Signal Service. The immediate reasons given were: (*a*) the abolition by Congress of the Smithsonian franking privilege; (*b*) discontinuation by the Department of Agriculture of its coöperation in financing the publication of the data; and (*c*) the failure of the First National Bank, containing Smithsonian funds (*Smithsonian Institution Report,* 1874 :286). It may be noted that all three of the acts probably were direct effects of the then prevailing depression. In June, 1874, the Surgeon General's Office of the War Department transferred to the Signal Service its extensive meteorological records, dating from 1816, and arranged that the incoming reports from its 123 observers should be transmitted also (175—1874 :89). In this way the Signal Service acquired some 400 additional voluntary observers. It is recorded, however, that lack of interest in them by the Signal Service caused many of them to cease taking observations (1), at least until the Signal Corps later came under the administration of General A. W. Greely.

By coöperation between the Navy and War Departments, the Signal Service furnished meteorological instruments through the Bureau of Navigation to all naval vessels, whose officers, under order from the Secretary of the Navy on December 25, 1876, made observations and reported the resulting data to the Signal Service (175—1877–78 :9). This was part of the international coöperation discussed below.

Gradually the Signal Corps built up a very large corps of voluntary observers distributed throughout the country. By the time the work was transferred to the Department of Agriculture in 1891, the Signal Corps was receiving reports from 119 military posts through the coöperation of the Medical Department of the Army (45 :45–51 ; 175—1891 :21), more than three hundred rainfall reports monthly from the Navy Hydrographic Office, about forty such reports monthly from the U. S. Geological Survey, and still others from the Lifesaving Service of the Treasury Department, provided the Signal Corps maintained the necessary telegraph lines to the isolated lifesaving stations (1 :282).

Coöperating State weather services: In 1875 a State Weather Service was created on a modest scale by the Legislature of Iowa. Missouri later took similar action. By 1881, the Signal Corps, foreseeing the possibilities in the movement, had sent a letter to the Governor of each State to suggest the establishment of coöperating State services, and late in 1882 Major Dunwoody of the Corps made a tour of the States to encourage such organization (1–260 ; 175—1882 :761–70). While these were created in and by the States, and virtually all with small State appropriations, their officers had the Federal franking privilege and their observers received the Federal publications (1 ; 23). Gradually the services lost their State character and became part of the Federal organization (188 :11). They served, however, to expand greatly the number of observers throughout the country.

In California, a representative State, official observation and publication of aerographic data began with the State Agricultural Society, created and chartered by the Legislature, its *Transactions* printed by the State, and for years its premiums and prizes furnished from the State treasury. From 1864 to 1874 its *Transactions* (30) contained an annual meteorological report by Dr. Thomas M. Logan, M.D., who was a coöperative observer for the Smithsonian Institution, and Meteorologist to the Society. In 1873 his report contained data from the Signal Service station at San Diego. After his death, and the transfer of Smithsonian observers to the Signal Service in 1874, there were but fragmentary data from 1875 to 1878 and none at all in 1879 and 1880, by reason, probably, of the previously noted Signal Service neglect of the voluntary observers. Beginning in 1881, following a change in leadership and policy in the Signal Corps, and coincident with the development of State coöperation, the *Transactions* contained an annual "Rainfall and Weather Review" by the Signal Corps officer for the State, increasing from 4 pages then to more than 150 pages in 1886, the observer having been made Meteorologist to the Society in 1885. At the very close of this period (1891) the Society published a comprehensive summary of the climate of California and Nevada, prepared by the Signal Service, with special reference to irrigation problems (58). Coöperation from 1891 onward is discussed under the Weather Bureau Period.

There also was wide coöperation with colleges, many of them State institutions, in the collection and exchange of data on weather (1:282), as well as in magnetic observations. Coöperation with the Smithsonian Institution in the compilation of aerographic data has been discussed in the preceding section on Historical Development.

International coöperation.—International coöperation began almost with the inception of the national weather service. Late in 1871, exchange of observations was begun with the Canadian Meteorological Service (175—1872:82). An international series of simultaneous daily meteorological observations, made at specified hours, was begun in 1874, as recommended by the Vienna Congress of 1873. The daily reports totaled 214 and were exchanged twice a month (175—1874:89). A *Bulletin of International Simultaneous*

Observations, containing the results of the daily simultaneous observations, was published daily in quarto form by the United States Signal Service from July 1, 1875, through to 1887, with monthly and annual summaries to the end of 1889. The publication of an international daily weather chart was begun by the Signal Service on July 1, 1878, for the first time in world history, and was the direct result of world-wide coöperation by the civilized powers. As a part of this program of international coöperation, the naval and commercial vessels of the collaborating countries aided by making observations at sea and transmitting the results when they reached port. This important work was begun in 1871 and thereafter was steadily extended (175—1877–78 :149). Through coöperation with the State Department, United States consular officers throughout the world were instructed to accept and forward without charge all such records of meteorological observations left with them by shipmasters for this purpose (74).

By action of the International Meteorological Conference, arrangements were made for extensive international coöperation in a study of the climatic factors in polar regions. After preliminary investigations in 1871, 1877, and 1881 (1 :260), the period from July, 1882, to August, 1883, was designated the International Polar Year, for which the nations composing the conference laid down a comprehensive plan (181) and conducted extensive research. The United States manned two stations in the Arctic, one at Point Barrow, and the other, by the ill-fated Greely expedition, at Fort Conger, Lady Franklin Bay (27 :476).

The publications listed in the Literature Cited at the end of the chapter which have been cited in this section on the Signal Service Period are Nos. 1, 23, 27, 30, 45, 58, 74, 175, 176, 177, 178, 170, 180, 181, 182, 183, 184, and 188.

Weather Bureau Period, 1891–

By act of October 1, 1890, the Congress (26 U. S. Stat. L, 653) created the Weather Bureau (55 :64–66; 188) in the U. S. Department of Agriculture and transferred thereto all the work of collecting and disseminating climatic information which had been delegated to the Signal Service in 1870. This action was due in part to the enormously increased and still increasing service to

agriculture rendered by the national weather service, and in part
to the growing desire to separate civilian and military duties. Many
publications contain shorter or longer accounts of the history and
activities of the Weather Bureau, including its research program
in aerography (4; 13; 26; 34; 48; 56; 59; 69; 71; 73; 85; 108; 121;
122; 124; 130; 150; 151; 158; 188). Several papers are devoted
wholly or in part to the publications of the Bureau (49; 67; 87;
171; 186; 187; 188; 194).

On taking over the work from the Signal Corps, the newly created Weather Bureau found already well developed the collection
of aerographic observational data (both terrestrial and marine),
the compilation, interpretation, and publication of results, and the
forecasting of expected weather nationally and for special industries. The civilian scientists were transferred to the staff of the
Weather Bureau and certain specially trained Signal Corps officers were detailed, through coöperation of the War Department,
to aid in the Bureau's meteorological service. This continued for
many years, until prohibited by the Congress in 1898, when the
outbreak of war required all army officers for military duties
(152—24:11). Necessarily, much attention was given to better
training of personnel, and to this end the Bureau officers coöperated with educational institutions in promoting and giving courses
in meteorology.

The Weather Bureau continued the *Monthly Weather Review*
(155) started by the Signal Service, and in 1914 founded a series
of *Supplements* to it (156), of which thirty-four have been issued.
In 1892 it founded a series of octavo numbered bulletins (152), discontinued in 1913, and in 1893 it founded a series of quarto bulletins, designated by letters (153)—also discontinued in 1913, as
were all Department of Agriculture "Bureau" series.

The Weather Bureau has functions in the field of meteorology
or aerography which, for convenience in discussion, may be arranged in three groups, i.e., investigations, observations, and forecasts (including warnings). Investigations include the study of
meteorological manifestations, the analysis of accumulated data,
the deduction of meteorologic laws, and the study of relations
between weather and the production of animal and plant life.
Observations include the determination and recording of daily or

shorter-period aerographical data for permanent tabulation, and for immediate interpretation in terms of coming weather. Forecasts include the assembling, charting, and interpretation of the results of the daily or shorter-period observation in the light of research, and the various forecasting and warning services by which this information is made promptly available to the public.

Organization and program.—The organization of the Weather Bureau does not conform to these three divisions of function (148). In fact, the Bureau is less definitely organized, as to location and personnel, on the basis of either function or activity, than are most units of government. This doubtless is due in part to the fundamental difference in the materials with which this agency deals, and therefore an equally fundamental difference in methods of research and of service. Probably also it is conditioned on the relatively recent development of meteorology as a science, and the consequent limited full-time personnel and the lack of specialization within it.

The American Society of Civil Engineers, through a special committee, recently has made a survey (15A) of the organization, personnel, equipment, and procedure of the Weather Bureau, and has recommended, among other things, that its program of fundamental research coöperative with other Federal, State, and municipal agencies, and with scientific institutions and commercial agencies and organizations, be greatly expanded (*op. cit.*, p. 155).

In the Weather Bureau at Washington is a quasi-"Branch of Investigation and Service." It comprises twelve administrative and investigative divisions, namely, Climatological, Aerological, Marine, Meteorological Physics, Agricultural Meteorology, River and Flood, Solar Radiation, Instrument, Forecast, District Forecasting, Library, and Monthly Weather Review (a journal). These are small divisions, manned by one to five or six technical employees each. Nine of these represent the research function, while two, Forecasts and District Forecasting, represent the extension function. The Weather Bureau has no regulatory functions.

For forecasting purposes the country is divided into five Forecast Districts, with headquarters at Washington, D. C., Chicago, New Orleans, Denver, and San Francisco. These are intimately concerned with the publication and dissemination of forecasts and warnings for their respective districts. They are supervised by the District Forecasting Division in Washington, D. C., but have no administrative responsibility for the State headquarters or other principal observing stations within their districts.

For each State (with exceptions noted), including Alaska, a State Climatological Section headquarters is maintained, usually at the capital, but sometimes at a metropolis or at the seat of the State university. The entire New England area is classed as if one State, and Delaware and Maryland likewise are consolidated. These headquarters compile and publish the monthly and annual tabulations and discussions of weather data, and also are the local observing station for that city. These State headquarters (successors to the former State weather services in most States) are administratively responsible for the other principal observing stations and for the much larger number of voluntary observers in their States.

Probably no other government agency, except the Division of Crop and Livestock Estimates in the Bureau of Agricultural Economics of the Federal Department of Agriculture, depends so fully on a large volunteer force for its basic data.

The Western District and the State of California will serve to illustrate the setup. Forecast District Four, with headquarters at San Francisco, comprises five Western States—California, Nevada, Oregon, Washington, and Idaho. In California, the Weather Bureau maintains twelve meteorological stations of the first order, of which one is District and State Headquarters, 10 (including this one) are general weather stations, one (Pomona) is a special fruit-frost-service station, and one (Oakland Airport) is a special airways-service station. A first-order station is one where full-time and permanent technical employees of the Weather Bureau are located. Nine separate activities are listed for the San Francisco (District Headquarters) station, including meteorological observations and reports, climatology, agricultural meteorology, marine meteorology, general forecasts and warnings, forest fire-weather warning service, fruit-frost service, aviation forecasts and warnings, commercial airways service. Fewer activities are located at the eleven other first-order stations.

In addition to the dozen principal or first-order stations mentioned, there are some 190 other locations in California where general meteorological records are taken, making 200 in all. There are also some 70 additional points, or 270 in all, at which at least daily precipitation records are taken. During the winter season, special snowfall records are obtained, especially in the mountain areas. Most of these stations are manned by coöperative (voluntary) observers, serving without compensation. There are numerous paid observers, also, such as rainfall, mountain-snowfall, weather and crop, fruit-frost, and river observers, who take only certain classes of observations, for which they receive a nominal compensation.

The Weather Bureau has a widespread and diverse program of research (109) fundamental to its forecasting and warning services. This program of investigation begins with the taking and assembling of twice-daily or thrice-daily observations from its many stations. The nucleus of the research system is the individual observing station (91), of which there are 6000 or more in the United States and are said to be more than 31,000 in the world. Some reports are immediately charted and interpreted for the regular forecasts and warnings. All are tabulated and published for further critical study and interpretation. This insures that the permanent record of an enormous body of observational data collected by the Bureau personnel and an army of observational observers, for purposes of daily forecast, finally serves the much higher purpose of permanent climatological knowledge. This record becomes increasingly valuable with the steady lengthening of the period of years it covers. From these and other fundamental research are deduced the laws governing the origin, dimensions, direction, speed of movement, and intensity of cyclones (not tornadoes, but "lows," low-pressure areas, or storms) and anticyclones ("highs," high-pressure areas, or "fairs"). The research field may be said to include the making of observations, the compilation and analysis of observed results, the deduction of meteorological and climatic laws, and the study of climatic and weather effects on the development and distribution of plants and animals.

The expenditures for direct research in the meteorological phases of climatology have been relatively small during the more than forty years since the Weather Bureau was established. The quality of the leadership in the Federal meteorological service, and outside of it, however, has been such that great advances have been made in the science of climatology, as well as in meteorological service to the public.

Some of the activities, especially among those carried on during the World War, are so intimately concerned with both observations (research) and forecasting (extension), that it is difficult to assign them wholly to either subject. Some therefore are likely to be discussed under one head and others, obviously closely related, to be found under the other.

The publications in the list of Literature Cited at the end of the chapter which are cited in this general section on the Weather Bureau Period are Nos. 4, 13, 15A, 26, 34, 48, 49, 55, 56, 59, 67, 69, 71, 73, 85, 87, 91, 108, 109, 121, 122, 124, 130, 148, 150, 151, 152, 153, 155, 156, 158, 171, 186, 187, 188, and 194.

For convenience of presentation, the research activities of the Weather Bureau may be divided into three groups, concerned respectively with terrestrial, marine, and aerological or free-air aerography. All of these had been developed by the weather service of the Signal Corps, as had also the river-gaging studies which are a necessary outgrowth of precipitation studies and are the basis for flood forecasting.

Terrestrial aerography.—The basis of the study of terrestrial aerographics is the taking of frequent observations on the temperature, pressure, and humidity of the air; on the quantity, kind, and character of the precipitation and of cloudiness; on the quality and character of evaporation; and on the direction and velocity of the air movement, or wind, at stations on the land surface. These observations require large numbers of observing stations, widely scattered over the entire country, as previously stated. The Weather Bureau employs full-time paid observers at first-order or principal stations, and volunteers at the great majority of the stations. Many of the records are taken by self-recording instruments. Others must be obtained at some points, and some at all points, by the individual observers. All the instruments used, whether by paid or volunteer observers, are furnished and kept in repair by the Bureau. The volunteer observers serve either without pay, other than publication, or are paid a small sum for each record taken. To obtain and maintain this large staff of observers requires widespread coöperation with individuals, institutions, commercial organizations, and many agencies of government at the different levels, Federal, State, and municipal.

State weather services coöperating: The promotion of the establishment of State weather services by the Signal Corps during the period from 1881 to 1891 already has been recounted (p. 109, above). This was continued by the Weather Bureau. In 1893, Dunwoody, the Signal Corps officer who helped to organize the services, and who had been detailed to the Weather Bureau, discussed this work before the International Meteorological Congress at Chicago (46). The Weather Bureau published the proceedings of the first to the fourth annual meetings of the American Association of State Weather Services (152—7) from 1893 to 1896, by which time most of them had been absorbed by the Federal system and the meeting had become a convention of Weather Bureau officials (152—24).

The early history of coöperative relations in weather observations in California during the Signal Service period already has been given (p. 110, above). The coöperation with the State Agricultural Society was continued by the Weather Bureau. In his report for 1891, the first year of the Weather Bureau, Mr. James A. Barwick, former Signal Corps observer in California, signs himself, "Observer United States Weather Bureau, Director State Weather Service, and Meteorologist to the State Agricultural Society" (30—1891:217). Extensive coöperative annual reviews, twenty to forty pages each, of the weather of California were published in the *Transactions* for 1892 to 1895, inclusive. No transactions were printed in 1896, 1897, and 1898, owing to lack of State appropriations, and the issues for 1899, 1900, and 1901 (the final volume) were brief and only the last contained any weather data.

With January, 1897, the Weather Bureau began the publication of volume 1 of the "California Section of the Climate and Crop Service of the Weather Bureau," known since 1914 as *Climatological Data, California Section* (154). The issues for January and February, 1897, bore also the phrase, "In coöperation with the State Agricultural Society" (by whom it was printed), but the State Printing Office then was abolished, the journal was moved to San Francisco, and thereafter was published by the Weather Bureau. Precipitation data from some twenty-five lighthouses, furnished by the district lighthouse inspector, were published therein from January, 1897, to June, 1909. Since 1922 the section director has been authorized to publish precipitation data by fiscal years, which correspond to rainfall years in California, rather than by calendar years as formerly and elsewhere (150—1922:92, and 1923:123).

In 1903, Professor McAdie (102) of the Weather Bureau published his *Climatology of California,* based on Federal-State coöperative data. He acknowledged the coöperation of the Geological Survey in furnishing high-altitude rainfall data, and of the University of California, through Professors Davidson and LeConte, in revising tables of elevations. In 1899 was published *The Climate of San Francisco* (107) which was brought up to date again in 1913 (103), both editions containing coöperative data. In 1912 appeared the comprehensive *Summary of the Climatological Data for the United States* (Weather Bureau *Bulletin W*). It was issued in 106 sections, separately paged, of which sections 13 to 16 contained the data for California (104) to the end of 1909 or 1910. These sections are revised and brought up to date from time to time.

The University of California has maintained a coöperative observing station for many years. During the period from 1886 to 1927 it published the local data monthly (31). A twenty-year synopsis (100 B) of the meteorological observations at this station was published in 1908. The Lick Observatory of the University also was equipped with instruments by the Signal Corps and Weather Bureau, and furnished data for the Federal publications on California climate and also presented them in its own early publications (128).

Coöperation in providing station quarters: In 1923, the Weather Bureau was receiving free station quarters and accommodations in seventy-eight Federal buildings throughout the United States, other than the forty-six buildings owned by the Bureau itself. It had quarters also in five State or other public buildings. Thus 83 stations, or 37 per cent, were provided by public coöperation, out of a total of 225 principal stations in that year. These buildings, of course, are used for the forecasting and warning service as well as for the research program. During the World War, through cooperation of the Navy Department's coast patrol, temporary residence buildings were furnished for the use of assistant observers at points on the coast of Washington (150—1918:61). In 1920, a severe storm threatened the Bureau's observatory building at Cape Henry, Virginia, which was saved by sandbag bulkheads built in part by officers and men of the Army Engineer Corps, from Fort Strong (150—1920:69).

Coöperation in weather observations: Many Federal, State, and other public agencies coöperate by installing instruments and making observations for the Weather Bureau. This is especially true of the Federal and State agricultural experiment substations scattered widely over the country. The situation in California is typical of the country at large.

Of the two hundred stations in California where general meteorological records are taken daily, ten principal stations are manned by full-time Weather Bureau employees. At about fifteen stations the observer is the coöperating representative of some other Federal bureau or equivalent unit. Among these are the Forest Service with five observers, the Bureau of Plant Industry with four, the National Park Service and the Reclamation Service with three each, and possibly the Smithsonian Institution with one. Employees of State agencies man at least four more of these stations. They are located at the University of California, the University Farm at Davis, the Lick Observatory on Mount Hamilton, and the State hospital at Napa, respectively. Two other official coöperators are the city of Oakland, through the Chabot Observatory, and the South San Joaquin Irrigation District. In addition to these are special rainfall, snowfall, and river-gaging stations maintained by or in coöperation with other Federal, State, or county agencies, and discussed in other sections of this chapter. A few stations are located at other educational institutions than those maintained by the State. Many commercial agencies also are represented, including railroad, power, lumber, sugar, salt, oil, water, and fruit companies. Most of the observers are private citizens, interested in the subject, and willing to aid by devoting specified time to the collection of weather data. This widespread coöperation tends to show the general appreciation of the public service rendered.

Aerographic observations are as much needed in remote, inaccessible, and often nearly uninhabited portions of the country as in the accessible and populous portions. To obtain such records the Weather Bureau secures the coöperation of those government agencies which by the nature of their duties must maintain stations and employees in these remote parts. By the aid of the Forest Service of the Department of Agriculture, and the Bureaus of Indian Affairs and Reclamation in the Department of the Interior, observations are made at many otherwise impossible locations in the inaccessible or uninhabited mountains and deserts of fourteen western States. All needed instruments are furnished by the Weather Bureau (150—1919 :63, 65, and 69, and 1923 :124). Similar valuable coöperation exists with the Coast Guard of the Department of the Treasury at their isolated coastal stations. The station staff make observations with Weather Bureau instruments, and report them over telegraph and telephone lines provided by the Bureau (150—1917–20), which in turn furnishes the Coast Guard stations with weather forecasts.

In coöperation with the Bureau of Lighthouses, Department of Commerce, a new type of weather station was established in 1916 aboard coastal lightships equipped with wireless apparatus. Instruments for measuring pressure, temperature, and wind velocity (150—1916 :53) were furnished by the Weather Bureau and observations made by the lighthouse keepers.

Coöperation in instrument and equipment improvement: Because of the closing of the European sources of scientific instruments during the World War, the Weather Bureau coöperated with the War and Navy Departments in the repair of instruments for meteorological work and in constructing those needed for special uses (150—1918 :70). In coöperation with the Bureau of Standards, Department of Commerce, the wind tunnel of the latter is used in standardizing Weather Bureau anemometers (150—1922 : 96, and 1923 :129). When a new type of anemometer was devised, the tunnel tests were repeated on it.

The Weather Bureau in 1923 took part in a coöperation sponsored by the Federal Bureau of Standards to devise standards of equipment for insuring protection of buildings against lightning, a subject in which the Weather Bureau had conducted research for many years.

Coöperation in use of telegraph lines: The Weather Bureau is obliged to establish and maintain telegraph or telephone lines to many isolated observing and storm-warning stations along the ocean coasts and Great Lake shores. Widespread coöperation exists in all phases of this activity in which the Coast Guard of the Treasury is an important collaborator because of the location of its stations. Making of observations by Coast Guard employees already has been noted. The Weather Bureau lines often are the only means of communication between Coast Guard stations and the outer world. The Coast Guard therefore coöperates largely in the maintenance of such lines, and in their prompt repair after damage by severe storms. In some cases, Coast Guard telephone lines are carried on Weather Bureau poles (150—1915–20). For three years or more, the Coast Guard and Weather Bureau jointly maintained the line from Mt. Tamalpais to San Francisco (150—1917–20).

The Departments of Navy and War make increasing use of Weather Bureau telegraph and telephone lines and facilities. The Navy uses the Bureau telegraph at Norfolk extensively, and four important naval stations with a large volume of messages enjoy the main line connection to the naval base at Norfolk (150—1919:62). During the World War, the Sand Key, Florida, Station of the Bureau was taken over by the Navy Department, which purchased and laid a new cable (150—1919:63). The station was returned to the Weather Bureau on July 1, 1919 (*op. cit.*, p. 59), but the Navy still owns the cable (150—1920:76).

The War Department has helped to improve parts of telegraph lines useful to it, and allows the Weather Bureau the use of a conductor in the Oregon military cable (150—1920:78). To facilitate the operations of the Spruce Production Division of the Signal Corps of the Army throughout the war, much reconstruction was effected by the Bureau in the Tatoosh Island–Port Angeles telegraph line, and a temporary office was opened at the military camp at Joyce, Washington (150—1919:64).

By order of the Postmaster General, Weather Bureau contracts with telegraph companies for 1920 and during Federal control were not subject to increased rates, nor were rates raised for wire and battery service from river gages (150—1919:59).

Coöperation in agricultural aerographics: The weather work of the Signal Service was extended to agriculture by special act of Congress in 1872. The coöperative activities of that agency in meteorological research, including that in the field of agriculture, have been noted (pp. 107, *et sqq.*, above). Two items not mentioned there are more pertinent to the present discussion. In 1882 the Signal Service published (44) some tables of rainfall and temperature compared with crop production in which the data on crops yields were prepared by the Commissioner of Agriculture. Just at the time of the transfer of the weather service to the Department of Agriculture in 1891, the Signal Service prepared a very comprehensive report on the relations between climates and crops (2). This compiled and summarized the views of the best experimentalists and observers so far as these had been published up to 1891.

With the transfer of the work to the Department of Agriculture, the research program in agricultural meteorology (crops, livestock, and soils) was greatly increased. In 1892, two papers discussing soils were published. Hilgard, of the University of California, treated the relations of soils to climate (83), and Whitney (193) of Maryland the properties of soils in relation to moisture and crop production. Neither makes any statement of the terms of coöperation between the State universities and the Department of Agriculture. A Division of Agricultural Soils had been organized in the Weather Bureau and was made an independent Division in 1894, with Whitney in charge. In 1896, Irish of the Federal Department of Agriculture published on the climate, soil characteristics, and irrigation methods of California, using coöperative rainfall data for the period from 1850 to 1890 (89). In 1893, Professor Mell of the Alabama Polytechnic Institute and Alabama Weather Service, with the coöperation of the officers of many State weather services and directors of State agricultural experiment stations, compiled extensive information on the climatology of the cotton plant, which the Bureau published (113).

In 1914, a coöperative study was begun with the Bureau of Plant Industry on the relation of the farm enterprise to geographic factors, the Weather Bureau compiling data on precipitation and frost (151—1914:53). In 1916 a Division of Agricultural Meteorology was organized in the Weather Bureau. Correspondence was had with the directors of the State agricultural experiment stations regarding coöperation in the determination of critical periods in the growth of various crops and the effect of weather on crop growth, as well as on insect and fungus injury. Extensive tests were planned. Aerographic instruments were loaned to the Massachusetts Agricultural College with which to study the effect of weather on the apple crop, and also to Dr. Felt, State Entomologist of New York, for a study of codling moth, and to the Bureau of Entomology to study conditions affecting insect damage to fruit trees (151—1916 :60).

In 1915, the preparation of an *Atlas of American Agriculture* (147) was begun as a coöperative project by the various Bureaus of the U. S. Department of Agriculture. The Weather Bureau contributed "Part II, Climate," which was published in sections, beginning in 1918. The parts issued are "A, Precipitation and Humidity" (95) ; "B, Temperature, Sunshine, and Wind" (96) ; and "I, Frost and the Growing Season" (129).

In 1915, Lamb of the Forest Service prepared for publication (97) by the Weather Bureau a tabular and graphic calendar of the leafing, flowering, and seeding of the common trees of the eastern United States, showing these developments in relation to seasonal progress. In 1918, Hopkins of the U. S. Bureau of Entomology prepared for publication by the Bureau (84) one of the first of several statements of his so-called bioclimatic law. In the paper he acknowledges the coöperation of the Office of Farm Management, the Bureau of Plant Industry, and the Weather Bureau, all of the Federal Department of Agriculture, in providing data for the study. In 1923 the Weather Bureau published a paper on the relation of thermal belts to fruit growing in North Carolina (41), which resulted from coöperative studies of the Bureau and the State horticulturist and State Department of Agriculture. In 1931, the Bureau published a selected and annotated bibliography of the influence of weather on crops, covering the period from 1900 to 1930 (68). In 1931 also it published (53) data on soil temperatures derived from thirty-two stations in the United States and obtained through the coöperation of many of the agricultural experiment stations. Many similar instances could be cited but these serve to picture the wide range of relations which occur from time to time.

Evaporation records are of great agricultural importance, both from the standpoint of crop growth and from that of water storage and use. Records of evaporation, begun in 1907, have been collected for more than twenty-five years in coöperation with various other Federal and State agencies (22). Owing to diverse water surfaces, lack of uniform temperatures, etc., the earlier data could not be coördinated. As a result, standardized equipment and procedure were agreed upon and stations, called Class A Stations, equipped as fast as funds permitted. In 1916 there were 8, in 1919 there were 38, and by 1922 there were 47 such stations making monthly reports. The results were published by State sections and summarized annually by the Weather Bureau (150—1915–22). Special evaporation studies on reservoirs, irrigation ditches, and irrigated fields, as well as the river-gaging studies, will be discussed in the chapter on Water Resources, in the volume on Natural Resources.

The Weather Bureau served on several important coöperating interbureau or departmental committees dating from about 1922. They made studies of the problems of Range, Spring Wheat, Cotton, Extension, the Ozark Region, etc., and they coöperate as needed with each other and with the State agricultural colleges, through the agricultural experiment stations and extension services.

River gaging and flood research: Floods, like droughts, hot winds, and frosts, are a manifest result of meteorologic processes. Because of their tremendous power in causing death and destruction, they are the subject of intensive research, directed into three major channels. First, the effect on river stages produced by given intensities and durations of precipitation over given portions or all of the watershed. Second, the antecedent relation of a given stage at a given place to stages which will develop later at points lower down in the drainage basin. Third, the relation of topography and vegetative cover, or of changes in the latter, such as deforestation or shift in the proportion of tilled to pasture land, to the rapidity of runoff, with precipitations of given intensity and duration. Closely tied up with these researches are those concerned with erosion of land surfaces and the silting of channels, reservoirs, and agricultural lands, which are considered in the chapter on Soils and also under Land Resources and Water Resources.

The study and recording of river stages was committed to the Signal Service in 1871 by a clause in the appropriation act (188), and observations were begun in 1873. The development of the work from that time on is given in the general papers cited above under the Signal Service and Weather Bureau Periods, and also in some devoted wholly to this subject (54; 65; 79; 120; 131; 132). In the earlier years, river stages were recorded by municipal authorities at Pittsburgh, Cincinnati, Cairo, St. Louis, etc. (120:131). By 1893, river stages were being recorded at 191 stations, throughout the country, by the Weather Bureau alone (131; 132). The Engineer Corps of the Army, which has charge of navigable rivers and of much flood-control activity, made observations of river stages on many streams prior to the work of the Signal Service, and has coöperated ever since (120). Some coöperation existed with the Mississippi River Commission, which printed annually the records of stages at other than Weather Bureau stations, and the Missouri River Commission, which printed these records at irregular intervals. Both commissions maintained gages at desirable points not covered by the Weather Bureau (132). In 1877, steps were taken to extend the river-gaging service to California, and by 1880 there had been established six special stations in that State and Oregon (120:14).

The Surface-Water Division of the Water-Resources Branch of the U. S. Geological Survey maintains many stream-gaging stations, some independently and many more in coöperation with Federal, State, municipal, and private agencies (88:52). Most of their work is directly for water-supply purposes, but some of it is of value in the studies of the flood problems as outlined above. In a comprehensive report on the rivers and floods of the Sacramento and San Joaquin watersheds, the Weather Bureau (145) in 1913 acknowledged the coöperation of the Geological Survey and of the Marysville Levee Commission, and also the use of data from previous coöperative publications.

In recent years there has developed a widespread coöperation in the gaging of streams. Federal agencies taking part and sharing the expenses in many cases include Weather Bureau and Forest Service in the Department of Agriculture, the Water Resources Branch of the Geological Survey, and the Bureaus of Indian Affairs and Reclamation in the Department of the Interior, the Army Engineer Corps of the War Department, and such independent agencies as the Missippi River Commission and others.

There is coöperation also in some cases from State engineers, State foresters, and others, as in Nebraska, where the Flood Service on the Platte River is maintained in coöperation with the Nebraska Department of Public Works, which supplies both gages and gage readers. In the Los Angeles district of California, coöperative rainfall measurements with reference to flood warnings are made in the Los Angeles National Forest by the Board of Supervisors of Los Angeles County, in coöperation with the U. S. Forest Service which in turn represents other Federal agencies contributing to the cost. A somewhat similar coöperation exists in San Bernardino County.

Closely correlated with the work of stream gaging, as an antecedent to flood forecasting, is the measurement of snowfall in the mountain areas. As early as 1908, the Weather Bureau and the Geological Survey and the then Reclamation Service of the Interior Department agreed to assist each other in establishing stations, obtaining observers, and discussing the records (22). Other Federal agencies, especially the Forest Service, have taken a larger part in this coöperation in recent years. City officials here and there, as for example in Salt Lake City, have given coöperation in the interest of their water supply.

Unclassified coöperation during the World War: On the entrance of the United States into the war in April, 1917, the Secretary of Agriculture offered the Secretary of War the fullest coöperation of the Weather Bureau, which was heartily accepted. This service covered forecasting in aid of military operations at home and abroad, aerological observations for aviators, balloonists, and artillerists, and assistance to marine interests and coast patrol (150—1917:47). There was intimate coöperation with the Signal Corps in the training of meteorologists, first at Weather Bureau stations, and then by detailing two Bureau men to give full courses in meteorology to a large special body of soldiers in camp at College Station, Texas (150—1918:59). Special coöperation was given the Signal Corps at its Balloon School at Omaha, Nebraska, through equipping it with a full set of instruments and allowing a Bureau officer to be commissioned and given charge of the school during most of the war period (116).

The Aviation and Medical Services of the Army were furnished with the data necessary to determine proper locations for aviation fields, hospitals, etc. (150—1918:64). On request of other Departments and for the use of the Peace Conference at Paris, the Weather Bureau prepared a vast quantity of data on the climate of Africa, with special reference to the former German colonies (150—1919:67).

A brief summary of all wartime coöperation of the Weather Bureau was published in the *Monthly Weather Review* in 1917 (32), in its annual report for 1918 (p. 59), and in a mimeographed account of all war activities of the Department of Agriculture (116).

Coöperation in international aerography: Coöperation of the United States with other countries was begun by the international conference of 1853, as already noted. Relations in this field during the Signal Service period have been outlined (p. 110 above). The activities then established have been enlarged and new ones added in the more than forty years since. The International Meteorological Organization is the official body representing the joint activities of the coöperating nations. It is purely administrative and discusses scientific problems only as they relate to administration, the International Union of Geodesy and Geophysics being the purely scientific international body of similar composition. The meteorological organization acts through (*a*) International Meteorological Conferences of directors of meteorological services, (*b*) the International Meteorological Committee, and (*c*) various commissions (155—51). The international conferences are held at intervals of a few years. The international committee is appointed at each conference and is the executive committee until and for the next conference. The Chief of the U. S. Weather Bureau is a member of the committee, and the Bureau is represented on the commissions (110). The new international code proposed by the Commission on Weather Telegraphy was promptly adopted and used by twenty-two nations.

In 1893, a special International Meteorological Congress was held in Chicago under the auspices of the Congress Auxiliary of the World's Columbian Exposition. The secretary of the Congress was the librarian of the U. S. Weather Bureau, and report of its proceedings was published by the Bureau in a volume of nearly 800 pages, of which one fourth comprised papers on history and bibliography (51).

But few reports of terrestrial aerographic observations were received from the various foreign countries before the World War, although coöperation with Canada had been arranged in 1871 by the Signal Service. The increasing scope of aviation especially requires much fuller international knowledge than previously was thought necessary, and expanding commercial activities also call for large-scale coöperative undertakings in aerography. By 1922, the U. S. Weather Bureau was receiving reports from 136 stations outside continental United States, including those from Alaska, Puerto Rico, etc., under coöperative arrangements made at small cost (150—1922:76).

In 1922, a daily exchange was arranged with the French Meteorological Service without cost, through the Office of Communications of the Navy Department (150—1922:76). In 1930, increased coöperation was effected with the Canadian Meteorological Service, covering the exchange of fuller data than previously had been furnished. In 1930, also, coöperation with the British Meteorological Service was extended to include twice-daily broadcasts of both land and ship data.

A few rainfall stations were established in Minnesota in 1917 on the United States portion of the watershed of the Lake of the Woods, and the results made available to the International Joint Commission which has jurisdiction over obstruction or diversion of waters forming or crossing the boundary between the United States and Canada (150—1917:57).

The Puerto Rico Section of the Weather Bureau was enlarged in 1920 to include the new West Indian Climatological Service (52), under the new plan of coöperation with the various foreign governments in that region (150—1920:92).

The climatic occurrences of Mexico are of concern to the United States, just as are those of Canada and the West Indies, and reports from the Mexican Meteorological Service long have been received. In 1930, the Weather Bureau published (126) a comprehensive discussion of the climate of Mexico, based on the full records of the Central Meteorological Observatory of Mexico, which coöperated in making the material available to a Bureau worker through a period of two months, and also in giving other assistance.

The publications listed in the Literature Cited at the end of the chapter which are cited in this section on Terrestrial Aerography are Nos. 2, 22, 30, 31, 32, 41, 44, 46, 51, 52, 53, 54, 65, 68, 79, 83, 84, 88, 89, 95, 96, 97, 100B, 102, 103, 104, 107, 110, 113, 116, 120, 126, 128, 129, 131, 132, 145, 147, 150, 151, 152—7, 24 and 27, 154, 155—51, 188, and 193.

Marine meteorology or aerography.—Observations on weather factors under marine conditions have exactly the same objectives and much the same procedure as those made on land in the study of terrestrial aerography. The chief difference is in the nature and location of the stations. Except for a few stations on small islands, a few others on offshore lightships, and an occasional anchored vessel engaged on oceanographic research, the observations must be made on moving vessels, never twice in the same place. Also the program must be essentially international in its organization.

The assembling and interpretation of aerographic data from the oceans dates from the time when Lieutenant Maury took charge of the Hydrographic Office of the Navy in 1844. The work became international by the agreement of the first International Meteorological Conference, held in Belgium in 1853, as a result of Maury's endeavors. In addition to the data on ocean temperatures and currents already discussed (p. 97, above), air temperatures and pressure, and wind direction and velocity, were reported by both naval and commercial vessels of the civilized nations from the beginning of the work. The general papers on the work of the Hydrographic Office have been cited in the discussion of the research on ocean currents. Aerographic data from oceanic areas are of great value in the intensive study of climatology and meteorology relating to land surfaces, as well as for use in the forecasting of immediate weather.

Work of the Signal Service: Systematic studies of marine meteorology were begun by the newly created weather service of the Signal Service in May, 1871. Circulars were sent then to navigators and vessel owners, requesting thrice-daily simultaneous observations at sea, the records to be transmitted to the War Department whenever the vessel arrived in port (3). These requests found much response and the results were used both in a study of marine meteorology and in the preparation of a daily weather chart of the northern hemisphere (188). Coöperative exchange of such meteorological information progressed through the action of international congresses until it resulted in the publication of the *Bulletin of International Meteorological Observations,* through the agency of of the United States. This daily bulletin was issued from January 1, 1875, until June 30, 1884. The issues appeared about one year after the date of the observations and were intended for use in climatological studies. The daily charts were published from January 1, 1875, to December 31, 1887, at which time the work in marine meteorology was transferred to the Hydrographic Office of the Navy Department. The studies are regarded as one of the finest pieces of international coöperation in precise scientific work that the world has ever seen, paralleled only by the studies of the International Polar Year in 1882–83 (3). In 1891, the Weather Bureau was created in the U. S. Department of Agriculture and took over the weather service of the Signal Corps.

Work of the Weather Bureau: When the Weather Bureau was created in 1891, the work in marine meteorology had been centered in the Hydrographic Office of the Navy Department since 1887. The Bureau had authority in law, however, for undertaking such investigations and was obliged to develop some of them in connection with its West Indies hurricane service particularly, for which increased appropriations were made by Congress in 1898. In 1904, an interdepartmental committee, representing the Departments of War, Navy, Agriculture, and Commerce and Labor, was appointed by the President to consider especially all questions of duplication and interference in the rapidly growing Federal activities in wireless telegraphy, and also to deal with duplication in meteorological work (33; 188).

The Weather Bureau, the Signal Corps of the Army, and especially the Bureau of Equipment of the Navy, all had equipped radio stations and were planning many more, while the Treasury Department was considering stations for the Lifesaving and Revenue Marine Services (now Coast Guard). Private stations, some on Federal reservations, were multiplying and interfering. The interdepartmental committee recommended that the Weather Bureau stations (all coastal) and equipment be transferred to the Navy Department, that the Navy be authorized to construct a complete system of necessary coastal and Great Lakes stations, and that the Signal Corps be permitted to construct necessary interior stations, provided they did not duplicate or interfere with naval radio stations.

The importance of wireless communication in obtaining weather observations, and in transmitting forecasts, from and to remote or inaccessible points was obvious. The committee fully provided for this by requiring that all such reports from vessels of war or commerce, or from other sailing craft, be sent to the Weather Bureau instead of the Hydrographic Office, the responsibility for ocean meteorology being transferred to the Department of Agriculture; that the Navy wireless stations should receive and transmit, without charge, all incoming or outgoing meteorological information for the Bureau; that the Navy should request all its vessels to take observations and report them daily or oftener; and that the Bureau, in return, should provide the Hydrographic Office and other Federal units with all desired weather information, without charge. On its pilot charts the Hydrographic Office was to give full credit for Weather Bureau data. These recommendations were approved and put into operation by the President, an early instance of clear vision and effective coördination of related Federal activities.

Under the provisions of an act of Congress in 1910, the publishing of the pilot charts became a coöperative activity of the Weather Bureau and the Hydrographic Office. At a further conference between these two agencies in 1913, it was unanimously agreed that there still was some unnecessary duplication of work and that the Bureau would discontinue the publication of meteorological charts and would reapportion other marine work (150—1913 :65).

Under the agreements reached, a large program of coöperation with the Navy in marine meteorology was begun and has continued ever since. The collection of weather reports by radiogram was extended promptly by the Weather Bureau to commercial shipping also, as such vessels installed wireless apparatus. In 1906, this vessel-reporting service was established as a project, with 35 vessels actually reporting. Payments of 50 cents an observation and the costs of ship-to-shore transmission were made by the Bureau in special cases, while some companies required their masters to perform this service free. In 1922 more than 15,000 observations were received, from more than 300 ships. This service was in addition to the earlier established ship-reporting by mail on blanks furnished by the Weather Bureau. The World War interrupted both sets of observations, but by 1920 there were 2148 vessels reporting under the old system, and both were fast approaching prewar conditions. All reporting ships receive pilot charts and other resulting publications free of charge. A pamphlet describing the expanded and coördinated marine service developed by the Weather Bureau was issued in 1919 (159).

Coöperation with official agencies also increased after the war. Besides the regular data, the Weather Bureau furnished the Hydrographic Office with the track of important storms for use on its pilot charts (150—1920:83). The Hydrographic Office, in turn, assisted in revising a text on cyclonic storms (150—1923:127). More recently the Bureau has completed the revision of data for the vessel routes between Pacific Coast ports and the Panama Canal for publication on the pilot charts. It has furnished, moreover, an increased quantity of data for use as evidence in admiralty cases (150—1920:83). In 1921 the United States Shipping Board required the masters of all ships under its control to forward daily observations, without charge to the Bureau, when they were in certain specified ocean areas. Their ships in the Atlantic, and all ships in the Pacific ocean, report throughout the year. Others in the Atlantic, and those in the Caribbean Sea and the Gulf of Mexico, report only during the hurricane season, from June on into November. In 1923, the Commission on Marine Meteorology of the International Meteorological Organization provided an international code, consisting of four universal or international groups of figures and four other groups for national use (155—51). In 1931 the vessel weather code was published by the Weather Bureau for the use of coöperating vessels (161).

Since the agreements of 1904, the Weather Bureau has collected an immense quantity of data on ocean meteorology, including surface temperatures. Some of these are published regularly in the

Monthly Weather Review, especially those covering the Carribbean Sea and the north Atlantic Ocean. The Hydrographic Office of the Navy still collects records of ocean temperatures through naval and other vessels, as noted heretofore.

International radio coöperation: The development of radio transmission naturally increased the opportunity for effective international coöperation in obtaining observations from remote but very important parts of the earth, especially in the Arctic regions. In addition to the more than three hundred stations reporting daily or twice-daily by cable and telegraph, of which one-fifth were outside the United States, reports were received wholly or in part by radio from some sixty points throughout the world, by the end of 1922. All came over Navy or Army stations, the Signal Corps furnishing reports from two stations in Alaska (33). The Canadian Government also was planning a series of new stations in the Mackenzie River area, data from which would be sent to our Weather Bureau. There was an even greater increase in official broadcasting of forecasts and storm warnings. (See next section.)

By 1928, most of the coöperating nations were agreed that fuller data and more complete forecasts of ocean weather were needed, both for ships and planes. It was agreed further that the time was ripe for the designation, by each nation, of a certain number of its own ships to make observations at least twice and perhaps four times daily and to report them promptly by radio, for interchange among the contributing nations (150—1928:7). This was known as the selected-ship program. Different nations used different codes and desired observations at different hours. International conferences in 1928 and 1929 had arranged for the use of the international code (160) and for observations at specified times by the Greenwich meridian. This selected-ship plan allocates the ships to the nations in proportion to their total tonnage, contemplating eventually 1000 well-equipped ships, of which 225 would be of United States registry (35). United States ships west of longitude 35° W. report to stations in this country, and when east of 35° W. longitude, they report to European stations. Data are exchanged by shore stations at specified times. The United States and British services broadcast twice daily the international reports from both ship and land stations.

The publications listed in the Literature Cited at the end of the chapter which are cited in this section on Marine Meteorology are Nos. 3, 33, 35, 150, 155–51, 159, 160, 161, and 188.

Aerological or free-air studies.—Aerology, or aerography, is the science of the physics of the air. The term applies equally properly, therefore, to the aerographic studies at the earth's surface (terrestrial aerography) and over the water surfaces (marine aerography), which have just been discussed. The Weather Bureau, however, uses the term in the somewhat restricted and arbitrary sense of meaning the physics of the free air, or the atmosphere at sufficient heights above land and water surfaces to be relatively uninfluenced by either topography and artificial obstructions, on the one hand, or direct heating and cooling effects, on the other. In that restricted sense the word is used here.

Aerological information on upper-air conditions is obtained by means of kites, pilot balloons, and sounding balloons, and the self-recording instruments carried by the kites and sounding balloons. Daily flights are conducted when practicable at five special stations, none of them located in California. Less regular flights are made at all major stations. The instruments carried by the kites show atmospheric pressure, temperature, humidity, and the velocity and direction of the wind at all heights reached, the average being three kilometers, or about two miles. The strongly inflated pilot balloons carry no instruments, but computations from observations on them by means of a theodolite determine wind direction and velocity at different elevations. The sounding balloons carry light instruments, and ascend to heights not otherwise reached, in a few cases exceeding thirty kilometers or eighteen miles, where they explode and the instruments are carried down by means of a parachute.

Investigation of the free air has continued in connection with research on electricity since the days of Franklin. The early researches of the Weather Bureau in this field were concerned with lightning and the electricity of the air, in which the officials of three States worked together in supplying data (106). In 1904 an aerological station was established on Mount Weather in the Blue Ridge Mountains of Virginia (188). In 1914 this was discontinued and a site remote from the influence of mountain and ocean was sought in the Midwest, across which our cyclones and anticyclones travel. In 1915 the work was located temporarily in coöperation with the Signal Corps of the Army, at its balloon training station at Fort Omaha, Nebraska (25). In the same year, coöperative experiments were made over the ocean from the cutter *Seneca* of the Coast Guard of the Treasury Department (25). In 1915, also, the Bureau established its Drexel Aerological Station, at Drexel, Nebraska, where observations by kites began in October (150— 1916 :64).

In July and August, 1913, the Weather Bureau collaborated with the Smithsonian Institution in the expedition of the Astrophysical Observatory to points in southern California, including Catalina Island, Mt. Wilson, and Mt. Whitney. Balloon soundings were made at great elevations (150—1914 :55). The experiments were continued in July, 1914 (150—1915 :74).

Coöperation during the World War: With the entry of the United States into the World War in 1917, the Weather Bureau immediately coöperated with the Departments of Navy and War in aerological observations to provide information for aviators, balloonists, and artillerists. The official in charge of aerological investigations was commissioned a major and established complete collaboration between the Weather Bureau and those stations independently established by the Signal Corps of the Army (150— 1917 :48), the Bureau compiling both sets of data. Free-air wind data were furnished from the Bureau's Drexel station to the Signal Corps balloon training school at Fort Omaha. The officers and men of that school also used the kite field at Drexel for their training and experiments (150—1917 :51–52). Under an item in the War Department appropriation bill, five more aerological stations were established by the Weather Bureau in the Central States (150— 1918 :62, and 1919 :60–61). Coöperation was effected with the Navy Department for free-air observations at their training bases, including San Diego, California, in aid of aeronautics and ballistics (150—1917 :51).

Coöperation with the War Department included also the joint preparation of papers on meteorology and aeronautics, and related subjects; information on free-air conditions in this country and in Europe; instrumental equipment for the American Expeditionary

Force at camps in this country and overseas; the testing of search-lights and methods of detecting moving objects at night by their aid; and the setting up of temporary field stations at several camps in the United States (150—1918:63). Frequent conferences were held with the aeronautic branches of the Army and the Navy in order to insure close coöperation in all activities. The aerological activities of the Weather Bureau during the war were reviewed at its close (60; 116).

Postwar coöperation: The rapid development of aviation, both official and commercial, after the war made the need of extensive and accurate information about the upper air more imperative than ever. Numerous stations had been established and equipped by the meteorological services of the Army and Navy during the war. At its close some of these were transferred to the Weather Bureau and some were retained by the military organizations. The records accumulated at the latter, including the Navy stations in the Canal Zone and the Dominican Republic, were made available to the Weather Bureau for reduction and study (150—1920:80, 1922:88–89, and 1923:122). The Bureau, in turn, shared its information with the military departments and with the postal aviation service. In coöperation with the Air-Mail Service, an analysis was made of the air-mail flight records, in relation to kite and balloon data, and a paper on the wind factor in flight was published (64). Standardized data on the atmosphere, for all seasons, and for altitudes up to 65,000 feet, were prepared for the National Advisory Committee for Aeronautics, and were adopted as standard for the United States by that committee in 1922 (150—1922: 90). In 1923 the Weather Bureau represented the Department of Agriculture on a joint committee, comprising representatives from the Departments of Commerce, Navy, Post Office, and War, as well as from all commercial interests, in preparing an aeronautical safety code (150—1923:122). In connection with air charting, close coöperation is maintained with the Section of Aerial Navigation, of the Division of Maritime Security, in the Hydrographic Office of the Bureau of Navigation, Department of the Navy.

Aerological survey of the United States: This survey utilizes the information obtained from the aerological observations described above, and summarizes them for use in several fields of investigation, including statistical compilations for the entire country, upper-air conditions in cyclones and anticyclones, development of relations between these conditions and the formation and movement of the cyclones and anticyclones, and, finally, determination of the daily variations in the several meteorological elements at different heights. The aerological observations thus have the same relation to the aerological survey which meteorological observations bear to climatology.

The voluminous data accumulated during the years of observations by Weather Bureau and military agencies are being analyzed and published as fast as possible, those obtained by kites (61) and by pilot balloons (62) already having appeared. More recently an aerological code for pilot balloons has been published (162). While much aerological investigation has been made necessary by the development of aviation, it is interesting to note that the airplane itself now contributes to this research, as in a recent survey of cloud and fog conditions along the southern California coast (16).

International coöperation: The International Commission for the Exploration of the Upper Atmosphere, one of those created by the International Meteorological Organization, maintains an extensive program of international aerological research. Formerly they set individual days on which the various coöperating nations made free-air observations (150—1913:67, and 1914:54–55), but in recent years they fix certain months as "international months," during which the research shall be continued. The Weather Bureau coöperates by studies made at one or another of its aerological stations (133; 134), and has published the aerological code used (162).

In 1921 the director of the Brazilian Meteorological Service asked the help of the Weather Bureau in organizing and establishing an aerological service for Brazil. In coöperation with a Brazilian representative in Washington, the plans were made, materials selected and purchased, and two Bureau specialists released to proceed to Brazil and help to inaugurate the service there (150—1922:89).

The aerographic investigations made during the International Polar Year of 1882–83 have been discussed under the Signal Service Period. In the second International Polar Year, which began on August 1, 1932, a large volume of aerological investigation was conducted by means of pilot balloons at the United States cooperating station at Point Barrow, Alaska. Dr. Millikan of the California Institute of Technology also has coöperated with the Weather Bureau there in his studies of cosmic rays (149—11:188).

The publications listed in the Literature Cited at the end of the chapter which are cited in this section on Aerological Studies are Nos. 16, 25, 60, 61, 62, 64, 106, 116, 133, 134, 149, 150, 162, and 188.

4. FORECASTING AND WARNING SERVICES

THE EXTENSIVE PROGRAM of research, much of it coöperative, which supports the forecasting services has just been described. Forecasting and warning services are a form of extension. These and not investigations were the primary thought of Congress when it created a weather service in the Army Signal Service in 1870. From the very beginning, the major emphasis, as we have seen, has been on applied or practical meteorology. The organic act of 1890, creating the Weather Bureau in the U. S. Department of Agriculture on July 1, 1891, named eight duties in applied meteorology, and ended with a simple clause authorizing "the taking of such meteorological observations as may be necessary to establish and record the climatic conditions of the United States, or are essential for the proper execution of the foregoing duties" (which were forecasting and warning).

In recent years the service activities of the Weather Bureau, some of them of rather spectacular nature, have captured the popular imagination. Numerous writers, both official and private, have written general accounts of them in popular style (15B; 21; 75; 81; 115; 116; 141; 144; 157; 188; 191; 192).

The general manifestations of weather, lows or storm periods (cyclones) and highs or fair periods (anticyclones), tend to move in a general southeasterly direction across North America. Knowing their location, extent, intensities, and direction and rate of movement, an experienced forecaster can predict the time of incidence and the character of the weather about to occur in the near and distant areas affected by the movements. He uses likewise the same sort of knowledge of tropical storms approaching or entering the country from the southeast. Forecasting therefore is based on reports of conditions actually existing in all parts of the country, or in areas surrounding it, at specified hours. For this purpose the regular instrumental and visual observations are taken twice daily, at 8 A.M. and 8 P.M., 75th meridian time, at approximately three hundred primary or first-order stations distributed throughout the country, including Alaska and the West Indies. A first-order station, it will be remembered, is one at which there is a permanent full-time employee of the Weather Bureau.

These observations cover the several elements of meteorological conditions, including temperature, precipitation, humidity, barometric pressure (reduced to mean sea level), wind direction and velocity, cloudiness, etc. This information is coded, telegraphed to Washington and the other forecast centers by means of a special circuit system devised coöperatively by the Bureau and the Western Union Telegraph Company, and then redistributed as far as necessary to major stations throughout the country, all within about forty-five minutes. On these observations, plus some received by radio, telegraph, or cable, from Canada, Mexico, and certain vessels at sea, are based the twice-daily forecasts of weather, both national and regional, for the coming twenty-four hours and for longer periods (188). Forecasts may be divided into two classes, general forecasts, and special forecasts and warnings.

GENERAL FORECASTS

There is little or no coöperation in the actual making of forecasts but there is widespread coöperation in the assembling of the necessary observational reports and in the dissemination of forecast information. The chief element in both operations is speed. When taken, the observations must be transmitted with the utmost dispatch in order to arrive in time to be used for the forecast issued an hour or so later. When made, the forecast must be disseminated with the utmost dispatch if it is to serve as advance information to agriculture, industry, and commerce.

Assembling of Forecast Information

Reports of observations in continental United States reach the Weather Bureau chiefly by way of the telegraph circuit system developed by the Bureau and the Western Union Telegraph Company, as noted above. From the more remote and inaccessible coastal stations, however, as well as from Alaska, the West Indies, and necessary areas at sea, other means must be employed. This gives rise to coöperation with official agencies, both national and international.

National coöperation in assembling data.—By the agreement reached in the interdepartmental conference of 1904, the Weather Bureau gave up its wireless stations and equipment in favor of the Navy Department, and that agency, in turn, agreed to handle all incoming and outgoing weather information promptly and without cost to the Weather Bureau. In 1923 the Bureau recorded that the Navy had continued to perform this service in an excellent spirit of coöperation (33). The service included forwarding of reports gathered by Navy radio stations at isolated points in the Great Lakes area and along the northern Pacific Coast (150—1917:56). The naval Office of Communications aids essentially in gathering the twice-daily reports from some ten of the dozen observing stations in Alaska which furnish forecast reports, the other two being forwarded by the Signal Corps of the Army (150—1923:108). The Alaskan service began in 1907, from one station (Nome). The Navy radio stations also pick up and transmit reports from vessels at sea, including our naval vessels, all of which report regularly. In 1923 the forecasting ability of the Hawaiian Island district was greatly strengthened by the coöperation of the Navy Department in transmitting to Honolulu the daily observations from sixteen stations distributed from California to Alaska (150—1923:107).

International coöperation in assembling data.—The coöperative arrangements with foreign countries in conducting meteorologic research already have been discussed. Similar coöperation exists in making the observations from strategic points immediately available to the United States as an aid to its forecast service. Besides those received by commercial telegraph and cable, there are the reports picked up and transmitted by the naval radio stations from many points in the arctic regions, in interior Canada, in Mexico and the West Indies, and in the Orient. Not only does the United States receive these reports but in its turn it supplies various foreign nations with similar information from this country and adjacent waters to be used in forecasting their own weather. This exchange of information is performed also by the naval radio stations, under the agreement of 1904. The Signal Corps of the Army, also, has coöperated since 1922 in transmitting promptly the special early morning and afternoon observations made at its stations in the eastern United States as a basis for forecasts to aviators (33). Collection of information from the West Indies by radio began in 1914, and transmission of information to France by radio began in 1919 (33).

Distribution of General Forecasts

There always has been large coöperation of various agencies in effecting the prompt and widespread distribution of forecasts and warnings. This began in the very early days of Signal Service responsibility for weather information. The Post Office began coöperation with the Signal Service in 1872, when the Postmaster General instructed postmasters to forward forecast bulletins promptly and to post them conspicuously in their offices. In 1873 the printing of a *Post Office Bulletin* was begun at fifteen central stations from weather matter telegraphed by the Signal Service. This bulletin was distributed to some 3391 post offices which could be reached promptly from the central stations. In 1894, soon after the Weather Bureau was created, the logotype or rubberstamped mailing card for local forecasts was developed. It was distributed by postmen locally and by mail to points which could be reached by 4 P.M. Again the Post Office Department coöperated to effect speedy handling of these cards (140). There also was much commercial coöperation in making forecasts public during this period.

The general forecasting program centers on the twice-daily report of observations. These are made, recorded, coded, telegraphed, decoded, charted, and interpreted, and the resulting forecast published in the space of about two hours (188:21). The morning forecasts are telegraphed to some 1600 principal points for dissemination by telegraph, telephone, radio, and mail, as well as local posting in public buildings and commercial establishments, and printing in the evening newspapers. The evening forecasts are distributed chiefly through the press associations for publication in morning papers. Both sets are widely distributed by commercial and official radio stations. As early as 1922, it was estimated that about one fourth of the then approximately four hundred licensed stations were broadcasting weather reports. The percentage as well as the number has greatly increased since then. The Bureau of Navigation of the Department of Commerce assigned a wave length of 485 meters for broadcasting weather forecasts and market reports (150—1922:74).

Navy department coöperation.—In accordance with the interdepartmental radio and weather agreement of 1904, a very large volume of coöperation has been built up in the field of radio broadcasting of weather reports by the various naval radio stations (33). At first it was largely for the benefit of shipping, but covered the regular weather forecasts and not merely storm and hurricane warnings. It began with two stations, Arlington, Virginia, and Key West, Florida, on the Atlantic Coast in 1913, and a Great Lakes broadcast was added in 1914, also from the Arlington naval station. In 1917 the Great Lakes Naval Training Station took over the Great Lakes work. In 1916, however, the Great Lakes station had begun coöperation by broadcasting the regular forecasts and reports to some 270 amateur operators who posted the information for the public. Wireless stations operated by State universities also began broadcasting the weather news and market reports about this time, beginning with Ohio and North Dakota (150—1913–16). In 1919, the wind and weather forecasts and statements of port conditions were extended to cover the Gulf of Mexico as well as the Atlantic Ocean, and in 1920 the naval radio station at Point Isabel, Texas, undertook to cover the Mexican Gulf and the Western Caribbean Sea by an evening broadcast. In the same year the naval radio station at San Juan, Puerto Rico, started the same evening service for the eastern Caribbean Sea and the south Atlantic Ocean.

In 1921, in response to public demand, the Arlington naval radio station began twice-daily broadcasting and on a much enlarged scope of material. In 1922 the Great Lakes station began the same enlarged program as part of a general plan of coöperation in official broadcasting worked out by the Interdepartmental Radio Committee. This program included the weekly crop and weather summaries, as well as twice-daily weather forecasts. The Arlington program included also upper-air or aerological information for aviators, obtained from three Weather Bureau stations, five Navy Department stations, and one Signal Corps aerological station. This activity was especially requested by the air services of the Army and the Navy. In 1921, also, a localized broadcasting of weather information was begun from many smaller naval radio stations for the benefit of vessels and others not equipped to receive on the higher wave lengths used by the high-powered stations. In 1922 the enlarged twice-daily broadcast was begun from the Navy radio station on Yerba Buena (Goat) Island in San Francisco Bay, including free-air data from several aerological stations operated by the Weather Bureau, Signal Corps, and Navy Department. At the same time the the program of localized low-power broadcasting was begun from five smaller naval stations, including those at San Pedro and Eureka, California (33). In 1923, the Arlington naval station increased its broadcasts to thrice daily. The broadcasting is done directly from the Weather Bureau through telephone connection with the station.

International coöperation in distribution.—The international coöperation in assembling the data for forecasts has been described, including our transmission of data to many foreign countries. Naturally, each country must prepare and distribute its own forecasts. International coöperation in distribution lies chiefly in radio broadcasts to the vessels of all nations, discussed above under Navy Department coöperation. One special attempt in this field looks toward the preparation and distribution of forecasts by suitably manned vessels in mid ocean. About 1922, the French Meteorological Service assisted the French freighter *Jacques Cartier* to make forecasts en route by means of reports from vessels and shore stations, and to broadcast them immediately for the benefit of Atlantic shipping. Officials of the Weather Bureau accepted an invitation to make a round trip on this ship to observe and assist in the development, which was done (80). As a result, plans were worked out for a similar service by ships of American registry. The United States Shipping Board approved the plan and offered to provide the facilities on three of its North Atlantic vessels (150—1923 :111). Chief advantages of this system would be knowledge of local conditions, prompt distribution of forecasts, and service to smaller vessels not reached by the powerful shore stations.

The publications listed in Literature Cited at the end of the chapter which are cited in this combined Introductory and General Forecast section are Nos. 15B, 21, 33, 75, 80, 81, 115, 116, 140, 141, 144, 150, 157, 188, 191, and 192.

SPECIAL FORECASTS AND WARNINGS

The special services may be classified roughly into five groups: storm warnings for shipping; agricultural warnings, including those for protection of products; flood warnings; aviation forecasts; and miscellaneous services.

Storm Warnings for Shipping

The chief reason for the establishment of the weather service in the Army Signal Service in 1870 was the terrible losses of life and property caused by sudden and violent storms on the Great Lakes, as noted in the historical review. These warnings still are an important part of the work and now cover not only the lakes but the coasts and oceans, and the hurricane area in the Caribbean Sea, the Gulf of Mexico, and the adjacent American coasts. The warning signals are displayed at more than four hundred points. The abundant coöperation of the Navy Department in distributing forecasts of storms from its larger and smaller radio stations has been discussed under distribution of general forecasts. In or about 1916, the Coast Guard of the Treasury Department undertook to display storm signals at their stations, thus reducing the expense of the Weather Bureau.

Agricultural Forecasts and Warnings

The work of the Signal Corps weather service was extended to agricultural areas in 1872. Since that time there has been a steady increase in the number and efficiency of these services (70; 82; 108). They include frost and cold-wave warnings in the areas producing fruits and truck crops; cold-wave warnings to shippers and carriers of perishable agricultural products; harvest-weather forecasts in important grain and hay districts, as well as for cotton, tobacco, and rice; spraying-weather forecasts for the fruit industries; special rain warnings in the fruit-drying season, and in fruit-picking and root-crop–digging seasons; heavy-snow warnings to livestock growers, shippers, and carriers; drought warnings in grazing and irrigation areas; special weather forecasts in the lambing and shearing seasons in sheep-raising areas; fire-weather warnings in forest areas; and others of similar nature. These and the regular forecasts are used protectively by a thousand and one other commercial activities. These various services are described in the annual reports (150; 151), and the descriptive publications previously listed.

In 1918, a special weather and crop service was inagurated in San Francisco, for the seven western States. During the summer, a weekly bulletin was issued, much on the order of the bulletins of the various State climatological sections.

Some of these protective services will be presented in the chapters on Plant Industries and Animal Industries, or in that on Forests in the volume on Natural Resources. There is some official coöperation in these undertakings. The agricultural extension service in the State colleges of agriculture promotes the dissemination of these special forecasts in many ways, including college broadcasting.

There is full coöperation between the Weather Bureau and the Federal Forest Service in the handling of fire-weather forecasts (137) and in the publishing of information (138; 155—51:561–81), with some help from the State foresters. The Weather Bureau and the Forest Service, in coöperation with the State of California, have equipped and manned a forecasting truck which attends large going fires in that State and forecasts coming weather while the fire lasts (137). The California legislature has published a paper by the State Forester, containing a large bibliography of the influence of forests on climatic factors (125).

There is some coöperation also between Federal and State agencies in the frost-warning service for fruit and truck-crop industries, as also in the fruit-spraying service. In the frost-warning service (105) to protect the citrus industry, the bulletin issued by the Weather Bureau (66) was republished, with additions, by the California State Board of Horticulture. There is some Federal-State coöperation likewise in the fruit-spraying forecasts service

(150—1923 :107), the State officials aiding especially in the prompt distribution of the forecasts.

In 1914, there was begun a coöperation of the Weather Bureau and the Federal Bureau of Statistics (now Agricultural Economics) in the publication of monthly summaries of weather and crop conditions in each State. In 1916, coöperation began with the Office of Markets and Rural Organization (also now included in the Bureau of Agricultural Economics) in the publication of daily market reports on the strawberry crop during the shipping season (150— 1916 :60). This crop is very sensitive to climatic influences.

Flood-Warning Service

The issuing of flood warnings was made an official duty of the Weather Service of the Army Signal Service in 1871, and has been continued by that agency and the Weather Bureau ever since. Fundamental to a flood-warning service is stream gaging, which has been fully discussed under research in terrestrial aerography. There naturally can be little coöperation in issuing flood warnings, which remains the duty of the Weather Bureau experts. In disseminating their warnings, however, there is widespread but unofficial coöperation by Federal, State, and municipal, as well as commercial, agencies. The service was established in the Sacramento and San Joaquin drainage basins at an early day, and the work has been gradually extended.

Two new river districts were established in California in 1917 to give flood-warning services, one on the Los Angeles River, with headquarters at Los Angeles, and the other for the Eel River, with headquarters at Eureka.

Aviation Forecasts

The rapid development of aviation has made necessary an entirely new type of weather forecast, namely, one that gives information on conditions in the upper air as well as near the surface of the earth, and at frequent intervals instead of only twice or thrice daily. Information necessary for aviators regarding surface conditions is derived from the regular observing stations of the Weather Bureau. Knowledge regarding conditions in the upper air must come from the aerological studies described above under

Aerological Research. As noted in that section of this chapter, such stations are maintained by the Weather Bureau, by the Army Signal Corps, and by the Navy Department. The two military services have coöperated most heartily in enabling the Weather Bureau to perform this important new service for official as well as commercial aviation (47).

The making of daily aviation forecasts was begun in 1918 in coöperation with the Army Signal Corps, and for use of the air services of the two military departments and the air-mail service of the Post Office Department. By 1922 the United States had been divided into fourteen zones for these daily aviation forecasts, which were furnished to the officials and employees of the three departments concerned and to all the flying fields of the country. In addition, more detailed twice-daily forecasts were furnished for the Army Air Service on three major routes leading from the District of Columbia to Dayton, Ohio, to New York, and to Norfolk, Virginia (150—1922:71).

In the meantime, closer coöperation with the Army Air Service was developed by the Weather Bureau through arranged visits of Army aviators to Weather Bureau stations, to get acquainted with personnel, learn of existing facilities, discuss common problems, and arrange the detail of obtaining weather information promptly as required. Reprints of prepared papers on weather and aeronautics were furnished to all aviators in the military and naval service. Weather Bureau meteorologists arrange series of lectures on meteorology and aerology, including physics of the air, air currents, etc., for Army and other government aviators. Circulars explaining these coöperative activities were mailed to all field stations and military and naval services, and their importance stressed by the Chief of the Army Air Service.

Similar coöperation was entered upon with the Bureau of Aeronautics of the Navy Department, and Weather Bureau forecasts and weather reports also were furnished to all naval flying bases. A naval flying officer has been given desk space and facilities in the forecast room of the Weather Bureau at Washington, D. C., where he prepares a daily weather map and makes forecasts in collaboration with the official Bureau forecasters, and telephones these directly to various naval bases. The same methods were employed in spreading a knowledge of the service among Navy aviators. As a result, Army and Navy flying fields call Weather Bureau stations for a special forecast whenever flying operations are contemplated, and individual aviators away from stations call convenient Bureau stations for information at any time.

The Weather Bureau and the two flying services coöperated in a preliminary meteorological survey for commercial and official airship bases on the Atlantic Coast (185).

Under the Air Commerce Act of 1926, it was made the duty of the Weather Bureau to establish such stations, make such observations and investigations, and furnish such forecasts, as were necessary to the safety and efficiency of air navigation. It was made the duty of the Secretary of Commerce to make recommendations to the Secretary of Agriculture as to meteorological services necessary for aviation. Funds for this work were made available to the Weather Bureau thereafter, in its appropriation bill, on the specific recommendation of the Secretary of Commerce as to needs. Hearty coöperation between the two departments was maintained in this important work (63; 149–11:64; 150–1928).

Information and forecast services have been provided by the Weather Bureau expressly in furtherance of many special aviation events, such as the Army and Navy balloon races, the Navy seaplane flight across the Atlantic in 1919, the Army transcontinental reliability airplane race, the Navy hydroplane recruiting tour, the national balloon race, and many others of later date. Such coöperation becomes international with the arrival of our aircraft abroad or with the visits of foreign aircraft to this country, such as the visit of the British Dirigible R-34 in 1919 and the more recent visit of the German *Graf Zeppelin*.

In performing this extensive forecasting service at airports, the Weather Bureau receives coöperation from municipal officers as well as from the representatives of commercial airports and aviation companies, the former providing facilities and quarters for Bureau employees at the airports. As aviation is only an infant industry, it seems probable that both the services rendered by the Weather Bureau and the coöperation given to it by public and private agencies will steadily increase in future years.

Miscellaneous Special Services

In 1919 the Weather Bureau was specifically authorized to set up a highways service, for showing weather conditions and the actual and probable conditions of highways. It was designed for the use of motorists, truckers, and the public generally (28).

For many years the Bureau has given special attention to supplying homeseekers with information regarding weather and climate in different parts of the country (192). This was especially important as the more favorable portions of the agricultural area became settled and land seekers were forced more and more into the less favorable parts. This information has been given direct to applicants, and also to State agencies such as departments of immigration, etc.

Another special use of the extensive data accumulated and disseminated by the Weather Bureau is as evidence in courts of law. There are many cases in which judgment or action may have depended on visibility, cloudiness, slipperiness, etc. (40).

The Weather Bureau has encouraged the teaching of meteorology in the public schools, from grade and high schools to colleges and universities (191). It has helped educational authorities to formulate courses, when requested, and has published courses proposed by those in the educational field (14).

Wartime coöperation.—Immediately on the entrance of the United States into the World War, the Secretary of Agriculture offered the military and naval authorities the fullest use of the facilities of the Weather Bureau. The chief forecasting activities were concerned with weather conditions for the movement of troops and supplies on land and sea, special information for operations in the air, and assistance to the shore patrol (150—1917:47). Other services had to do with the conditions affecting the location and sanitation of camps and hospitals, and operations at camps and naval stations. One of the foremost officials in the forecasting service was commissioned a major in the Signal Officers' Reserve Corps. Coöperation was effected with both the British and French Meteorological Services (116; 150—1917:48, and 1918:58).

The publications listed in the Literature Cited at the end of the chapter which are cited in this section on Special Forecasts are

Nos. 14, 28, 40, 47, 63, 66, 70, 82, 105, 108, 116, 125, 137, 138, 149–11, 150, 151, 155–51, 185, 191, and 192.

5. Summary of Coöperation

In both the research and the extension (forecast) activities relating to climate and weather, there is wide though often informal coöperation.

RESEARCH IN CLIMATIC FACTORS

Solar radiation.—Federal agencies engaged are the Astrophysical Observatory of the Smithsonian Institution and the Weather Bureau of the U. S. Department of Agriculture, while the Naval Observatory determines sun-spot data. The Weather Bureau and the Astrophysical Observatory occasionally collaborate on problems. In a few cases there is limited State and county collaboration. Both observatories furnish data for regular publication in the *Monthly Weather Review*. All three Federal agencies coöperate with the International Meteorological Organization or the International Geodetic and Geophysical Union in allocated research.

Ocean currents and temperatures.—For ninety years the Navy Hydrographic Office has collected ocean data as part of a formal and increasingly extensive international coöperation. There is minor State collaboration. Since 1904 the previously independent work of the Weather Bureau has been coördinated by formal agreement. The Coast and Geodetic Survey has charge of similar current studies along ocean coasts, and receives coöperation from units of the Commerce, Navy, and War Departments, and State, county, and municipal officials. It coöperates internationally in exchange of data.

Aerography covers terrestrial, marine, and free-air meteorology. Terrestrial aerography has been the official concern successively of the Medical Department of the Army, the Smithsonian Institution, the Signal Service of the Army, and, finally, the Weather Bureau of the Department of Agriculture, for more than 115 years. These and many other Federal and State units have coöperated extensively in collecting and publishing the data, and in furnishing quarters for weather stations. Many local official agencies record observations. There is much coöperation with Federal, State, and municipal engineering agencies in river gaging and flood recording. Since 1874 there has been increasing international coöperation through the International Meteorological Organization. The United States has been the chief publishing agency for international data, and has shared in the researches of the two International Polar Years.

In marine aerography there is wide coöperation from Navy and Shipping Board vessels. The international coöperation is of long standing and very extensive. Here again the United States has been a leader in the publication and distribution of international data. In aerological or free-air research, there has been intermittent coöperation with the Signal Corps of the Army and with some other Federal units. There also has been extensive international coöperation in polar-year research.

WEATHER FORECASTS AND WARNINGS

Assembling observations.—By formal agreement the Navy Office of Communications coöperates extensively with the Weather Bureau in assembling from Alaska and vessels at sea the observations needed in making forecasts, and also transmits Pacific Coast observations for Hawaiian forecasting. The Army Signal Corps likewise transmits some Alaskan data, and furnishes observations as bases for special aviation forecasts between the twice-daily regular forecasts. In international coöperation, the Navy radio stations gather needed observations from stations in Canada, Mexico, the West Indies, and the Orient, and exchange our data with the same nations.

Distributing regular forecasts.—Since 1872 the Post Office Department has coöperated in speeding the transmission and distribution of forecasts. Since 1913, under formal agreement, there has been increasing coöperation by the Navy Office of Communications in broadcasting forecasts and warnings. The program has been steadily increased in scope of material, frequency of broadcast, and area covered, which now includes the entire United States and the Caribbean region. International coöperation occurs regularly in transmitting forecasts to vessels at sea, and occasionally in special activities.

Special forecasts and warnings.—The Coast Guard coöperates in the display of storm warnings to shipping. In special forecasts

and warnings for agriculture there is minor coöperation by interested State and local agencies. In aviation forecasts, however, there
is abundant and formal coöperation. In 1918 the Weather Bureau
and the Signal Corps began coöperative supplying of aerological
data to the Air Services of the Navy and War Departments and
the air-mail service of the Post Office Department. Still closer relations with the military departments have developed in making
flying-weather forecasts, locating air bases, etc. Under law, the
Aeronautics Branch of the Department of Commerce and the
Weather Bureau coöperate in assuring necessary forecasts for
commercial aviation. There is international coöperation relating to
official flights to and from foreign countries.

6. Literature Cited

1. Abbe, Cleveland. The meteorological work of the U. S. Signal Service,
1870 to 1891. U. S. Dept. Agric., Weather Bur., Bul. 11:232–85, 1894. (See
Entry No. 51.)

2. Abbe, Cleveland. A first report on the relations between climates and
crops. U. S. Dept. Agric., Weather Bur., Bul. 36:1–386, 1905.

3. A[bbe], C[leveland]. International simultaneous observations. Mo.
Weather Rev. 42:675–76, 1914.

4. Abbe, Cleveland. How the United States Weather Bureau was started.
Sci. Amer. 114:529, May 20, 1916.

5. Abbot, C. G. The solar constant of radiation. Science (n.s.) 39:335–48,
March 6, 1914.

6. Abbot, C. G. Extracts from the Annual Report of the Smithsonian Astrophysical Observatory. Mo. Weather Rev. 42:621–23, 1914.

7. Abbot, C. G. Measurements of the solar constant of radiation. Mo. Weather
Rev. 47:85–87, 1919.

The second and third articles in the series appeared as contributions under the name
of C. G. Abbot (Mo. Weather Rev. 47:499, 658–59, 1919). Thereafter the data were
usually transmitted without specific titles.

8. Abbot, C. G. Montezuma pyrheliometry, 1920–1926. Mo. Weather Rev.
Suppl. 27:1–15, 1 fig., 1926.

9. Abbot, C. G. Weather dominated by solar changes. Smithsn. Misc. Collect.
85(1):1–8, figs. 1–4, 1931.

10. Abbot, C. G., and Mrs. A. M. Bond. Periodicity in solar variation. Proc.
Nat. Acad. Sci. 19:361–70, figs. 1–7, 1933.

11. Abbot, C. G., and colleagues. Values of the solar constant, 1920–1922.
Mo. Weather Rev. 51:71–81, figs. 1–8, 1923.

12. Abbot, C. G., F. E. Fowle, and L. B. Aldrich. The great solar cooker on
Mount Wilson, California. Ann. Astrophys. Observ. Smithsn. Inst. 4:311–18,
1922.

13. Alexander, William H. The U. S. Weather Bureau and its work. Cleveland Engin. Soc. Jour. 5:321–38, illus., 1913.

14. Allen, W. N. A course in meteorology and physical geography. U. S. Dept. Agric., Weather Bur., Bul. 39:1–35, 1911.

15A. American Society of Civil Engineers. Meteorological data: Progress report of special committee. Proc. Amer. Soc. Civil Engin. 59(1):153–82, figs. 1–9, 1933.

15B. Ames, Allan P. Doing business by the weather map. World's Work 28:186–91, 1914.

16. Anderson, Joseph B. Observations from airplanes of cloud and fog conditions along the southern California coast. Mo. Weather Rev. 59:264–70, 1931.

Atlas of American Agriculture. See U. S. Department of Agriculture.

17. Beehler, W. H. Relations between the barometric pressure and the strength and direction of ocean currents. U. S. Dept. Agric., Weather Bur., Bul. 11:177–95, pl. 7, 1894. (See Entry No. 51.)

18. Beehler, W. H. Origin and work of the Division of Marine Meteorology, Hydrographic Office. Proc. U. S. Naval Inst. 19:267–81, 1893.

19. Beehler, W. H. The origin and work of the Division of Marine Meteorology. U. S. Dept. Agric., Weather Bur., Bul. 11:221–32, 1894. (See Entry No. 51.)

20. Benjamin, Marcus. Meteorology: 647–78. *In* The Smithsonian Institution, 1846–1896. The history of its first half century. 856 p. (Washington: Government Printing Office, 1897.)

21. Bigelow, F[rank] H. Work of the meteorologist for the benefit of agriculture, commerce, and navigation. U. S. Dept. Agric., Yearbook 1899 (Sep. 183):71–92, pls. 1–2, 1900.

22. Bigelow, Frank H. Mountain snowfall observations and evaporation investigations in the United States. U. S. Dept. Agric., Yearbook 1910 (Sep. 547):407–12, pl. 26, 1911.

23. Birkhimer, William E. Sketch of the work of the Signal Service Bureau for the agriculturist. U. S. Dept. Agric., Misc. Spec. Rept. 9:191–96, 1885.

24. [Blair, Wm. R., and] W. R. Gregg. Free-air data in southern California, July and August, 1913. Mo. Weather Rev. 42:410–26, figs. 1–15, 1914.

Under the above title are two separate contributions, as follows: (*a*) The free balloon observations, pp. 410–19, anonymous but presumably by Wm. R. Blair; and (*b*) The captive balloon and mountain observations on and near Mount Whitney, pp. 419–26, by W. R. Gregg.

25. Blair, Wm. R., *et al.* 1. Sounding balloon ascensions at Fort Omaha, Neb., May 8, 1915 (pp. 7–10, figs. 1–3); 2. Meteorological observations on board the U. S. Coast Guard Cutter *Seneca*, April to July, 1915 (pp. 11–28, figs. 4–13). Mo. Weather Rev. Suppl. 3:1–28, figs. 1–13, 1916.

26. Bliss, George S. The weather business; a history of weather records and the work of the U. S. Weather Bureau. Sci Amer. Suppl. 84:110–11, August 18, 1917.

27. Börgen, C. The international polar expeditions, 1882–83. U. S. Dept. Agric., Weather Bur., Bul. 11:469–85, 1894. (See Entry No. 51.)

28. Bowie, E. H. Work of the Weather Bureau and its relation to transportation. Sci. Amer. Suppl. 62:818–19, November 17, 1906.

Brookings Institution. See Institute for Government Research.

29. Brown, Ralph Minthorne. Bibliography of Commander Matthew Fontaine Maury, including a biographical sketch. Va. Polytech. Inst. Bul. 24 (2):1–61, 1 pl., December 1, 1930.

30. California State Agricultural Society. Transactions of the California State Agricultural Society for the year ――― 1858–1901. 8vo. (Sacramento: State Printer)

31. California. University. Meteorological synopsis of Berkeley. Univ. Calif., December, 1886, to June, 1927. 4to, monthly.

This synopsis was issued in two consecutive series of monthly pamphlets. Series 1, not designated by series or volume number, was issued by the Students' Observatory from December, 1886, to June, 1912, under the title, *Meteorological synopsis of Berkeley for the month of* ―――, ―――. Series 2, designated by series, volume, and issue numbers, was issued by the Department of Geography from July, 1912, to June, 1927, as volumes 1 to 15, under the title, *Meteorological synopsis of Berkeley: Summary of observations at the Meteorological Station for the month of* ―――, ―――.

32. Calvert, E[dgar] B. The Weather Bureau and the war. Mo. Weather Rev. 45:411–12, 1917.

Abstract of longer article published in Weather Bureau Topics and Personnel (Washington.)

33. Calvert, E[dgar] B. History of radio in relation to the work of the Weather Bureau. Mo. Weather Rev. 51:1–9, 1923.

Complete chronological history of the subject.

34. Calvert, E[dgar] B. [compiler]. The Weather Bureau. U. S. Dept. Agric., Misc. Publ. 114:i–iv, 1–34, figs. 11, 4″ × 6½″, 1931. (History, organization, and work of the Weather Bureau. See also Entry No. 158.)

35. Calvert, Edgar B. The selected-ship program for ocean-weather reporting by radio. Mo. Weather Rev. 59:185–86, 1931.

36. Clark, A. H. Navy's oceanographic program. Science (n.s.) 61:269–76, March 13, 1925.

Coast Survey. See U. S. Department of Commerce, Coast and Geodetic Survey.

37. Coffin, J. H. Results of meteorological observations made under the direction of the United States Patent Office and the Smithsonian Institution, from the year 1854 to 1859, inclusive, being a report of the Commissioner of Patents made at the First Session of the Thirty-sixth Congress. U. S. Cong. 36th, 1st Sess., S. Doc. vol. 1: I–L, 1–1219. (Washington, 4to, 1861.)

38. Coolidge, Richard H., and Lorin Blodget. Army meteorological register, for twelve years from 1843 to 1854, inclusive, compiled from observations made by the officers of the Medical Department of the Army, at the military posts of the United States. U. S. Dept. War, Surgeon General's Office, xi, 766 p., 10 folded charts, 4to, 1855.

39. Corbin, D. F. M. Life of Matthew Fontaine Maury. 326 p. (London: Sampson Law, Marston, Searle & Rivington, Ltd., 1888)

40. Cox, Henry J. Use of Bureau records in court. U. S. Dept. Agric., Yearbook 1903 (Sep. 307):303–12, 1903.

41. Cox, Henry J. Thermal belts and fruit growing in North Carolina. Mo. Weather Rev. Suppl. 19:1–106, front. and figs. 1–78, 1923.

42. Curtis, George E. Smithsonian meteorological tables. 2nd rev. ed. Smithsn. Misc. Collect. [Publ.] 1032:i–lix, 1–274, 1897. Based on Guyot's meteorological and physical tables.
The original edition of the present work was issued in 1893.

43. Davis, William Morris. The Redfield and Espy period. U. S. Dept. Agric., Weather Bur., Bul. 11:305–16, 1894. (See Entry No. 51.)

44. Dunwoody, H. H. C. Signal Service tables of rainfall and temperature compared with crop production. U. S. Dept. War, Signal Service Professional Papers 10:1–15, 4to, 1882.

45. Dunwoody, H. H. C. Charts and tables showing geographic distribution of rainfall in the United States. U. S. Dept. War, Signal Service Professional Papers 9:1–51, maps, 4to, 1883.

46. Dunwoody, H. H. C. State weather service organizations. U. S. Dept. Agric., Weather Bur., Bul. 11:285–91, 1894. (See Entry No. 51.)

47. Edholm, C. L. Airmen and the Weather Bureau—partners. Sci. Amer. 116:342, April 7, 1917.

48. Eisenhower, M. S., and A. P. Chew. The United States Department of Agriculture: Its growth, structure, and functions. U. S. Dept. Agric., Misc. Publ., 88:i–iv, 1–147, 21 charts (unnumbered), Sept. 1, 1930.

49. Everhart, Elfrida. Weather Bureau. Pp. 72–75. *In her* Handbook of United States public documents 320 p. (Minneapolis: Wilson, 1910)

50. Farrall, A. W. The solar heater. Calif. Agric. Exp. Sta., Bul. 469:3–30, figs. 1–21, June, 1929.

51. Fassig, Oliver L. [secretary and editor]. Report of the International Meteorological Congress held at Chicago, Ill., August 21–24, 1893, under the auspices of the Congress Auxiliary of the World's Columbian Exposition. U. S. Dept. Agric., Weather Bur., Bul. 11:1–772, pls. 1–43, many text figs., 1894. (Section IV. History and Bibliography, pp. 207–394.) (See Entries Nos. 1, 17, 19, 27, 43, 46, 72, 76, 99, 101, 132, 139.)

52. Fassig, Oliver L. The work of the Weather Bureau in the West Indies. Mo. Weather Rev. 47:850–51, 1919.

53. Fitton, Edith M., and Charles F. Brooks. Soil temperatures in the United States. Mo. Weather Rev. 59:6–16, figs. 1–7, 1931.

54. Frankenfield, Harry C. Extension of the river and flood service of the Weather Bureau. U. S. Dept. Agric., Yearbook 1905 (Sep. 379):231–40, 1906.

55. Gates, Otis H. [compiler] Chapter 2. The Weather Bureau. Pp. 64–70. *In* Laws applicable to the United States Department of Agriculture, 1923. iv, 897 p. (Washington: Government Printing Office, 1924)

56. Gauss, H. C. The Weather Bureau. Pp. 757–72. *In his* The American government, organization and officials. 871 p. (New York: Hamersly, 1908)

57. Gherardi. W. R. Special notice to mariners; One hundredth anniversary number, 1830–1930; The Hydrographic Office of the Navy. 18 p., 6 charts, 11 half-tones, U. S. Navy Hydrographic Office, Washington, 4to, 1930.

58. Glassford, W. A. Climate of California and Nevada, with particular reference to the rainfall and temperature and their influence upon the irrigation problems of the two States. Trans. Calif. State Agric. Soc. 1891:255–98, 1892.

59A. Greathouse, Charles H. [compiler]. Historical sketch of the U. S. Department of Agriculture; its objects and present organization. U. S. Dept. Agric., Div. of Publ., Bul. 3:1–74, front. and 2 pls., 9 unnumbered figs. (halftones), 1898; rev. ed., same paging, 1898. (Weather Bureau, p. 33.)

59B. Greathouse, Charles H. [compiler]. Historical sketch of the U. S. Department of Agriculture; its objects and present organization. U. S. Dept. Agric., Div. of Publ., Bul. 3, 2d rev. ed., 1–97, front. and 2 pls., 9 unnumbered figs. (half-tones), 1907. (Weather Bureau, pp. 47–48.)

60. Gregg, Willis R[ay]. Aerological investigations of the Weather Bureau during the War. Mo. Weather Rev. 47:205–10, 1919.

61. Gregg, Willis R[ay]. An aerological survey of the United States. Part 1: Results of observations by means of kites. Mo. Weather Rev. Suppl. 20:1–78, figs. 1–25, 1922.

The Suppl. No. is given wrongly as 22 in the bibliography of Part 2; see next entry.

62. Gregg, Willis Ray. An aerological survey of the United States. Part 2: Results of observations by means of pilot balloons. Mo. Weather Rev. Suppl. 26:1–60, figs. 1–14, 1926.

In the bibliography of this part, the Suppl. No. in which Part 1 was published is erroneously given as 22 instead of 20.

63. Gregg, Willis Ray. Weather service for commercial aviators is further extended. U. S. Dept. Agric., Yearbook 1927:684–86, 1928.

64. Gregg, Willis Ray, and J. Parker Van Zandt. The wind factor in flight: An analysis of one year's record of the air mail. Mo. Weather Rev. 51:111–25, 1923.

65. Grosvenor, Gilbert H. Our heralds of storm and flood, being an account of the various activities of the United States Weather Bureau in saving life and property. Century Mag. 70:161–78, 1905.

66. Hammon, W. H. Frost: When to expect it and how to lessen the injury therefrom. U. S. Dept. Agric., Weather Bur., Bul. 23:1–37, 1899.

67. Handy, R. B., and Minna A. Cannon. List by titles of publications of the United States Department of Agriculture from 1840 to June, 1901, inclusive. U. S. Dept. Agric., Div. Publ., Bul. 6:1–216, 1902. (Weather Bureau, pp. 199–216.)

68. Hannay, A. M. The influence of weather on crops: 1900–1930. A selected and annotated bibliography. U. S. Dept. Agric., Misc. Publ. 118:1–246, 1931.

69. Harrington, Mark W. Special report of the Chief of the Weather Bureau to the Secretary of Agriculture. 26 p. (Washington: Government Printing Office, 1891)

On the organization and activities of the Weather Bureau soon after transfer from the Signal Service.

70. Harrington, Mark W. Meteorological work for agricultural institutions. U. S. Dept. Agric., Off. Exp. Stat., Bul. 10:1–23, 1892. (Bibliography of recent works, except Federal, pp. 22–23.)

71. Haskin, Frederic J. The American government. 2 p. l., 9–388 p. (New York: J. J. Little and Ives Co., 1912). (Weather Bureau, pp. 145–56) Rev. ed., 5–484 p. (Washington: F. J. Haskin, 1924) (Weather Bureau, pp. 227–36)

71A. Haskin, Frederic J. The American government today. x, 470 p. (New York: Grosset & Dunlap, 1935) (Weather Bureau, pp. 143–50.)

Complete revision of author's former work, published under the title "The American government."

72. Hautreux, A. [Lieutenant, French Navy]. North Atlantic currents and surface temperatures. U. S. Dept. Agric., Weather Bur., Bul. 11:192–204, pls. 8–10, 1894. (See Entry No. 51.)

73. Hawkinson, Wendell Louise. The administration and organization of the United States Weather Bureau. Univ. Calif., Dept. Pol. Sci. Thesis (M. A.). 72 p., typw. 1922.

In University and University Bureau of Public Administration libraries, Berkeley, California.

74. Hazen, W. B. Memoranda on useful information for ship-masters, issued by the Chief Signal Officer of the United States Army. 9 p., 2 figs. U. S. War Dept., Office Chief Signal Officer, 1882.

75. Heiskell, Henry L. The commercial weather map of the United States Weather Bureau. U. S. Dept. Agric., Yearbook 1912 (Sep. 612):537–39, 1913.

76. Henry, Alfred J[udson]. Early individual observers in the United States. U. S. Dept. Agric., Weather Bur., Bul. 11:291–302, 1894. (See Entry No. 51.)

77. Henry, Alfred J[udson]. Wind velocity and fluctuations of water level on Lake Erie. U. S. Dept. Agric., Weather Bur., Bul. J:1–22, with 25 full-page unnumbered figs. (1 map, 24 charts), 4to, 1902.

78. Henry, Alfred Judson. Climatology of the United States. U. S. Dept. Agric., Weather Bur., Bul. Q:1–1012, pls. 1–34, figs. 1–7, 4to, 1906. (California, pp. 972–1006.)

79. Henry, Alfred J[udson]. The river service of the Weather Bureau. Second Pan-American Scientific Congress, Proc. 2(2):671–75, 1915–16.

80. Henry, A[lfred] J[udson]. Weather forecasting from ships at sea. Mo. Weather Rev. 51:188–90, 1923.

81. Henry, Alfred Judson. Weather forecasting from synoptic charts. U. S. Dept. Agric., Misc. Publ. 71:1–80, figs. 1–31, 1930. (Historical review, pp. 1–14).

82. Hermann, Charles F. von. How farmers may utilize the special warnings of the Weather Bureau. U. S. Dept. Agric., Yearbook 1909:387–98, 1910.

83. Hilgard, E. W. A report on the relations of soil to climate. U. S. Dept. Agric., Weather Bur., Bul. 3:1–59, 1892.

84. Hopkins, Andrew Delmar. Periodical events and natural laws as guides to agricultural research and practice. Mo. Weather Rev. Suppl. 9:1–42, figs. 1–24, 1918.

85. Horner, Donald W. United States Weather Bureau and its work. Nautical Mag. [London] 101:493–95, 1919.

86. Hughes, W. S. Founding and development of Hydrographic Office. 71 p. U. S. Hydrographic Office, Washington. 1887.

87. Hunt, Mabel G. List of publications of the United States Department of Agriculture from January, 1901, to December, 1925, inclusive (compiled by comparison with the originals). U. S. Dept. Agric., Misc. Publ. 9:i–vi, 1–182, 1927. (Weather Bureau, pp. 171–73, 180–82.)

"Supplementary to Bulletin No. 6, Division of Publications, issued in 1902, but duplicating that list for months of January–June, 1901."

88. Institute for Government Research of the Brookings Institution. The U. S. Geological Survey; Its history, activities, and organization. Institute for Government Research, Service Monograph 1:1–163. (New York: D. Appleton and Co., 1918)

89. Irish, Charles W. Climate, soil characteristics, and irrigation methods of California. U. S. Dept. Agric., Yearbook 1895 (Sep. 46):475–86, figs. 123–27, pls. 6–7, 1896.

90. Jones, E. Lester. The neglected waters of the Pacific Coast: Washington, Oregon, and California. U. S. Dept. Commerce, Coast and Geodetic Survey, Spec. Publ. 48:1–21, pls. 1–15, incl. charts, 1918.

91. Kenealy, James. Weather Bureau stations and their duties. U. S. Dept. Agric., Yearbook 1903 (Sep. 301):109–20, 1904.

92. Kimball, Herbert H. Solar radiation study reveals facts highly important to farmers. U. S. Dept. Agric., Yearbook 1928:549–51, fig. 211, 1929.

93. Kimball, Herbert H., and Hermann E. Hobbs. A new form of thermoelectric recording pyrheliometer. Mo. Weather Rev. 51:239–42, figs. 1–4, 1923.

94. Kimball, H[erbert] H., and B. G. MacIntire. Efficiency of smoke screens as a protection from frost. Mo. Weather Rev. 51:396–99, fig. 1, 1923.

95. Kincer, J[oseph] B. Precipitation and humidity. 48 p., maps (mostly col.), charts, 1922. *In* U. S. Dept. Agric., Atlas of American Agriculture, Part II, Climate. 1936. (See Entry No. 147.)

96. Kincer, Joseph B. Temperature, sunshine, and wind. 34 pp., maps (mostly col.), and charts, 1928. *In* U. S. Dept. Agric., Atlas of American Agriculture, Part II, Climate. 1936. (See Entry No. 147.)

97. Lamb, George N. A calendar of the leafing, flowering, and seeding of the common trees of the eastern United States. Mo. Weather Rev. Suppl. 2:1–19, 4 full-page graphs, 1915.

98. Langley, S. P. Researches on solar heat and its absorption by the earth's atmosphere. A report of the Mount Whitney Expedition. U. S. War Dept., Signal Service Professional Papers 15:1–242, figs. 1–20, pls. 1–21, 4to. 1884.

99. Langley, S. P. The meteorological work of the Smithsonian Institution. U. S. Dept. Agric., Weather Bur., Bul. 11:216–20, 1894. (See Entry No. 51.)

100A. Lapham, Julia A. Storm Signal service. Earth and Air [Rochester] 1:3–5, February, 1901.

100B. Leuschner, Armin O. Twenty-year synopsis of meteorological observations made at Berkeley, 1887 July 1, to 1907 June 30. Univ. of Calif. Chronicle 10:467–73, 1908.

101. McAdie, Alexander G. Simultaneous meteorological observations in the United States during the Eighteenth Century. U. S. Dept. Agric., Weather Bur., Bul. 11:303–04, 1894. (See Entry No. 51.)

102. McAdie, Alexander G. Climatology of California. U. S. Dept. Agric., Weather Bur., Bul. L:1–270, front. (map), pls. 1–12, and figs. 1–31, 4to, 1903.

103. McAdie, A[lexander] G. The climate of San Francisco. U. S. Dept., Agric., Weather Bur., Bul. 44:1–33, figs. 1–14, 1913.

104. McAdie, Alexander G. Summary of the climatological data for the United States, by sections; . . . Sec. 13.—Southern California and Owens Valley, pp. 1–16; Sec. 14.—Central and southern California, pp. 1–22; Sec. 15.—Northeastern California, pp. 1–20; Sec. 16.—Northwestern California, pp. 1–8. U. S. Dept. Agric., Weather Bur., Bul. W (sections paged separately, Sections 1–57 comprising vol. 1, and Sections 58–106 comprising vol. 2). 4to, 1912.

105. McAdie, Alexander G. Frost fighting. U. S. Dept. Agric., Weather Bur., Bul. 29:1–15, figs. 1–9 (on 6 pls.), 1900.

106. McAdie, Alexander G., and Alfred J[udson] Henry. Lightning and the electricity of the air. In two parts. I. Lightning and the electricity of the air, by McAdie, pp. 9–44, 15 figs. II. Loss of life and property by lightning, by Henry, pp. 45–74, pls. 1–4. U. S. Dept. Agric., Weather Bur., Bul. 26:1–74, illus., 1899.

107. McAdie, Alexander G., and George H. Willson. The climate of San Francisco, California. U. S. Dept. Agric., Weather Bur., Bul. 28:1–30, 7 unnumbered figs. (charts), 1899.

108. Marvin, Charles F. Organization of meteorology and seismology in the United States. Proc. 2nd Pan-American Scientific Congress, Washington, 1915–1916, 2(2):768–79, 1916.

109. Marvin, Charles F. Status and problems of meteorology. Proc. Nat. Acad. Sci. 6:561–72, October, 1920.

110. Marvin, C[harles] F. Locarno meeting of the Meteorological Committee, October, 1931. Mo. Weather Rev. 59:481, 1931.

111A. Marvin, C[harles] F., assisted by H[erbert] H. Kimball. Smithsonian meteorological tables, 4th rev. ed. Smithsn. Misc. Collect. 69(1):1–261, 1918. [Publ. no.] 2493. (See Entry No. 42.)

111B. Marvin, C[harles] F., assisted by H[erbert] H. Kimball. Smithsonian meteorological tables, 5th rev. ed. Smithsn. Misc. Collect. 86:i–lxxxvi, 1–282, 1931. Publ. No. 3116.

112. Maurer, J. Meeting of the Commission for Radiation Researches. Mo. Weather Rev. 51:526–29, 1923.

113. Mell, P. H. Report on the climatology of the cotton plant. U. S. Dept. Agric., Weather Bur., Bul. 8:1–68, charts 1–7, 1893.

114. Mendenhall, T. C. One hundredth anniversary of the U. S. Coast and Geodetic Survey. Science (n.s.) 44:45–50, 1916.

115. Merritt, Dixon. The United States Department of Agriculture: What it is and how it serves. U. S. Dept. Agric., 47 p., mim., 8½″ × 11″, [About 1920]. (Weather Bureau, pp. 7–11.)

116. Merritt, Dixon. Department of Agriculture in the War. U. S. Dept. Agric., Press Service, 208 p., mim., 8½″ × 11″, [about 1920]. (Weather Bureau, pp. 19–23.)

117. Miller, Eric R. The evolution of meteorological institutions in the United States. Mo. Weather Rev. 59:1–6, 1931. (Historical review with names, agencies, and dates; extensive bibliography, pp. 5–6.)

118. Miller, Eric R. New light on the beginnings of the Weather Bureau from the papers of Increase A. Lapham. Mo. Weather Rev. 59:65–70, 1931.

119. Miller, Eric R. The pioneer meteorological work of Elias Loomis at Western Reserve College, Hudson, Ohio, 1837–1844. Mo. Weather Rev. 59:194–95, 1931.

Monthly Weather Review, and Monthly Weather Review Supplement. See U. S. Department of Agriculture, Weather Bureau.

120. Moore, Willis L. (with assistance of others). The work of the Weather Bureau in connection with the rivers of the United States. U. S. Dept. Agric., Weather Bur., Bul. 17:1–106, figs. 1–3, 1896.

Contains much history of the early development of river and flood service by Federal agencies.

121. Moore, Willis L. The Weather Bureau. U. S. Dept. Agric., Yearbook 1897:59–76, 1898.

122. Moore, Willis L. New work in the Weather Bureau. U. S. Dept. Agric., Yearbook 1898:81–86, 1899.

123. Moore, Willis L. Weather forecasting: Some facts, historical, practical, and theoretical. U. S. Dept. Agric., Weather Bur., Bul. 25:1–16, 1899.

Reprinted from The Forum, May, 1898, where it appeared under the title, "Some facts about weather forecasting: Historical, practical, theoretical."

124. Moore, Willis L. The Weather Bureau . . . Presented to the guests of the convention of Weather Bureau officials, at Milwaukee, Wis., August 27–29, 1901. 19 p. (Chicago, 1901)

125. Munns, E. N. A bibliography of the influence of forests on climatic factors. Pp. 134–43. *In his* Erosion and flood problems in California. (Sacramento, State Printing Office, 1923)

California State Board of Forestry, Report to the Legislature on Senate concurrent resolution No. 27 (Legislature of 1921), pp. 9–165.

126. Page, John L. Climate of Mexico. Mo. Weather Rev. Suppl. 33:1–30, figs. 1–41, 1930.

127. Pillsbury, J. E. Ocean currents and deep-sea explorations of the United States Coast and Geodetic Survey. Pp. 40–46. *In* Centennial celebration of the United States Coast and Geodetic Survey, April 5 and 6, 1916. U. S. Dept. Commerce, Coast and Geodetic Survey, unnumbered publ., 196 p., 45 figs., 1916.

128. Reed, William Gardner. Meteorology at the Lick Observatory. Mo. Weather Rev. 42:339–45, figs. 1–4, 1914.

129. Reed, William Gardner. Frost and the growing season. 12 p. with charts and maps (mostly col.), July 15, 1918. *In* U. S. Dept. Agric., Atlas of American Agriculture, Part II, Climate. 1936. (See entry No. 147.)

130. Rolt-Wheeler, Francis W. The boy with the U. S. weather men. 336 p., 72 illus. (Author's U. S. service series; Boston: Lothrop, 1917.)

131. Russell, Thomas. River stages. U. S. Dept. Agric., Report of the Chief of the Weather Bureau, 1891–92: 483–504, 1893. 4to.

132. Russell, Thomas. River stage predictions in the United States. U. S. Dept. Agric., Weather Bur., Bul., 11:89–94, 1894. (See Entry No. 51.)

133. Samuels, L. T. Sounding-balloon observations made at Broken Arrow, Okla., during the International Month, December, 1929. Mo. Weather Rev. 59: 297–309, figs. 1–8, 1931.

134. Samuels, L. T. Sounding-balloon observations at Royal Center, Ind., during the International Month, September, 1930. Mo. Weather Rev. 59:417–26, figs. 1–6, 1931.

135. Schott, Charles A. Tables and results of the precipitation, in rain and snow, in the United States, and at some stations in adjacent parts of North America, and in Central and South America. (Collected by the Smithsonian Institution.) Smithsn. Contrib. Knowl. 222:1–175, diag. 1–8, pls. 1–5, folded unnumbered maps, 3; 4to, May, 1872; 2nd ed. *ibid.*, 353:i–xx, 1–249, 1881.

136. Schott, Charles A. Tables, distribution, and variations of the atmospheric temperature in the United States, and some adjacent parts of America. (Collected by the Smithsonian Institution.) Smithsn. Contrib. Knowl. 277: i–xvi, 1–345, illus. by unnumbered diag. and maps, 4to, 1876.

137. Show, S. B. Meteorology and the forest-fire problem. Mo. Weather Rev. 59:432–33, 1931.

138. Show, S. B., and E. I. Kotok. Weather conditions and forest fires in California. U. S. Dept. Agric., Dept. Circ. 354:1–24, figs. 1–9, 1925.

139. Smart, Charles. The connection of the Army Medical Department with the development of meteorology in the United States. U. S. Dept. Agric., Weather Bur., Bul. 11:207–16, 1894. (See Entry No. 51.)
History of official meteorological work and records from May 2, 1814, to 1870.

140. Smith, George W. Forecast distribution. Mo. Weather Rev. 42:541–45, 1 pl., 1914.

141. Smith, J. Warren. Speaking of the weather. U. S. Dept. Agric., Yearbook 1920 (Sep. 838):181–202, 1921.
Lists the various services, with illustrations of each.

142. Smithsonian Institution. Annals of the Astrophysical Observatory of the Smithsonian Institution. 1, by Langley and Abbot, 1900; 2, by Abbot and Fowle, 1908; 3, by Abbot, Fowle, and Aldrich, 1913; 4, by Abbot, Fowle, and Aldrich, 1922.
Smithsonian Institution. Smithsonian Meteorological Tables. See Curtis, Entry No. 42, and Marvin, Nos. 111A and 111B.

143. Southerland, W. H. H. Hydrographic Office of the United States. Nat. Geogr. Mag. 14:61–75, 1903.

144. Talman, Charles F. The farmer and the Weather Bureau; the latest chapter in the story of practical meteorology in America and its application to agriculture and horticulture. Sci. Amer. (n.s.) 104:175–76, 187–89, 1911.

145. Taylor, Nathaniel R. The rivers and floods of the Sacramento and San Joaquin watersheds. U. S. Dept. Agric., Weather Bur., Bul. 43:1–92, figs. 1–48, 1913.

146. Tittman, O. H. Work of the Coast and Geodetic Survey. Science 18:33–40, 1903.

United States Coast Survey and United States Coast and Geodetic Survey. See U. S. Dept. of Commerce, Coast and Geodetic Survey.

147. U. S. Department of Agriculture, Bureau of Agricultural Economics. Atlas of American agriculture: physical basis, including land relief, climate, soils, and natural vegetation of the United States. Prepared under the supervision of O. E. Baker. 4 vols. in 1, illus., maps, tables, diagrs. (Washington: Government Printing Office, 1936)

Sections on Cotton and Rural Population were printed as separates and not included in this volume.

148. U. S. Department of Agriculture. List of technical workers in the Department of Agriculture and outline of Department functions, 1931. U. S. Dept. Agric., Misc. Publ. 123:1–165, 1931. (Weather Bureau, pp. 127–34.)

149. U. S. Department of Agriculture. Official Record 1–11, 1922–32. 4to., weekly.

150. U. S. Department of Agriculture, Weather Bureau. Report of the Chief of the Weather Bureau. 1891–. *In* Annual Reports of the Department of Agriculture for the year ending June 30, ――― [year]. Report of the Secretary of Agriculture. Reports of Chiefs.

Beginning with 1891, an octavo annual administrative report was published. From 1891 to 1920, inclusive, and for 1922 and 1923, the reports of Chiefs of Offices, Divisions, and Bureaus are included with report of the Secretary in a consecutively paged volume. For 1921 and 1924 to date all these reports have been paged and issued separately. Most of them have been printed, some have been multigraphed, and some have been mimeographed, as that of the Weather Bureau in 1928.

151. U. S. Department of Agriculture, Weather Bureau. Report of the Chief of the Weather Bureau, 1891–92–. Washington, 4to, 1893–.

These quarto annual reports are printed under concurrent resolution of the Congress, which specifies that 1000 copies will be for the use of the Senate, 2000 copies for the use of the House of Representatives, and the specified remainder for the use of the Weather Bureau. Besides an administrative section, they contain extensive meteorological data.

152. U. S. Department of Agriculture, Weather Bureau. Bulletins 1–44, 8vo, 1892–1913.

153. U. S. Department of Agriculture, Weather Bureau. Bulletins A–Z, 4to, 1893–1913.

154. U. S. Department of Agriculture, Weather Bureau. Climatological Data, California Section. Vols. 1–36, 1897–32. San Francisco, Calif., 4to, monthly issues with annual summary.

The title of this publication has been modified several times in these 36 years, and other changes made.

155. U. S. Department of Agriculture, Weather Bureau. Monthly Weather Review 19(7)–61, 4to, July, 1891–1933.

For previous volumes, see U. S. Department of War, Signal Service.

156. U. S. Department of Agriculture, Weather Bureau. Monthly Weather Review Supplements 1–34, 4to, 1914–30.

157. U. S. Department of Agriculture, Weather Bureau. Does the Weather Bureau make good? Answer by the maritime, agricultural, and commercial in-

terests of the United States, and by the American press. (Symposium.) 65 p. (Washington, 1909.)

158. U. S. Department of Agriculture, Weather Bureau. The Weather Bureau. Prepared under the direction of Willis L. Moore, Chief. 39 p., unnumbered publ., 4" × 6½", 1912; rev. ed., 58 p., 10 figs., 1915; rev. ed., by Henry E. Williams, 59 p., 1921; rev. ed., by Henry E. Williams and E. B. Calvert, 55 p., 11 figs., 1923. (For 1931 revision, see Entry No. 34, Calvert.)

159. U. S. Department of Agriculture, Weather Bureau. The marine meteorological service of the United States. 22 p. (Washington: Government Printing Office, 1919)

160. U. S. Department of Agriculture, Weather Bureau. International radio weather code for use on United States selected ships. 14 p. (Washington: Government Printing Office, 4to, 1930)

161. U. S. Department of Agriculture, Weather Bureau. Vessel weather code for transmission of weather observations from ships by radio. 24 p. (Washington, Government Printing Office, 4to, 1931)

162. U. S. Department of Agriculture, Weather Bureau. Aerological Code (pilot balloons) 1930. 18 p. (Washington, Government Printing Office., 4to, 1930)

163. U. S. Department of Commerce, Coast and Geodetic Survey. Annual report of the Director of the United States Coast and Geodetic Survey to the Secretary of Commerce for the fiscal year ending June 30, ———. 1834–.
Titles of publication have differed slightly, even in recent years.

164. U. S. Department of Commerce, Coast and Geodetic Survey. The United States Coast and Geodetic Survey: its work, methods, and organization. Spec. Publ. 23 (rev. ed.): i–vi, 1–111, front., 36 figs., 8vo, 1929.
Previous editions, with slightly differing titles, in 1893, 1909, and 1920.

165. U. S. [Department of Commerce,] Coast and Geodetic Survey. Bibliography. Descriptive catalogue of publications relating to U. S. Coast and Geodetic Survey. 1807–1890. Compiled by Goodfellow, Sinclair and Baylor. Report for 1891. Appendix No. 11. 474 p. (Washington: Government Printing Office, 1892)

166. U. S. [Department of Commerce,] Coast and Geodetic Survey. Bibliography . . . relating to the Coast and Geodetic Survey, 1807–1896. Spec. Publ. 3: 1–118, 1898.

167. U. S. Department of Commerce, Coast and Geodetic Survey. Centennial celebration of the United States Coast and Geodetic Survey, April 5 and 6, 1916. 196 p., 45 figs. (Washington: Government Printing Office, 1916)

168. U. S. Department of Commerce, Coast and Geodetic Survey. Tides and currents in San Francisco Bay. Spec. Publ. 115:1–125, 39 figs., 1925.

169. U. S. Department of Commerce, Coast and Geodetic Survey. Coastal currents along the Pacific Coast of the United States. Spec. Publ. 121:1–80, 23 illus., 1926.

170. U. S. Department of Commerce, Coast and Geodetic Survey. Tidal bench marks, State of California. Spec. Publ. 141:1–62, map & 1 pl., 1928.

171. U. S. Department of the Interior, Bureau of Education. Guide to U. S. government publications. Education Bulletin 1918 (2). 206 p. (Weather Bureau, pp. 91–92.)

172. U. S. Department of the Navy, Bureau of Navigation, Hydrographic Office. Annual report of the Hydrographic Office for the fiscal year ———. 1869–. Washington, 8vo. (Subtitle: Appendix No. 1 to the Annual Report of the Chief of the Bureau of Navigation, ———.)

173. U. S. Department of the Navy, Bureau of Navigation, Hydrographic Office. The origin and mission of the Hydrographic Office. Reprint of Hydrographic Information (from the Pilot Charts and Hydrographic Bulletin) No. 9, rev.:1–14, 8vo, January 3, 1918. (Original edition, January 1, 1910.)

174. U. S. Department of the Navy, Naval Observatory. Annual report of the Naval Observatory for the fiscal year ———. (Report of Superintendent of Naval Observatory.) 1847–. Washington. 8vo.

Usually about 20–30 pages, but the Report for 1928 is larger—38 p.—and contains discussion of organization, and a folded organization chart. What might be called the Annual Report for 1846 appears in the appendix to the Washington Observations for 1845.

175. U. S. Department of War, Signal Service. Annual report of the Chief Signal Officer (of the Army) to the Secretary of War for the year ended (June 30) ———. 1871–91. Washington. 8vo.

176. U. S. Department of War, Signal Service. Monthly Weather Review 1–19(6), 4to, July, 1872–June, 1891.

Volume and issue numbers were first assigned in February, 1883, which was designated vol. 11, No. 2. Publication was begun with July, 1872 (not January, 1873, as stated by Weber, Service Monograph 9:15) and the 6 issues of 1872 and the 12 issues of 1873 constitute vol. 1. For continuation, see U. S. Department of Agriculture, Weather Bureau.

177. U. S. Department of War, Signal Service. Professional Papers 1–18, 8vo, 1881–85. (Nos. 9, 10, and 15 cited under authors. *See* Dunwoody, Entries Nos. 44 and 45, and Langley, Entry No. 98.)

178. U. S. Department of War, Signal Service. Government telegrams and reports for the benefit of commerce. 22 p. Washington, Office of the Chief Signal Officer. 8vo. (No date but almost certainly 1870.)

179. U. S. Department of War, Signal Service. Memoranda on the work accomplished by the Signal Service of the United States. 25 p. Washington, Office of the Chief Signal Officer, 8vo, 1881.

180. U. S. Department of War, Signal Corps. The necessity of a permanent organization for the Signal Corps. 30 p. Washington, Office of the Chief Signal Officer, 8vo, 1882.

181. U. S. [Department of War, Signal Office]. Memoranda on International scientific coöperation in meteorology, magnetism, etc. 7 p. Washington, Office of the Chief Signal Officer, 8vo, 1882.

182. U. S. [Department of War, Signal Service]. History of the United States Signal Service, with catalogue of its exhibit at the International Fisheries Exposition, London, 1883. 28 p. Washington, 8vo, 1883.

183. U. S. [Department of War, Signal Service]. History of the Signal Service, with catalogue of publications, instruments, and stations. 39 p. Washington, 8vo, 1884. (List of publications of Signal Office, pp. 27–28.)

184. U. S. Department of War, Signal Corps. Publications of the U. S. Signal Service from 1861 to July 1, 1891. Ann. Rept., office of the Chief Signal Officer, 1891:389–409, 1892.

185. Van Orman, Ward T. A preliminary meteorological survey for airship bases on the Middle Atlantic seaboard. Mo. Weather Rev. 59:57–64, 21 figs., 1931.

186. Walling, William English, and Harry W. Laidler. State socialism: pro and con. Official documents and other authoritative selections, showing the world-wide replacement of private by governmental industry before and during the war. With a chapter on municipal socialism, by Evans Clark. 649 p. (Weather, pp. 138–143.) (New York: Henry Holt & Co., 1917)

187. Ward, R. DeC. Recent publications of the Weather Bureau. Amer. Geogr. Soc. Bul. 42:110–12, February, 1910.

188. Weber, Gustavus A. The Weather Bureau: its history, activities, and organization. Institute for Government Research, Service Monograph 9:[i]–xii, 1–87. (New York: D. Appleton Co., 8vo, 1922)

189. Weber, Gustavus A. The Coast and Geodetic Survey: its history, activities, and organization. Institute for Government Research, Service Monograph 16:[i]–xii, 1–107. (Bibliography, pp. 94–103.) (Baltimore: Johns Hopkins Press, 1923)

190. Weber, Gustavus A. The Hydrographic Office: its history, activities, and organization. Institute for Government Research, Service Monograph 42:[i]–xii, 1–112. (Appendices 1–6, incl. Bibliography.) (Baltimore: Johns Hopkins Press, 1926)

191. Weeks, John R. The Weather Bureau and the public schools. U. S. Dept. Agric., Yearbook 1907:267–76, 1908.

192. Wells, E. L. The Weather Bureau and the home-seeker. U. S. Dept. Agric., Yearbook 1904:353–58, 1905.

193. Whitney, Milton. Some physical properties of soils in their relation to moisture and crop distribution. U. S. Dept. Agric., Weather Bur., Bul. 4:1–90, 1 unnumbered diag., 1892.

194. Wiest, Edward. Agricultural organization in the United States. xxiii, 618 p. University of Kentucky, Lexington, 1923. (The University of Kentucky: Studies in Economics and Sociology, vol. 2.) (Weather Bureau, pp. 149–61, and map.)

195. Wilkins, H. T. Sleuth hounds of the sea. Popular Mechanics 43:579–82, 1925.

196. Winterhalter, Captain. Work of the Hydrographic Office as an aid to the maritime interests and to the naval militia. Naval Militia Association of the U. S., Trans., December 9, 1909:63–78. 1910.

197. Winters, S. R. Weather and the ocean currents. Popular Mechanics 43:787–90, 1925.

198. Wyckoff, A. B. Hydrographic work of U. S. Navy. Journ. of Franklin Inst. 121:349–61, 1886.

199. Yowell, Everett I. The Cincinnati Observatory—birthplace of the U. S. Weather Bureau. Univ. of Cincinnati Record 9:10–12, 1913.

Chapter III: SOILS AND SOIL MANAGEMENT

[Because each chapter covers a different subject and therefore will be used chiefly by a different constituency, it seems desirable to make each one complete and self-contained. For this reason, among others, a complete table of chapter contents is placed at the beginning of each chapter, rather than at the front of the volume. A list of all literature cited in the chapter will be found at the end of the chapter and the numbers in parentheses in the text refer the reader to the corresponding entries in this list. All entry numbers occurring in each major section of a chapter also are listed in numerical sequence at the end of that section, thus forming what is in effect a section list of literature cited. These features all should prove of great convenience to readers.]

CHAPTER CONTENTS

Chapter III

SOILS AND SOIL MANAGEMENT

1. Introduction

THIS STUDY of the development and extent of official relations in soil investigations may be separated, for convenience, into five sections: 1. Introduction; 2. Historical Development to 1895; 3. Soil Fertility and Soil Amendments (Manures and Fertilizers); 4. Soil Survey, Classification, and Mapping; 5. Soil Erosion and Protection. These are listed in the general order in which they have developed.

THE SOIL

Soil has been described as the greatest natural resource of the nation (148).* It is here treated from the standpoints both of agriculture and of natural resources. For the widening of the perspective of the nonagricultural reader it seems worth while to quote a description of the soil which illuminates the important interrelations therein (77:7):

The soil is of three parts, one solid, another fluid, and the third gaseous. The solid part is made up of both organic and inorganic matter in fragmentary or granular condition; the fluid part is a solution consisting of water carrying more or less organic and mineral matter; the gaseous part consists of air (nitrogen and oxygen) mixed with aqueous vapor, carbon dioxide, and other gases. The solid part forms the body and the fluid part the circulatory medium of the soil on which plants grow and animals live; the gaseous part permeates the body of the soil and passes through it in a manner which is sometimes likened to breath.

It should be noted also that soils are in a state of continual evolution. Like animal and plant organisms, soils are being acted upon constantly by agencies and forces from within and from without. Some of these are constructive and some are destructive. All are modifying. The physical and chemical action of water, temperature, and plant growth gradually reduces rock to soil. Wind, water, and burrowing animals (large and small) transport and mix different soil materials. Mixing, water percolation, the incorporation

---

* Numbers in parentheses refer to the Literature Cited, at the end of the chapter.

of plant and animal remains, and the actions of myriads of organisms forming the microflora and microfauna of the soil, unite to effect continual changes in its chemical and physical properties.

A vast amount of research has been conducted upon the physical and chemical properties of soils by State and Federal researchers. Most of it, naturally, is laboratory investigation and has not been done in coöperation, under the prevailing procedure in soil research. A few studies on the effects of climate on soils have had minor coöperative aspects. Considering the placement of the original Division of Soils in the Weather Bureau, perhaps it is surprising that there have not been broader relations in this field. Beginning in 1908, the Federal Office of Cereal Investigations and Laboratory of Vegetable Physiological Investigations, in coöperation with various States, including California, transferred soil plats from their original localities to several other States in order to determine the effect on wheat, as discussed in the chapter on Plant Industries. Some years later the California Agricultural Experiment Station made a detailed study of the effects of California climate on the physical properties of the soils transported to California (74). Recently the Wyoming Station and the Soil Survey collaborated in some studies on the effects of vegetation and climate on soil profiles (111).

AGENCIES CONCERNED IN SOIL STUDIES

The one Federal agency directly charged with soil studies is the present Soil Investigations branch of the Bureau of Chemistry and Soils in the U. S. Department of Agriculture. From 1901 to 1927, partly inclusive, it was the Bureau of Soils, and before that it had been the Division of Soils. The comparable State agency is the department or division of soils (or agronomy, or crops and soils) in the State colleges of agriculture and agricultural experiment stations.

Federal and State agencies responsible for the administration, appraisal, reclamation, or efficient and economic use of the public domain, those concerned with the location and construction of public works, such as highways, canals, irrigation works, parks, etc., and those interested in agricultural finance, constitute a group with a large secondary official interest in the soil problem. They include, among Federal units, the Forest Service, Bureau of Public Roads, Bureau of Agricultural Engineering, and Bureau of Agricultural Economics in the Department of Agriculture; the General Land Office, the Geological Survey, the National Park Service, and the Bureaus of Reclamation and Indian Affairs in the Department of the Interior, and all the various agricultural credit agencies which are now being combined in the Farm Credit Administration. Comparable agencies in the State governments and divisions in the State agricultural experiment stations have the same interest.

A third group, having an indirect official interest, includes those concerned with such activities as the production and protection of plant and livestock industries, and the location and operation of camps, playgrounds, hospitals, etc. Reference will be made to the coöperation of all these Federal, State, county, and municipal agencies, and still others, in one phase or another of the soil-investigation activities discussed in this chapter. In addition, many commercial agencies, with objectives and responsibilities similar to those of the official agencies, are interested in the results of soil investigations and sometimes contribute to the expenses of conducting them.

2. HISTORICAL DEVELOPMENT

WHEN AMERICAN AGRICULTURE expanded from the more or less acid soils of the Atlantic seaboard to the great interior basin, a sense of the influence of soil differences began to develop. Climatic differences were more apparent, however, and somewhat overshadowed the effects of variations in the soil. The widespread search made abroad for new kinds and varieties of crops was in response to the needs of the new environment. Soil analysis, naturally, was an outgrowth of the development of agricultural chemistry and therefore did not progress far until well after the epoch-making publication of Liebig in 1840.

Official attention to soils and their amendments (fertilizers and manures) by the Federal government may be said to date from 1839, when Congress made a small appropriation to the Patent Office in the State Department for "the collection of agricultural statistics and for other purposes" (139). General chemical work was undertaken, including presently a study of the chemical nature of soils and of manures and fertilizers. In 1849, the Department of the Interior was created and the Patent Office transferred thereto. The agricultural activities were organized as an Agricultural Division, and the work rapidly expanded. The annual report on agriculture (134) thereafter was issued in a separate volume from the regular Patent Office report. It soon was decided to place the Agricultural Division under the leadership of an expert agriculturist. One of the first contributions of this officer was a comprehensive article in 1851 on the study of soils (70). In 1857, specific investigations of sugar-cane soils were made, and in 1858 the work was extended to tobacco soils (139).

In 1862, the U. S. Department of Agriculture was created, under a commissioner. The first annual report of the Commissioner (119), for 1862, referred to the need and value of soil studies, and minor soil analyses were made in succeeding years. Dr. Antisell, appointed chemist in 1866, immediately included analyses of soils and fertilizers in the activities of his Division. This work was continued with varying emphasis throughout the developmental period of the Department in the twenty-five years from 1862 to 1887.

FEDERAL-STATE RELATIONS BEFORE 1895

With the growth of the Federal Department of Agriculture and the rapid development of the State colleges of agriculture and departments of agriculture, it was inevitable, as likewise desirable, that coöperative relations also should develop.

One of the earliest instances of Federal-State relations in this field was the publication in the report of the Commissioner of the U. S. Department of Agriculture for 1878 of a paper by Hilgard of the University of California on the agriculture and soils of that State (59).

Association of Official Agricultural Chemists

The Association of Official Agricultural Chemists grew out of previous conventions of agricultural chemists, both official and commercial, of which two were held in 1880 (the first at the U. S. Department of Agriculture), another in 1881, and two in 1884. The second of these, held in September, 1884, effected a permanent organization under the name "Association of Official Agricultural Chemists," and resolved itself into the first annual meeting of the Association (156). It was composed of the official chemists of the Federal and State departments of agriculture, of State agricultural colleges and experiment stations, and of some local official boards of agriculture. Several of the early meetings of the Association were held in the buildings of the U. S. Department of Agriculture, others in the U. S. National Museum. In 1887 the constitution was amended to permit the membership of official chemists who were not engaged in regulatory activities, including those of the U. S. Treasury Department.

The growing importance of fertilizers, and the impossibility of determining quality by visual inspection, had made their analysis and the establishment of standards of quality imperative as a measure for the protection of farmers and dealers. The official chemists were interested in the problem of methods of analysis, and especially in uniformity of method, and their Association was the outgrowth of several previous meetings on methods (156). The early years of this movement had been devoted exclusively to fertilizers, and only after the organization of the official chemists did it gradually extend its scope to cover soils, food, feed, and other materials, beginning with food stuffs and dairy products in 1886.

The official chemists' Association created committees, each responsible for determining methods of analysis in one group of agricultural substances. By October, 1895, there were submitted to the Secretary of Agriculture, for his approval, committee reports containing the analytic methods adopted by the Association for soils and fertilizers, as well as for six other groups of materials. These findings, as modified from time to time by the official committees, and then approved by the Association and adopted by the official agencies, are the standards not only for the coöperating Federal and State agencies represented in the Association, but also for the commercial interests involved, and for courts of justice in all levels of jurisdiction (139 :56–57). Just as for several other organizations composed of Federal and State officials, the Department of Agriculture published the *Proceedings* of the Association of Official Agricultural Chemists for many years (5). Eventually the association was recognized by law as an official adviser to the Federal government. This widespread and long-continued coöperation has resulted in uniformity of method in chemical analyses of agricultural materials, and has done much to stimulate coöperation in other fields.

State Agricultural Experiment Stations

In 1887 the Hatch Act, creating the system of Federally-assisted State agricultural experiment stations, became effective and Federal-State relations in research were officially begun. The Appropriation Act of March 2, 1889, for the U. S. Department of Agriculture, provided that the experiment stations should "devote a portion of their work to the examination and classification of the soils of their respective States and Territories" (139 :89). In response to this suggestion, Federal-State coöperation in this work was begun on a small scale in several States. It still was concerned chiefly with chemical examination of the soils.

One of the largest problems confronting the newly organized experiment stations was that of the growing use of fertilizers. Much loosely organized experimentation had already been begun, the results of which could not be interpreted for general application. As a result, representatives of the experiment stations met with officials of the U. S. Department of Agriculture in Washington, in March, 1889, to plan coöperatively for uniform methods of fertilizer experiments which would give the results wider significence (132). Following the conference, directions for conducting such experiments were published by the Department (133) for the use of the stations.

In 1891, when Whitney was engaged to conduct investigations of agricultural soils for the U. S. Weather Bureau, he began the systematic collection of soil samples in coöperation with the Maryland Experiment Station and Johns Hopkins University. In 1892 he collaborated with Professor Hilgard of the University of California in assembling an extensive collection of soil samples from nearly all the States and Territories for exhibition at the World Columbian Exposition in Chicago in 1893. By arrangement with the State collectors, duplicate samples for the Federal Bureau were obtained from many States. Other samples were obtained from Alabama and California in the course of the work done for the soils publications in the Tenth Census, and a few were obtained from State geological surveys. By 1899 the collection numbered some 4000 samples (140).

ORIGIN OF THE FEDERAL DIVISION OF SOILS

The widespread scientific interest which had developed in the study of soils is indicated by the publication of a comprehensive paper on the origin and nature of soils by the U. S. Geological Survey in 1891 (98). In 1891, also, the Weather Bureau, transferred in that year from the Army Signal Corps to the Department of Agriculture, began the investigation of the relation of climatic factors to soils and published two papers thereon in 1892, as previously noted in the chapter on Climate (p. 122). This study resulted in the formation of a Division of Agricultural Soils in the Weather Bureau in February, 1894, and the selection of Professor Milton Whitney, of Maryland Agricultural College, as its head on March 3 of that year (139).

Interest in soil erosion and protection often is assumed to be of later development than the activities in soil characteristics and amendments. In 1894, however, the U. S. Department of Agriculture published a popular bulletin on how to prevent and reclaim washed soils (121). This was a joint production of the Divisions of Chemistry, Soils, Forestry, and Botany, prepared under the direction of Assistant Secretary Dabney, who was from the South where the destructive effects of erosion first became evident.

In his annual report for 1894, the Secretary of Agriculture recommended to Congress the creation of an independent Division for the study of soils. By the appropriation act effective July 1, 1895, the Division of Agricultural Soils was removed from the Weather Bureau and given independent status. The name was changed to Division of Soils in 1897 and to Bureau of Soils in 1901 (139). The establishment of the independent Division marks the close of the period of Historical Development and ushers in the period of soils studies organized on a broad basis. From the foregoing discussion it is seen that the three major divisions of such studies, soil classification, soil amendments, and soil erosion and protection, all had their origin in the previous period. Their development on a large scale characterizes the new period beginning in 1895. As noted at the beginning of this chapter, the discussion of the activities in the period from 1895 to date will be presented under three heads, namely, Soil Amendments, Soil Surveys, and Soil Erosion. All that need be added here is a note on the general development of official relations and on general publications relating to history, laws, or publications.

Development of Official Relations

During the thirty years since the Federal Bureau of Soils was organized in 1901, the growth of coöperation in this field has been marked. In soil surveys, in soil-fertility studies, in the surveys for natural fertilizer resources, in methods of fertilizer manufacture and use, and in studies of soil microbiology alike, the same fact of increasing interrelations has prevailed. The soil-erosion investigations, of comparatively recent origin, have been widely coöperative from the start. In the increasing development of coöperation, relations have been effected between various Federal agencies, between Federal and State agencies, and between both groups and local governmental agencies, and with commercial organizations. While this has been the general trend in all the fields of official activity, it is perhaps more noticeable with respect to soil investigations, because here the earlier work was noncoöperative to a larger extent than on the part of the closely related Bureau of Chemistry, for example, which dates from the same year but developed widespread coöperative relations more rapidly. The actual relations will be pictured in the succeeding sections.

In the field of teaching, also, there have been coöperative relations. In 1916 the Section of Agricultural Education, U. S. States Relations Service, collaborated with the Division of Soils of the University of Wisconsin in preparing a series of extension courses in soils (154). For many years the colleges of agriculture, through their soils specialists, have collaborated in the improvement of soils teaching, through joint committees and conferences (67).

Publications Relating to Development

There are several individual publications, or series of publications, which deal with the activities and relations of the Division of Soils and the subsequent Bureau of Soils, with more or less attention to the historic development of soil studies (24; 43; 54; 72; 81:20–22; 120B:61–66; 125; 126; 127; 137:168–72; 139; 141; 142; 145; 147; 155:142–47).

Some of these, and others, are concerned with lists of the publications on soils issued by the Federal government (55; 64; 65; 139: 190–211). Still others contain extracts from the laws under which the work is authorized and conducted, or reports are published (51: Sections 10 and 128; 128; 139:180–84).

The publications listed in the Literature Cited at the end of the chapter which have been cited in this section on Historical Development are Nos. 5, 24, 43, 51, 54, 55, 59, 64, 65, 67, 70, 72, 81, 98, 119, 120B, 121, 125, 126, 127, 128, 132, 133, 134, 137, 139, 140, 141, 142, 145, 147, 154, 155, and 156.

3. Soil Fertility and Soil Amendments

General agricultural chemistry long antedated specific soil chemistry. Fertilizer and fertility studies, therefore, were within the province of official agencies charged with chemical investigation for a long time, both before and after the organization of separate agencies devoted to soil studies.

The effect of fertilizing substances was one of the earliest phases of soil study to attract attention. The influence of leguminous crops and of manures on the growth of subsequent crops was observed by the Romans. The Atlantic Coast Amerinds used dead fish as fertilizer and taught the practice to the early colonists from England. Question of the actual chemical composition of the soil arose later. These facts were noted in the preceding section on Historical Development. The question of fertilizers now has come to be one of major importance. It is the province of one of the three coördinate branches of the present Bureau of Chemistry and Soils, namely, the Fertilizer and Fixed Nitrogen Investigations, as well as of the Division of Soil Fertility which constitutes a large part of the Branch of Soil Investigation of the same Bureau.[*]

The coöperative activities in this section of the chapter on soils may be presented under four headings, namely: (*a*) Soil and Fertilizer Analyses; (*b*) Soil Fertility Experiments; (*c*) Soil Microbiol-

[*] Since retransferred to the Bureau of Plant Industry.

ogy Studies; and (*d*) Investigations of Natural Fertilizer Sources, including experimental manufacturing of some fertilizers.

SOIL AND FERTILIZER ANALYSES

The major coöperation of Federal and State agencies in this field has been through the activities of the Association of Official Agricultural Chemists. Its creation and scope were related in the section on Historical Development, above. It is composed of the official chemists of the U. S. Department of Agriculture and other Federal units, of the State departments of agriculture, and of the State colleges of agriculture and agricultural experiment stations. The soils chemists of the Bureaus (and preceding Divisions) of Chemistry and of Soils have been members of the Association and have served as members and chairmen (later called referees) of the subcommittees charged with determining methods of analysis for specific substances in this field. Continued refinements have been made in these methods and reported annually to the Association. They may be found in the annual reports (5) and in special bulletins of the Bureau of Chemistry containing revised methods of analysis.

Soil Analyses

The Division of Soils and the Division of Chemistry coöperated in soil analyses from the founding of the former in 1895. At various times the Bureau of Soils and its successor, the Bureau of Chemistry and Soils, have called upon the State experiment stations for assistance in obtaining soil samples from different parts of the country. As recently as 1932 the Bureau published the results of studies on the hydrogen-ion concentration of the soils of the United States and Canada (120A—291), the samples being obtained through State and Provincial collaboration.

At recurring times, chemical analyses of soils have been made for numerous other Federal agencies, including especially the Bureau of Plant Industry (and its antecedent Divisions) of the Department of Agriculture, and the Geological Survey and the Bureau of Reclamation of the Department of the Interior. One of the special coöperations with the Bureau of Plant Industry was in determining the source of the barium found to be the toxic ingredient in certain stock-poisoning locoweeds (125—1908 :525). From 1923 to 1930, analyses of many soils were made for the Bureau of Standards of the Department of Commerce in furtherance of its studies on the destructive corrosion of pipe lines buried in the ground (125—1923 :5, 1930 :37, and 1931 :40).

In California the division of plant nutrition of the University of California College of Agriculture, at Berkeley and the laboratory of agricultural chemistry of the Citrus Experiment Station at Riverside have coöperated in a chemical and X-ray analysis of soils and soil-making materials (69).

Fertilizer Analyses

The fertilizer industry, as noted previously, was the first interest of agricultural chemistry to receive widespread public attention. Fraudulent practices were prevalent and it was quite impossible for the buyer to determine quality and value at the time of purchase. Laws requiring the control of the quality of fertilizers through analysis by State agencies were passed in many eastern States before the system of State agricultural experiment stations was established by the Congress in 1887. Some States had established State-supported experiment stations before 1887. In this early period the control of fertilizers sometimes was placed with the State department of agriculture and sometimes with the agricultural experiment station. Because fees were charged for analyses and licenses, a considerable revenue was assured to the agency exercising control, and this often led to antagonism on the part of the other agency. With the modern coördination of functions within the States, the State departments of agriculture usually are charged with the analysis and control of fertilizers, and the experiment station with the necessary research on their origin, handling, uses, and effects. There now is frequent coöperation between the two agencies in fertilizer matters affecting both.

In California the law enacted in 1903 (Calif. Stats., 1903 :259) specified that all fertilizer analyses should be made by the methods approved by the Association of Official Agricultural Chemists, and placed the enforcement in the hands of the director of the State experiment station. In 1919, when the State Department of Agriculture was created by the consolidation of numerous independent agencies, the administration of the fertilizer act was transferred to it. Because the State Department was not then equipped to handle the work, it was agreed betwen the two agencies to let it remain for another year in the experiment station, which accordingly coöperated to that extent (39) and, in recognition, had the department's appreciation in a foreword to the station bulletin of 1921 on commercial fertilizers (39 :91).

Later on, there developed a sentiment for including other agricultural minerals, such as limestone, sulphur, gypsum, etc., under State control. With the advice and assistance of the California Experiment Station, the Federal-State Agricultural Extension Service, and farm organizations, the California Agricultural Minerals Act of 1923 was drafted and enacted, and its enforcement vested in the State Department of Agriculture (33).

All of these statutes are presented in the 1931 compilation of the agricultural statutes of the State of California, Part 4 (25).

Street-Sweepings Disposal and Analyses

One of the problems of municipal authorities is the disposal of street sweepings. These often are collected at large expense and some revenue from them is greatly to be desired. Their value for agricultural fertilizer depends on the street surface from which they are collected, on the ordinances and administration governing the kinds and amounts of refuse that may be thrown into the streets, and on the period of our industrial development. Street surfaces consisting of dirt, gravel, or macadam furnish sweepings of low fertilizer value. In the days of universal horse power the sweepings from paved streets had a high value as fertilizer, especially on truck farms. With the advent of asphalt paving, the sweepings began to contain a new and suspectedly harmful substance. With the coming of the automobile, oils of possible harmful effect on soils began to appear in the sweepings. At the same time the gradual disappearance of the horse, especially from the cities, steadily reduced the proportion of manure to other wastes in the material gathered.

In 1897 the Bureau of Chemistry asked that officials of street-cleaning departments in 354 cities and towns of 10,000 or more inhabitants coöperate by providing information on the disposal of their street sweepings (139 :24). Information was received from

204 departments and the results were tabulated and published by the Bureau (45). Some years later, after soil fertility investigations had been transferred to the Bureau of Soils, that agency made a limited study of street sweepings as farm fertilizer, again from the standpoint of suspectedly harmful ingredients (101).

The publications listed in the Literature Cited at the end of the chapter which have been cited in this subsection on Soil and Fertilizer Analyses are Nos. 5, 25, 33, 39, 45, 69, 101, 120A, 125, and 139.

SOIL-FERTILITY STUDIES

Soil-fertility studies are concerned with the chemistry of the soil as it affects plant growth and composition. Obviously the official agencies charged with studies in the fields of chemistry, soils, and plant industry would be the ones interested in soil fertility. Historically, the Federal studies of soil fertility have been assigned to each of the three agencies in succession and now have gone back to their second love—to Soils. The work was started in the Division of Chemistry of the U. S. Department of Agriculture in 1894, transferred to the Bureau of Soils in 1904 (three years after both Divisions had become Bureaus), transferred as a Division to the Bureau of Plant Industry in 1915, and returned to Soils in 1927* when the separate Bureaus of Chemistry and Soils were united as a Bureau of Chemistry and Soils, with the Fixed Nitrogen Research Laboratory forming a third coördinate Branch therein. Throughout this period, the unit has developed an increasing program of coöperation with other Federal agencies, with State agencies, and occasionally with municipal agencies.

Under the Bureau of Chemistry

In 1894, Congress made a specific appropriation (continued to 1901) for investigations to determine the chemical character and physical properties of the typical soils of the United States, and especially the nature of their nitrifying organisms. The work was assigned to the Division of Chemistry. Through the coöperation of various State agricultural experiment stations, samples of typical soils were obtained, and the studies were made in an extensive

---

* See preceding footnote, p. 177.

series of pot cultures in a greenhouse in Washington, D. C. (139 : 23–24). In 1904 the Soil and Fertilizer Laboratory of the Bureau of Chemistry was discontinued and its work was transferred to the Bureau of Soils. In its place in the Bureau of Chemistry a Plant Analysis Laboratory was established.

Under the Bureau of Soils

During the eleven years from 1904 to 1915, while the soil-fertility studies were assigned to the Bureau of Soils, the field studies were greatly expanded. Only a minor part of the experiments, however, were conducted in coöperation with the State experiment stations.

While the Bureau of Chemistry was making the studies mentioned above, the Bureau of Soils had developed the method of growing plants in paraffined wire baskets and in soil extracts to determine the relative fertility of soils. Immediately on the transfer of the soil and fertilizer work from Chemistry to Soils, cooperative field experiments were begun. The object was to check the rapid wire-basket method of testing, requiring only three or four weeks, against the results from long-established fertilizer field plots of certain experiment stations, results requiring accumulated data of some ten years for reliable interpretation. During 1905, field parties of the Bureau of Soils coöperated with the Ohio and Rhode Island Experiment Stations in such experiments (125— 1905 :267). The results of the Ohio tests were published by the Ohio Station (106), and are mentioned here especially because they were made the basis of rather vigorous criticism of the Bureau by another station not concerned in the tests (57 ; 62). During 1907, similar studies were made in coöperation with the Pennsylvania Station, where the fertilizer plots were then twenty-five years old (125—1907 :434).

In 1910 there was published by Milton Whitney (149 ; 150 ; 151 ; 152 ; 153), Chief of the Bureau of Soils, a series of five bulletins dealing with fertilizers for soils to be used respectively in growing corn, cotton, potato, wheat, and miscellaneous crops. These were tabulations of some 1500 to more than 6000 individual tests of fertilizing substances for the various specified crops, made and published by the different State agricultural experiment stations of the country between 1887 and about 1907, and compiled and printed by the Federal government for the information of all the States.

In an extensive series of studies of the factors influencing soil fertility, a few of the experiments were conducted in coöperation with the New York Cornell and the Iowa Experiment Stations (95). In a similar extensive series of experiments on the fertility of soils as affected by manures, which were conducted on farms in many States, miscellaneous samples were tested at several State experiment stations (48).

In this period, also, was the beginning of the coöperation between the Bureau of Plant Industry and the Bureau of Soils which largely ceased in 1915 when soil-fertility investigations were transferred to Plant Industry, and was resumed on an extensive scale when the work was retransferred to the Bureau of Chemistry and Soils in 1927. An early instance of this coöperation was a joint study of the prairie soils of Alabama and Mississippi, with reference to the growing of alfalfa (12).

While the soil-fertility investigations were transferred bodily to the Bureau of Plant Industry, the Bureau of Soils still was concerned with the source, quality, and combinations of fertilizer materials as such. The problem of concentrated fertilizers, especially from the standpoint of increasing transportation charges on large quantities of inert matter, was of growing importance. So also was the possible harmful effect of more and more concentrated materials on germination of seeds and growth of crops. Coöperation was established with the Office of Soil-FertilityInvestigations in Plant Industry during this period, for the study of the latter problem (125—1926:9). Some of the published results will be noted in the section on the Bureau of Chemistry and Soils.

Under the Bureau of Plant Industry

As one of the chief lines of research in the Bureau of Plant Industry was the investigation and control of diseases of plants, it was only natural that the relation of soil reaction and fertility to the destructiveness of plant diseases should receive early attention from the Division of Soil-Fertility Investigations, soon after its transfer to that Bureau in 1915.

In the spring of 1917 large numbers of samples of soil were collected from two soil types in a coöperative study with the Maine Agricultural Experiment Station, with which the Bureau previously had been collaborating in the breeding of potatoes. The hydrogen-ion concentration was determined in the samples from both types, with relation to the prevalence of scab on the potatoes grown in each of the soils (52). In coöperation with the Pennsylvania Experiment Station, a determination was made of the botanical composition of a permanent pasture as influenced through a series of years by various fertilizers of different compositions. The results were published by authors representing both agencies (105).

In coöperation with the Office of Fruit-Disease Investigations of the Bureau, a study was made of the influence of soil conditions and management on the rosette disease of pecan orchards (103). Fertilizer studies of one kind or another were carried out also by other Offices of the Bureau of Plant Industry independently of the Office of Soil-Fertility Investigations. For instance, the Office of Western Irrigation Agriculture studied experimentally the effects of farm manures on irrigated crops at its field stations on the reclamation projects of the Department of the Interior at Huntley, Montana, Scottsbluff, Nebraska, and Belle Fourche, South Dakota, the first two in coöperation with the respective State agricultural experiment stations (96). At about the same time the Office of Physiology and Fermentation Investigations was coöperating with the Virginia Truck Experiment Station in a study of ash absorption by spinach from concentrated soil solutions (112). This was done under experiments in truck-crop production and disease prevention which were conducted coöperatively by the Bureau and the Virginia Station.

As early as 1916 some coöperation was had with the New York Cornell and the Pennsylvania Agricultural Experiment Stations in studies on harmful soil constituents (124—1916 :142).

Immediately after the War, field experiments were begun in Maine, New Jersey, New York, Pennsylvania, Virginia, North Carolina, South Carolina, Georgia, Florida, Arkansas, and Wisconsin, covering general tests of the sources, amounts, and ratios of fertilizers to be used in crop production. The experiments were conducted in coöperation with the State agricultural experiment stations, local associations, and other Offices of the U. S. Department of Agriculture (124—1919 :165). Following a conference of the Federal Department of Agriculture and seventeen States, a discussion of the desirability of correlation and coöperation in regard to soil-fertility investigations was presented before the Association of Land-Grant Colleges and Universities (*Proceedings,* 33 :227–29) in 1919. The results of ten years of experiments (1919–28) on two different soils, in coöperation with the South Carolina Station, mostly at the Pee Dee Branch Experiment Station at Florence, were published under Bureau authorship (120A— 226) in 1931.

Shortly before the transfer of the soil-fertility unit from Plant Industry to Chemistry and Soils in 1927, the coöperative testing of concentrated fertilizers, in contrast with ordinary mixtures, was begun in collaboration with several State experiment stations, on different soils and with different crops (93).

The Office of Tobacco and Plant-Nutrition Investigations, of the Bureau of Plant Industry, conducted extensive tests of fertilizers on tobacco in the South in coöperation with several States. The experiments were begun as early as 1913, before the transfer of soil-fertility investigations from the Bureau of Soils to that of Plant Industry, and apparently were carried on wholly independently of that unit after the transfer. The results for the years from 1913 to 1925 were published (83) by the Office with a statement of the coöperation which is explicit and prominently displayed, and therefore a model of such acknowledgements. It is printed three times in the bulletin: first, in a box on the inside of the front cover; second, in capital letters near the top of the title page, just below the names and scientific titles of the authors; and, third, in the text where the discussion of the locations of experimentation begins. The statement of coöperation is as follows:

The tests reported in this bulletin were made by the United States Department of Agriculture in coöperation with the North Carolina Department of Agriculture, the Virginia and North Carolina Agricultural Experiment Stations, the Georgia State College of Agriculture, and the Georgia Coastal Plain Experiment Station.

Not all coöperation in soil-fertility experimentation in the Bureau of Plant Industry ceased with the retransfer of the Division of Soil Fertility to the Bureau of Chemistry and Soils in 1927. The Division of Forage Crops and Diseases has worked with the department of agronomy of the Florida Experiment Station and the U. S. Golf Association in lawn-grass studies which include the influence of soil fertility (7) on the development of such grasses.

Under the Bureau of Chemistry and Soils

When Soil-Fertility Investigations were retransferred to the Soils Branch of the new Bureau (Chemistry and Soils), on July 1, 1927,* a fairly large volume of coöperative investigation was under way. This has been continued and expanded. One principal effect of the long sojourn of the unit in the Bureau of Plant Industry was the extensive study of soils and soil fertility in relation to plant diseases. This still forms one of the major lines of soil-fertility work in the new Bureau. It covers a wide range of crop plants, and the coöperation extends into many States.

The coöperative fertilizer studies cover many phases of the complex soil-fertility problem. Most important have been the sources of fertilizer materials, including nitrogenous fertilizers and especially synthetic nitrogen carriers; the safe and economical use of concentrated fertilizers, to avoid the costs and transportation charges of inert materials; and the broad questions of the influence of soil fertility on the quantity and quality of crop production, and especially on the development and destructiveness of plant diseases.

Some of the studies have included animal industry as well as plant industry units. Several years ago the "Sandhill Experiment Station" was established near Columbia, S. C., by the South Carolina station in coöperation with the Bureaus of Chemistry and Soils (Soil Fertility), Dairy Industry, and Plant Industry (Forage Crops), to conduct soil-improvement experiments on the type of soil indicated by the substation's name. Coöperating representatives of these three Bureaus are located at this State substation (1:83).

Field and truck crops.—Experiments on the effects of concentrated fertilizers on several crops grown on important soil types have been conducted by the Division of Soil Fertility during several recent years in coöperation with the State Experiment Sta-

---

* See previous footnote (p. 177).

tions of Florida, Georgia, North Carolina, and South Carolina, both on the station farms and on farmers' soils. The principal crops have been cotton, potatoes, and sweet potatoes.

Cotton: A study of the fertilizer requirements of cotton, including synthetic nitrogen and concentrated fertilizers on different soil types, was begun by the Bureau of Plant Industry in coöperation with experiment stations of Georgia and North Carolina, and continued by the Bureau of Chemistry and Soils. The experiments were conducted on farmers' land, controlled through the experiment stations in both States. A summary of both independent and coöperative studies on fertilizers for cotton soils was published by the Federal agency (*Miscellaneous Publication* 126) in 1931, and another (120A—452) on experiments with nitrogen fertilizers on cotton soils under joint authorship of the Federal Bureau of Chemistry and Soils and the North Carolina Agricultural Experiment Station in 1934.

Studies of the relation of soil to the cotton root-rot disease were begun in 1929 with the establishment of a laboratory at the University of Texas and of field tests at twelve locations on the black soils, including at least one in coöperation with the Texas Agricultural Experiment Station at Substation No. 5, at Temple. The coöperation included the Division of Western Irrigation Agriculture of the Bureau of Plant Industry, on its field station at San Antonio, Texas.

Potato: Coöperative investigations of the relation of soil fertility to all phases of potato production have been numerous and extensive. Field experiments on the effects of concentrated fertilizers and on the relation of soil fertility to composition, quality, and yield of tubers have been conducted for several years in coöperation with the State Experiment Stations of Maine, New York, New Jersey, Pennsylvania, and Virginia, the latter at the Truck Experiment Station. The work in Maine and Virginia is coöperative to some extent also with the Division of Horticultural Crops and Diseases in the Bureau of Plant Industry. The results of the experiments with concentrated fertilizers in Maine, begun in 1925, have been published by that station (20). So also have been the results of sixteen years of coöperative experiments on sources of nitrogen for potato fertilizers (2). Some of the Virginia data have just appeared (63). These three may be taken as fairly typical of the publications resulting from such coöperation.

In coöperation with the Michigan, New Jersey, and Ohio Stations, studies are being made on the effects of different placement methods for potato fertilizers on germination, stand, and yield (125—1931–32). A test of the effects of ordinary and concentrated fertilizers on fresh-cut and suberized seed-pieces, conducted in coöperation with the Bureau of Plant Industry, was concluded in 1931.

Potato and sweet potato: Experiments with concentrated fertilizers on both potatoes and sweet potatoes have been conducted coöperatively with the North Carolina station for several years. The results have been published by that station under joint authorship (104A). More recently the Federal Bureau has published the results for the years 1922–28 with a prominent cover-page statement of the coöperation (104B; 120A—335).

Sugar plants: The coöperation in soil-fertility studies on sugar plants has likewise been extensive. Five complete triangular experiments on sugar beets have been conducted in coöperation with the Division of Sugar Plant Investigations and the Division of Western Irrigation Agriculture of the Bureau of Plant Industry in four different States (124—1931 :48), in one of which there was some coöperation with the State experiment station. Similar experiments have been carried on for three years in coöperation with the Division of Western Irrigation Agriculture on field stations at Huntley, Montana, which is a State substation, and Newell, South Dakota (124—1931 :48). Direct coöperation with the Nebraska Experiment Station, also, is had at the Scottsbluff Substation in studying the effects of fertilizers applied to sugar beets in a rotation. Sugar-beet experimentation also is carried on at St. Paul, Minnesota, but apparently not in coöperation with the Minnesota Experiment Station.

A four-year test of fertilizers for sugar cane was completed in 1931 in coöperation with the Division of Sugar Plants on its sugar station at Houma, Louisiana, where the State Experiment Station coöperates through a resident employee (1 :35). At the same time, coöperative studies of sugar-cane soils, including a complete reconnaissance survey, have been conducted with the Louisiana Experiment Station in two subprojects.

Alfalfa: In coöperation with the Bureau of Plant Industry, the causes of alfalfa failure on the alluvial lands in the Mississippi Valley are being studied.

Fruits and nuts.—Peach: In coöperation with the North Carolina Station in 1926, a study was made of soils in which peach trees were dying, but without finding any soil conditions which could be considered as contributing causes. In coöperation with Georgia Agricultural Experiment Station, extensive studies are being made on the effect of varying quantities of nitrogen and potash on the time of maturity of peaches, and other studies of the effect of fertilizers, green manures, and tillage, on winter injury of peaches.

Pecan: In coöperation with the Bureaus of Entomology and Plant Industry, fertility studies are being made on pecan soils in Louisiana and Georgia, including the influence of cover crops and tillage. Similar coöperation covers the influence of fertilizers on the health of strawberry plants, flavor of the fruit, etc.

Mechanical distribution of fertilizers.—The placement of fertilizers is important from several viewpoints. It governs to some extent the quantity required and therefore the investment which must be made. More important still, it often has much to do with the germination of the seed and the health and vigor of the seedlings, and therefore with the final stand and yield obtained. Reference has been made above to placement studies of potato fertilizers conducted in coöperation with the Michigan, New Jersey, and Ohio Stations. Some of these studies have been conducted with the North Carolina and South Carolina (Coastal Plain Substation) Experiment Stations.

The Federal Bureau of Agricultural Engineering (until 1932 a Division of the Bureau of Public Roads) is concerned with the structures and equipment for storing and applying farm manures and commercial fertilizers. Since 1926 (125—1926 :9) the Division of Soil Fertility, now of the Bureau of Chemistry and Soils, has coöperated with the Bureau of Agricultural Engineering in conducting experiments on the drillability of fertilizers, especially of concentrated fertilizers in comparison with the ordinary mixtures. The two Bureaus issued joint publications in 1930 and 1932 on the results of these experiments (79 ; 80). The former (pp. 5–6) says that a questionnaire on practices was sent to each State station.

The publications listed in the Literature Cited at the end of this chapter which have been cited in this subsection on Soil-Fertility Studies are Nos. 1, 7, 12, 20, 21, 48, 52, 57, 62, 63, 79, 80, 83, 93, 95, 96, 103, 104A, 104B, 105, 106, 112, 120A, 124, 125, 139, 149, 150, 151, 152, and 153.

SOIL MICROBIOLOGY INVESTIGATIONS

Soil microbiology as treated here deals with the nonparasitic microorganisms inhabiting the soil. It is concerned with the effects they produce on the physical and chemical properties of soil through their ability to decompose animal and vegetable matter and to elaborate compounds readily assimilable by plants. These organisms include both a microflora chiefly bacteria and fungi, and a microfauna, including protozoans, nematodes, and other groups. The first group to be recognized as having large agricultural importance was that containing the nodule-forming bacteria which live symbiotically in the roots of legumes and enable them to obtain nitrogen from the air. Knowledge concerning the various groups of organisms is relatively new but is developing rapidly in recent years.

Most of the work with these microörganisms of the soil necessarily must be done in specially equipped laboratories rather than in the field, and therefore does not lend itself to coöperative activities as readily as do some other lines of research. Nevertheless, there has been a gradual and increasing development of institutional relations, involving numerous and widely diverse agencies.

Bacteria for Legume Inoculation

In the U. S. Department of Agriculture this line of investigation was begun on a small scale by the Division of Vegetable Physiology and Pathology about 1900, just before the inclusion of this unit as the Laboratory of Plant Physiology in the newly formed Bureau of Plant Industry on July 1, 1901. At first the work was confined to a study of methods of maintaining, multiplying, and distributing cultures of nodule-forming bacteria for use in inoculating soils where it was desired to grow alfalfa, clover, and other legumes, the problem being discussed fully in the *Yearbook* of the Department for 1902. An extensive distribution of cultures to growers was in progress by 1903, and had reached a quantity sufficient to inoculate more than 200,000 acres annually by 1915. In 1904 patents were applied for by the Department. By 1905 the distribution of pure cultures to manufacturers of inoculating material had begun. By 1907 some phases of the work were done in coöperation with the Missouri and Ohio Agricultural Experiment Stations. In or before that year the Laboratory was renamed the Office of Soil-Bacteriology and Water-Purification Investigations, and the study of other groups of soil-inhabiting bacteria was begun. In 1907 also the Office of Experiment Stations of the Department of Agriculture published a comprehensive review of investigations in soil bacteriology, prepared by the New Jersey Agricultural Experiment Station (135B).

By 1923 it was recorded that the Office of Soil Bacteriology was conducting experiments to determine the need for the inoculation of legumes in sixteen different States from the Atlantic to the Pacific and from New York to Georgia. No mention was made of any coöperation with State agencies (124—1923:281).

In 1927, when the Division of Soil Fertility was transferred from the Bureau of Plant Industry to the newly created Bureau of Chemistry and Soils, all the work with nonparasitic soil bacteria, molds, and other fungi, was transferred to the same Bureau and combined into a Division of Soil Microbiology.

Activities with legume-inoculating bacteria have increased in recent years. In coöperation with the Wisconsin Experiment Station, a study is being made on the variability of efficiency of the soybean-nodule organism in fixing nitrogen (124—1930:51). A somewhat similar study of the organism forming nodules on the Austrian winter pea has been made for the Iberia Livestock Experiment Station, Jeannerette, Louisiana, conducted jointly by the Bureaus of Animal and Plant Industry in coöperation with the Louisiana Experiment Station (71; 124—1931:59).

Under authority of Congress, the Division of Soil Microbiology is charged with the inspection of all inoculants for legumes. These now include the output of about fourteen State agricultural experiment stations, and some twenty-two commercial firms (124—1932:34). Pure cultures of substantially all the organisms used in the inoculation of the various legumes are maintained by the Division and are available for experiments by other bureaus and by the State agricultural colleges and experiment stations. From time to time, fresh cultures are furnished to the State institutions supplying inoculants (124—1931:59). The Division continues the distribution of inoculating cultures to farmers on request through members of the Congress, county extension agents, and the farmers themselves (124—1932:35). The number sent out is now about 5000 annually.

Other Soil-Inhabiting Organisms

By the year 1907, studies had been started in the Bureau of Plant Industry on other groups of soil-inhabiting bacteria, especially the nitrifying and denitrifying species. Much attention was being given to the development of dry-land farming at this time, and the question of humus formation from the decomposition of materials high in cellulose content, such as the grain straws, was becoming important in arid regions. By 1914, studies of the cellulose-dissolving bacteria were extensive. In 1915 all the work being done on soil microbiology in the Bureau of Chemistry was transferred to the Bureau of Plant Industry with the Division of Soil Fertility, and in 1927 the whole Division was returned to the Bureau of Chemistry and Soils. Before the work was transferred to the Bureau of Plant Industry in 1915, the Bureau of Chemistry and the Dairy Division of the Bureau of Animal Industry coöperated in a study of one group of the genus *Aspergillus* (110).

In 1919 there were published the results of an investigation of the oxidizing action of soil bacteria on certain harmful organic constituents of the soil (90), conducted jointly by the Division of Soil Fertility and the Alabama Agricultural Experiment Station. In 1923 the Division was engaged with the U. S. Geological Survey in an investigation of the formation of deposits of calcium carbonate by soil bacteria (124—1923:281).

Recently the Division of Soil Microbiology, in coöperation with the Lignin Laboratory of the Farm Waste Division of the Branch of Chemistry, has made a study of the decomposition of lignin by soil microörganisms and published a joint paper containing the results (125—1929:35).

In 1913 the Office of Biophysical Investigations of the U. S. Bureau of Plant Industry entered into coöperation with the California Agricultural Experiment Station through its Citrus Experiment Station at Riverside, on some phases of a study of the prevalent chlorosis of citrus trees. The relation of certain soil bacteria to the disease was shown, as also that some relief was obtained through the addition of straw to the soil in special ways (18). The work continued for several years and is more fully discussed in the chapter on Plant Industries, under Protection of Citrus Crops. A little later, the Office of Soil Bacteriology and Plant Nutrition Investigations of the same Bureau conducted some studies on the fixation of ammonia in soils (75), using the facilities of the Citrus Experiment Station for the work.

In California, the division of chemistry and plant nutrition in the Experiment Station studied the comparative nitrifying powers of some humid and some arid soils in about 1915. Portions of all soil samples collected throughout the State by the Federal-State coöperative soil survey were obtained through the division of soil technology at the Station. Samples also were obtained through the chemists or agronomists of virtually all the other States (73).

For several years the unit which is now the Division of Microbiology* in the Bureau of Chemistry and Soils has been building up a collection of living cultures of fungi and bacteria important to agriculture and allied industries. These organisms include not only the beneficial species but also some of the destructive ones, for purposes of identification and comparison. The Division determines many cultures for other governmental agencies, both domestic and foreign, and also for commercial agencies. It also furnishes type collections of important groups, such as *Aspergillus* and *Penicillium,* to State and other agencies needing them. The University of California has been the recipient of such material (125—1931:62). In the past few years the Division has cultured and identified numerous specimens taken from cases of human disease by officials of the U. S. Public Health Service of the Treasury Department and of the Bureau of Mines of the Department of Commerce (125—1929: 33, 1930:53, and 1931:62).

The publications listed in the Literature Cited at the end of the chapter which have been cited in this subsection on Soil Microbiology are Nos. 18, 71, 73, 75, 90, 110, 124, 125, and 135B.

* See previous footnote (p. 177).

INVESTIGATION OF NATURAL FERTILIZER RESOURCES

In March, 1911, the Congress made appropriation to the Department of Agriculture for "exploration and investigation within the United States to determine a possible source of supply of potash, nitrates, and other natural fertilizers" (36 U. S. Stat. L, 1235, 1236). This item was repeated for ten successive years thereafter. A preliminary report on the fertilizer resources of the United States as determined by this investigation was published by Cameron (29) of the Federal Bureau of Soils, in 1912, as Senate Document No. 190 of the Second Session of the 62d Congress. This extensive document consisted of a short paper by Cameron and some twenty appendixes containing papers and statistical matter by other specialists. The further activities under this and later acts of Congress are discussed below under natural resources of nitrogen, phosphates, and potash, respectively.

During the World War there was much Federal activity concerned with fertilizers, caused partly by the need of nitrogen for munitions manufacture, and partly by the need of increasing crop production per acre and per man. An Office of Fertilizer Control was established in the Department of Agriculture as a war-emergency measure under the Food-Control Act. The Division of Fertilizer Resources in the Bureau of Soils worked in the closest coöperation with this body. In 1917 and 1918 surveys were made through a series of questionnaires to determine lists of manufacturers of the various kinds of fertilizers, the materials used, available stocks, exports and imports (53), and the prices at which fertilizers were being sold. The Fertilizer Control, in coöperation with the Food Administration, made an investigation of all reducing plants for garbage, municipal and private (53). The inquiries into the prices at which fertilizers were being made available to farmers were carried on largely through the collaboration of the State agricultural extension services and the county agricultural agents, all of whom work in direct coöperation with the U. S. Department of Agriculture (129; 130). General regulations governing the importation, manufacture, storage, and distribution of fertilizers and fertilizer ingredients were promulgated by the President of the United States, under the authority of the National

Defense Act (157). After the close of the war, the Division of Fertilizer Resources in the Bureau of Soils took over the work of the Office of Fertilizer Control in licensing companies and supervising trade (125—1920:293).

Investigation of Sources of Nitrogen

Under the legislation just mentioned, explorations for nitrate deposits were made by the Bureau of Soils. Samples obtained were analyzed by the coöperative laboratory of the Mackay School of Mines, maintained jointly by the University of Nevada, the Bureau of Soils, and the Geological Survey (47:4). A census on nitrogenous fertilizers available in the United States was published (116) by the Bureau of Soils in 1913, the data on available quantities of dried blood and tankage (pp. 9–11) being contributed by the Bureau of Animal Industry.

As early as 1910, the Bureau of Soils compiled a comprehensive list of publications on the electric fixation of atmospheric nitrogen and the use of the resulting nitrate fertilizers (108). By 1913 they were conducting experiments in this field (139:106). In 1916, the National Defense Act (39 U. S. Stat. L, 166, 215) provided large sums for determining methods of nitrate production. From this act resulted the construction of the two Federal nitrate plants at Muscle Shoals and Sheffield, Alabama. There was much coöperation of Federal agencies in this work during the World War.

The plant of the Bureau of Soils at the Arlington Agricultural Experiment Farm, near Washington, for nitrogen fixation by the Haber process, was nearly complete at the time of the entry of this country into the war. Coöperative funds immediately were supplied from the Ordnance Office of the War Department, the plant rushed to completion, chemists obtained through the selective draft, and the practicability of fixation under our conditions demonstrated. One of the joint problems, in which the Bureau of Mines of the Interior Department also shared, was that relating to the oxidation of by-product ammonia to nitric acid (125—1917:223). Difficulties having arisen in the operation of the War Department's Haber-process plant at Sheffield, Alabama, a new coöperative agreement was entered into by the Nitrogen Division of the Ordnance Office in 1918, by which the two agencies operated the

Bureau of Soils plant day and night as a testing plant for solving some of the serious problems developed in operating the War Department's larger plant (82:104–6).

During the war the great need for nitrogen in the manufacture of explosives made it necessary to ration its fertilizer use on the farm, where also it was urgently needed in the production of wheat and cotton, and of pasturage for the livestock yielding the vitally needed milk, meat, and fats. The President designated the War Industries Board to purchase supplies of nitrate of soda, and the Secretary of Agriculture to sell them to farmers. The Department of Agriculture coöperated with the States through the county agricultural agents in handling the sales (123).

Early in the period of the World War, the need of grease and nitrogenous fertilizer led to systematic efforts by the Office of Fertilizer Control and the Division of Fertilizer Resources to obtain more efficient utilization of garbage in the larger cities. The matter was taken up with the mayors with a view to better operation of existing municipal garbage-rendering plants, and the installation of such plants where none existed (125—1918 :231).

Promptly after the close of the war, the Nitrogen Division of the Ordnance Office entered into coöperation with the Office of Soil Fertility Investigations of the Bureau of Plant Industry to carry on field and greenhouse experiments with atmospheric-nitrogen fertilizers. The field tests were conducted during the years 1919, 1920, and 1921, on about twenty acres of plots on the War Department reservation at Muscle Shoals, Alabama. In the first year they were supervised by the Bureau of Plant Industry and in the two following years by the newly created Fixed-Nitrogen Research Laboratory, which remained a part of the Nitrogen Division until June 30, 1921 (2). The greenhouse tests were made at the Arlington Experimental Farm (3). Material of similar character was prepared at Sheffield for the use of the Office of Tobacco Investigations.

Soon after the close of the World War, the Office of Soil Fertility Investigations coöperated with the Ordnance Office of the War Department and the National Research Council on a study of methods of utilizing surplus cannon powder and smokeless powder, including nitrated cellulose, as sources of nitrogenous fertilizer (124—1919 :166–67).

Some difficulties arose when cyanamid was used as the entire source of nitrogen in the fertilizer in conjunction with acid phosphate. Experiments in using basic phosphate with varying quantities of cyanamid in fertilizer tests on corn were conducted in coöperation with the Agricultural Experiment Stations of Indiana, Maryland, Pennsylvania, South Carolina, and Virginia (124—1924:37).

After the close of the war, the Fixed-Nitrogen Research Laboratory was established in Washington by the War Department to coördinate the accumulated knowledge of nitrogen fixation, to continue research, and to aid in the peace-time utilization of the two Government nitrate plants in Alabama (139:106–7). In 1921 the laboratory was transferred from the Department of War to the Department of Agriculture, because nitrogen primarily is a fertilizer ingredient under peace-time conditions (131). At first the War Department coöperated in maintaining the laboratory, through the transfer of funds.

By 1923 the studies of the Bureau of Soils on the Haber process of nitrogen fixation, in coöperation with the Fixed-Nitrogen Research Laboratory, had been completed, the coöperation was discontinued, and the results were being prepared for publication (125—1923 and 1924). The laboratory remained an independent unit until 1926, when it was attached to the Bureau of Soils for one year, and then, in 1927, became one of the three component branches of the united Bureau of Chemistry and Soils.

After its inclusion in the new Bureau, the Fixed-Nitrogen Research Laboratory coöperated with the Bureau of Standards of the Department of Commerce to study the deterioration of structural steel in the synthesis of ammonia. This resulted in the joint preparation of a publication (135A). A more recent coöperation with the Bureau of Standards covers tests of specific heats at low temperatures, heats of combustion, and free energies of organic substances suitable for use in nitrogen-fixation and fertilizer investigations (125—1931:76). A review of the methods of preparation, plant-food content, and properties of various new fertilizer materials and mixtures was prepared and incorporated in the report of the President's Muscle Shoals Commission (125—1932:42). Coöperative tests were conducted for the Bureau of Aeronautics of the

Navy Department on the catalytic purification of gases (125—1932:76). In the theoretical phases of the problems of the nitrogen-research laboratory, numerous collaborations were set up with many universities and other institutions and the results of the consequent research were made available to the laboratory without cost (125—1931:76).

About 1925 or 1926, the Bureau of Soils coöperated with the Federal Bureau of Biological Survey in a study of the utilization of the waste from meat-rabbit slaughtering in the manufacture of oil, grease, and nitrogen-bearing fertilizer. The results were published jointly in July, 1926 (138).

Investigation of Sources of Phosphates

In the winter of 1908–09, the Secretary of the Interior withdrew from all form of entry some 6700 square miles of public domain in western Wyoming, eastern Idaho, and northeastern Utah, pending determination of possible phosphate deposits therein. Extensive surveys were made in this area in 1909 by the U. S. Geological Survey in coöperation with the Bureau of Soils, which made the chemical tests of samples in the field (136A).

In the spring of 1911, the Congress directed that a survey be made of all the fertilizer resources of the country, including the phosphates, and made annual appropriations for the work for a period of some ten years (139:103). There was more or less coöperation with the field parties of the Geological Survey throughout the period.

In November, 1917, the Council of National Defense, through the National Research Council, called a meeting of agricultural workers to consider means of increasing the availability of the phosphorus in rock phosphate, so that it might be more readily used as a substitute for the increasingly expensive acid phosphate. Among the resulting coöperative experiments were those on composting phosphate rock with sulfur (44). In 1918 the Bureau of Soils published a summary of the experimental work done on raw rock phosphates by twenty of the State agricultural experiment stations (136B).

Since the transfer of Soil-Fertility Investigations from Plant Industry to the Bureau of Chemistry and Soils, there has been increasing coöperation with the agricultural experiment stations. Because Bureau tests showed that the availability of the products of reverted phosphoric acid to plants should be greater than was indicated by the official methods of measuring it, samples of the reverted forms were tested in coöperation with some twenty-five experiment stations and other institutions (125—1931:74).

Tests of the relative availability of water-insoluble phosphates in soils of varying acidity (pH) have been conducted in coöperation with the experiment stations of Connecticut, Delaware, Oklahoma, and West Virginia (125—1932:43). The effect of the fluorine content of phosphatic fertilizers on plant growth is being investigated coöperatively with the University of Arkansas (125—1932:43).

Investigation of Sources of Potash

As noted at the beginning of this section, exploration for natural sources of potash was begun in 1911 under an act of Congress providing for investigation of possible sources of all natural fertilizers. The appropriation for this investigation was repeated annually for ten successive years. The printed report published by Cameron (29) in 1912 with its numerous appendixes by other specialists dealt largely with sources of potash fertilizers. It included several papers on the giant kelps of the Pacific Coast, which are discussed more fully below. In another publication (28), Cameron discusses possible sources of potash, including Searles and Owens Lakes in California, and the kelp beds off the Pacific Coast, but makes no mention of any coöperation with State agencies.

In 1916 another appropriation item was added, providing for "the investigation and demonstration within the United States to determine the best method of obtaining potash on a commercial scale, including the establishment and equipment of such plants as may be necessary therefor ..." Large appropriations were made to the Bureau of Soils for the latter study and were continued for two or three more years (139:103–4). Following this, Brown again discusses the Searles Lake deposit and the kelps as potash sources and cites the need of State legislation and the efforts made to obtain it (22).

In 1911, also, the U. S. Geological Survey had been authorized to make borings to discover deeper layers of potash salts. There was more or less active coöperation by the two agencies thereafter in this work, in accordance with the Congressional enactment. Samples collected both independently and coöperatively by both agencies were analyzed, and the results published by the Bureau of Soils (115). Both the Bureau and the Geological Survey aided in the support of the coöperative laboratory at the Mackay School of Mines of the University of Nevada, at Reno (122), some of the results from which were published by the Bureau (159).

Again in 1924 the Congress considered authorizing the Bureau of Soils and the Geological Survey to make joint investigations of potash deposits and of improved methods of recovering potash from them, and the Committee on Mines and Mining of the House held hearings on the subject (117). The Bureau of Soils coöperated with the Bureau of Mines of the Department of Commerce in determining the feasibility of a new treatment of a Texan potash saline, *polyhalite.*

Kelps as sources of potash.—Among possible sources of potash for fertilizer use, the giant kelps of the Pacific shores already had been brought to public attention by Balch (6) in 1909. The appendixes to the paper by Cameron (29) which deal with the California kelps are those by Crandall (38), biologist of the Marine Biological Station at La Jolla, now the Scripps Institution of Oceanography of the University of California; McFarland (76), of Stanford University; Turrentine (113), of the U. S. Bureau of Soils; and Setchell (97), of the University of California. In 1912 and 1913 other papers dealing with the chemical and technological aspects of this partly coöperative investigation were published by Turrentine (114) and by Parker and Lindemuth (88), in a private journal.

In 1915 there was published *Bulletin 248* of the California Agricultural Experiment Station, by Professor John S. Burd (23), containing discussion of the fertilizing value of Pacific Coast kelps and conclusions from kelp studies made in the station laboratory. Acknowledgment was made of assistance from Professor Setchell of the University department of botany, from Professor McFarland of Stanford University, and from the U. S. Marine Hospital Service for the use of its wharf and drying shed at San Diego. Portions of the results were published independently by Hoagland (61), and

Stewart (107), in the Federal-State coöperatively managed *Journal of Agricultural Research*.

Coöperation of the Bureau of Soils with State agencies was continued, and in 1915 another publication appeared, under the authorship of Cameron (30) and Crandall of the Scripps Institution and Doctors Frye and Rigg of the University of Washington. Still later, from 1916 to 1920, large appropriations were made by Congress for investigations of domestic sources of potash, nitrates, and other fertilizing materials, the amount reaching nearly $200,000 in 1920. Part of these funds were expended for the erection and operation of a plant at Summerland, California, for producing potash from kelps. This plant began on a small scale in 1918 and operated on a larger scale in 1919 (125—1920 :17). Coöperative researches on the distillation products from kelps were arranged. At the University of North Carolina the Department of Chemistry studied the neutral oils derived from kelp tar. The U. S. Bureau of Mines made tests of the crude oils, redistilled oils, and kelp acids as flotation agents in the concentration of ores of various kinds (125—1920 :20). Active coöperation was maintained between the Bureau of Soils and the Scripps Institution in certain phases of this work at La Jolla and Summerland, especially in the study of the kelps themselves (15).

Toxicity of boron in potash fertilizers.—Following the location of potash deposits in arid western basins such as Searles Lake in California, potash fertilizers from these sources were placed on the market and widely used. Soon thereafter crop injury developed and finally was traced to boron, and the source of the boron was found in the Searles Lake deposit. The extensive research caused by the injection of the boron problem resulted in widespread coöperation by various agencies.

The Bureaus of Entomology, Chemistry, and Plant Industry of the U. S. Department of Agriculture, beginning in 1913, made extensive tests of boron as a larvacide for houseflies in stable manure, and of the possibility of injury to crops from the use of such treated manures as a fertilizer. Several publications resulted (34; 36 ; 37). A part of these experiments were conducted in winter at the Audubon Park Sugar Station of the Louisiana Experiment Station (35). Later results are reported in Department Bulletins

Nos. 245 and 408 of the U. S. Department of Agriculture, published in 1915 and 1916, respectively.

In 1918 or 1919, the Office of Soil-Fertility Investigations and the Office of Cotton and Truck-Disease Investigations, both of the Bureau of Plant Industry, conducted tests of crop injuries by fertilizers containing borax, in coöperation with farmers growing potatoes in Maine, New York, New Jersey, Virginia, and North Carolina, and cotton in North Carolina, South Carolina, and Georgia. Coöperation with the State stations is not mentioned (94) but other publications show that the coöperation included the Stations in Maine (19; 102), New Jersey (13; 102), and Virginia (102). The experiments in Alabama were conducted on the government reservation at Muscle Shoals, in coöperation with the Fixed-Nitrogen Research Laboratory (100; 102).

By 1922 the Bureau of Soils was able to show that when potash fertilizers from Searles Lake were made by a new process, the borax content was well within the margin of safety for crops, and therefore was very different from what it had been (125—1922:9).

The most extensive coöperation in the boron research was that organized by eight northeastern State experiment stations, namely, those of the six New England States, New York, and New Jersey. Experiments had been begun at the Maine Station, but at a meeting of the directors of the eight stations it was proposed to pool the efforts of all and share the expense. The Vermont Station offered an equipped greenhouse, which was accepted. The Maine Station was asked to be responsible for the plan of research, and the New Jersey Station to select the workers who should conduct the studies in Vermont. In reporting the results it was stated (85:81) that "the work here reported was undertaken and carried out under the joint auspices of eight different institutions in as many different States. In this respect it is believed that it establishes a new record for coöperation among experiment stations."

The publications listed in Literature Cited at the end of this chapter, which have been cited in this subsection on Investigation of Natural Fertilizer Resources are Nos. 2, 3, 6, 13, 15, 19, 22, 23, 28, 29, 30, 34, 35, 36, 37, 38, 44, 47, 53, 61, 76, 82, 85, 88, 94, 97, 100, 102, 107, 108, 113, 114, 115, 116, 117, 122, 123, 124, 125, 129, 130, 131, 135A, 136A, 136B, 138, 139, 157, and 159.

4. Soil Survey, Classification, and Mapping

THE SURVEY OF THE SOILS of the United States is the largest single activity of the Soil Investigations branch of the Bureau of Chemistry and Soils of the U. S. Department of Agriculture. It likewise is a major activity in the soils unit (Division of Soils, Soils and Crops, or Agronomy) in most of the State agricultural experiment stations. For convenience of discussion, the work will be presented in two subdivisions, namely, national soil survey, and special-purpose surveys, the latter including studies of special soils, such as alkali, peat, etc.

NATIONAL SOIL SURVEY

During most of the nineteenth century, the points of view in soils studies in this country had been those of chemical analysis and of response to fertilizers. A few forward-looking contributions with a much broader horizon have been mentioned, above, in the section on Historical Development, notably those of Hilgard and Shaler. Russian scientists had been engaged in the field study of soils, but their work was little known in America. The slow development of the broader view doubtless played some part in the delay in establishing a special-soils unit in the Federal Department of Agriculture. It is greatly to the credit of Whitney and his associates that the survey of soils in the field was begun only five years after the Division of Soils was created in the Weather Bureau and four years after it became an independent unit. The discussion of soil-survey activities will proceed along two lines, the development of methods and bases for soil classification and its publication, and the development of coöperation with State agencies, illustrated specifically by coöperation in California. It should be noted, however, that the two developments progressed together, a fact which intensified the complexity of the problem.

Development of Bases for Soil Classification

The field survey and classification of soils was begun on a small scale in 1899. Because of the previous emphasis on chemical analysis, there was only meager knowledge and experience as a background for a study of physical characteristics. A larger fund was obtained for the second year. The work grew rapidly and field men were being trained in increasing numbers. At first only the texture of the soil, or the fineness or coarseness of its particles, was considered in its classification. Little was known about American soils and the whole subject was in a formative state. Soon it was recognized, however, from actual field experience, that other characteristics, especially color, were of importance in soil differentiation.

At the beginning, there was no thought of determining broad general groups of soils, and then proceeding to more and more detailed subdivisions of these groups. Each area was surveyed in great detail, but no attempt was made to correlate the soils in one area with those in another. It soon was realized, however, that this method would result in a soil map of the United States detailed for each area but with the areas totally unrelated, and with no possibility of determining whether the soils in the separate areas were alike or were different. Search was made, therefore, for some basis on which the relationships of soils could be determined and shown.

The first basis chosen was geologic origin, as it was supposed that soils derived from similar geologic materials would be similar in their characteristics. Large soil "provinces" were established on this basis. For instance, the glacial province included all the glacial soils from New England to Montana, and the loessial province all the windblown soils of the western States. This method was employed until about 1917. It had the unfortunate effect of focusing attention on the geology of the areas surveyed, instead of on the characteristics of the soils themselves. In the meantime the Russian pedologists or edaphologists had established and published their more advanced view and in a German translation it had appeared in this country just before the outbreak of the World War. It confirmed American soil scientists in their growing conviction that the geologic basis of differentiation was inadequate and misleading.

The new concept of the soil was that of a body in a state of development or evolution, having characteristics which change gradually as that evolution proceeds. This standpoint was quickly accepted by American workers, and has been the basis for most of the recent work in the classification and mapping of soils. Under its impetus, the major study is that of the soil itself, and its varying characteristics. An immediate result of the new evolutionary concept was the soil profile as a picture record of the development of residual soils from parent material through subsoil to surface soil, and the recognition of the various soil horizons. On this basis some soils are recognized as mature, and others as immature or juvenile soils in varying stages of development.

The foregoing discussion of the progressive development of ideas regarding soils and the bases for their survey and classification is important here only because of the profound influence upon relations between the Federal government and the States during the period in which these ideas were being developed. In a period of rapid change not all minds act and react alike. Some move rapidly to new standpoints, while others are conservative or even reactionary. Thus, at every stage of the evolution of the soil concept, there was much diversity of opinion as to proper methods of classification. This fact made effective Federal-State coöperation more difficult than it otherwise would have been. Yet the necessity of uniformity of method and treatment remained as great as ever, if results in one area were to be interpreted in terms of those obtained in other areas. The very facts that rendered coöperation difficult to achieve likewise rendered it the more imperative, if survey results were to have their greatest usefulness.

Methods of Publication

There has been a gradual development, likewise, in the manner of publishing the results of the Federal and Federal-State soil surveys. The first volume, for the year 1899, was published by the Department of Agriculture (143) under the title, *Field Operations of the Division of Soils, 1899.* By joint resolution of February 23, 1901 (31 U. S. Stat. L, 1462), the Congress provided for the annual publication of the *Report on Field Operations of the Division of Soils* (144), beginning with 1900, as a Congressional document. Seventeen thousand copies were provided, of which 3000 were for the use of the Senate, 6000 for the House, and 8000 for the Department of Agriculture (51 :43). It soon was realized that publishing the results in an annual volume, only, was both unsatisfactory and uneconomical. Necessarily, the distribution of the publication containing the results of any given survey was delayed until all those for the year were ready, and persons wanting only a given area had to take the entire volume or nothing. Accordingly, by joint resolution of March 14, 1904 (33 U. S. Stat. L, 583), the Congress provided for only 10,500 copies of the annual report of field operations, of which 1500 were for the Senate, 3000 for the House, and 6000 for the Department, and, in addition, for advance sheets of each area surveyed, the number to be variable, as follows: 500 copies for each Senator from the State concerned, 2000 for each Representative from the Congressional district or districts covered by the survey, and 1000 copies for the Department of Agriculture (51 :52–53).

This plan of distribution was maintained until 1922, when the single bound volume, *Field Operations,* was discontinued altogether, because of the enormous size resulting from the surveys of one year, the great expense, the increasing delay in appearance, and the fact that few persons wanted the results in this form, unwieldly and geographically unassorted. The volume for 1922 comprised 2138 pages and was issued in 1928. Beginning with 1923, only the separate publications of each individual survey were issued. Those reports resulting from the field work of each year form a series for that year, and are numbered consecutively as they are completed. In general, it requires from three to five years after the survey is completed to interpret the results, prepare the text, check all doubtful points in the field, make the large detailed map and have it lithographed, and print the report and map. Because the change in style was not decided upon until 1928, all of the separate parts in Series 1923 and the earlier ones in Series 1924 were already printed with consecutive paging. Thereafter, each report is separately paged.

Federal Coöperation with the States

Special impetus to the study and classification of soils by the State agricultural experiment stations was given by a proviso in the annual appropriation bill of the U. S. Department of Agriculture for the fiscal year 1890. The item making the annual appropriation of $15,000 for each of the State experiment stations provided (25 U. S. Stat. L, 841)—

That, so far as practicable, all such stations shall devote a portion of their work to the examination and classification of the soils of their respective States and Territories, with a view to securing more extended knowledge and better development of their agricultural capacities.

Actual coöperation of the Federal Division of Soils with State agencies in the study of their soils seems to date from 1895, when it was stated that the Maryland Station, at its expense, had placed a man in the Division to work on Maryland soils under the direction of the divisional chief, who formerly was in that station. In the same year the Virginia State Board of Agriculture, by agreement with the Division, employed four men to work under the direction of its chief (apparently in the laboratory also, though statement is lacking). Other States also had asked for coöperation, either through their agricultural experiment stations or their State geological surveys (125—1895 :189).

Soil survey and mapping was begun by the Division of Soils in 1899. Coöperation with State agencies began in the same year. The Maryland Geological Survey entered into an agreement to help finance a survey in that State, the agricultural experiment station also coöperating by furnishing paid personnel. The work was begun immediately and colored maps prepared to accompany the manuscript results. In the same year the New Mexico Station coöperated in a survey of the alkali soils of the Pecos Valley. A survey of the alkali soils of the Salt Lake Valley was begun in July, 1899, in coöperation with the Utah Agricultural Experiment Station, and in the spring of 1900 the collaborative survey was continued in Sevier County, Utah. During the winter of 1899–1900, work was done jointly with the Louisiana Experiment Station, the two agencies sharing the expense but the Division of Soils to be responsible for the report and accompanying maps. During the same period a coöperative survey was made in the Salt River Valley of Arizona, the State Station furnishing an assistant for three months. By May, 1900, coöperative survey was under way in North Carolina, jointly with the State Department of Agriculture and the State Geological Survey. Some coöperative work on alkali soils had been planned in southern California, but apparently it was done finally by the Federal Division without assistance from the State.

These examples serve to show the ways in which coöperation in soil surveys developed and increased. In general, the amount contributed by the State agencies was much less than that by the Federal Division, and so it was for several years. Almost from the beginning of Federal field surveys in 1899, there was an increasing volume of requests from State agencies, asking the extension of the surveys into their States. The requests came from colleges of agriculture, agricultural experiment stations, State geological surveys, State boards of agriculture, members of Congress, county commissioners, and commercial sources. It was recognized from the beginning that the Division of Soils had men trained for survey and mapping, while most of the States did not, and that coöperation expanded the area covered by Federal funds and provided the States with trained workers. Comparatively little coöperative survey could be undertaken, however, because of lack of State funds.

In some States coöperation was effected for the survey of certain special areas, and was discontinued when these had been covered. In other States a program looking toward a more or less nearly complete State survey was planned. In Maryland and North Carolina, for instance, the coöperation begun in 1899 and 1900, respectively, with the State Geological Survey and the State Board of Agriculture, respectively, was continued during a long series of years. In 1907 the legislature of Alabama appropriated $10,000, to be repeated annually, for a coöperative soil survey under the supervision of the Federal Bureau of Soils. The Bureau was to set apart the same sum annually and the work was to be maintained continuously until the State survey was finished. The West Virginia Geological Survey paid all the expenses of the survey parties of the Bureau of Soils in that State (125—1908 :516).

In the mean time, special surveys of various sorts were undertaken with different States. In about 1910, for instance, the Bureau coöperated with the State Geological Survey of Washington in a survey of extensive logged and burned lands in the vicinity of Puget Sound. At about the same time a reconnaissance survey of the high plateau of western Pennsylvania was begun in coöperation with Pennsylvania State College.

By 1910 the question of active coöperation with all of the States had become very important, for several reasons. While there still was some opposition to the Federal survey, it was based for the most part on difference over what method of soil classification and mapping was to be employed. As pointed out by Secretary of Agriculture Wilson, however, in his report for 1911 (pp. 103–4), it was extremely important that any one method, once adopted, should be followed consistently (even though there were other methods equally good), in order that results should be comparable in different years and different States.

Other questions had to do with actual financial coöperation with the States. Where specific State appropriations had been made for State coöperation, the Bureau of Soils was obliged to spend more than the normal proportion of its own funds in that State, to the relative disadvantage of the work in other States. On the other hand, it was certain that if the Bureau did not enter into such coöperation, the States would proceed alone in their surveys and often by methods differing from each other and from that used by the Federal government, and the results unfortunately would not be comparable. For this reason, among others, it was considered highly desirable that unified methods should be insured by complete coöperation between Federal and State agencies on a single basis of classification.

While the greater part of the soil survey now in progress in the United States is under coöperation with the Soil-Survey Division of the U. S. Bureau of Chemistry and Soils, not all the problems of effective coöperation have been solved nor has all the survey been made coöperative. As late as 1928, the Bureau in its annual report stressed again the need of complete coöperation in order that there might be uniformity of treatment throughout the country, and in order also that the soil-fertility programs of the States might be tied in with the survey results (125—1928 :21). In 1930 (*op. cit.*, p. 40), the report recorded that coördination in soil classification had been effected with State organizations. Studies of soil profiles, increasingly important after the adoption of the evolutionary basis of soil classification, have been emphasized and enlarged throughout the United States, and determination of the pH (hydrogen-ion) values has been included. In Wisconsin, a study of the profiles of twenty-three soil types was begun in 1930 in coöperation with the Wisconsin Geological and Natural History Survey.

Coöperation in California

Coöperative soil surveys in any State may be illustrated well by what has been done in California, with regard to agencies, agreements, purposes, procedure, problems, and results. Soil survey was

begun in California independently by the Division of Soils of the
U. S. Department of Agriculture in 1900, and has been continued
in every year since that time except 1906 and 1911. It was not co-
operative with the State, however, until July 1, 1913. Similar work
was being done by the State agency during this period of independent operations.

For several years increasing requests for Federal participation
in the soil survey of California had been coming to the Department
from the Governor, members of Congress, county officials, and
commercial organizations. In 1913, Dr. Thomas F. Hunt, newly
appointed Dean of the University of California College of Agriculture and Director of the Experiment Station, proposed to the
Federal agency that the work be conducted in coöperation. This
proposal was accepted and the coöperative relation has been maintained without interruption ever since. The principal collaborating agencies are the Soil Survey (Division) of the Soil Investigations (Branch) of the Bureau of Chemistry and Soils in the U. S.
Department of Agriculture, and the Division of Soil Technology
of the College of Agriculture, University of California. On occasion, both coöperate with the U. S. Department of the Interior,
through the Geological Survey and the Bureau of Reclamation.

The purpose of this coöperative program is to survey, describe,
classify, and map the soils of California. The field survey determines the origin, characteristics, and distribution of the different
soil types occurring in the State, describes them, and classifies them
into groups and series. This classification then is correlated with
those made previously in other areas, either adjacent or noncontig-
uous. The distribution of the various soils of a given area is drafted
on field maps. When the field work has been completed, a full description of the soils of the area and their characteristics is written,
with a discussion of the general agriculture of the area, of the probable usefulness of different soil types for agricultural purposes,
and of their relation to commercial development. After the necessary interpretation, correlation, and editing, the text and maps are
published for the interested public.

Procedure in coöperative soil survey.—In coöperative soil surveys, a rather standardized procedure has been developed. This
standard procedure is followed in California.

In determining the areas to be surveyed in any State, the Federal law declares that they may be selected by the following agencies, in the order named : Members of Congress, the U. S. Department of Agriculture, other Federal departments, and State agencies. In actual fact, however, the first three all but never exercise their legal rights in this respect. Occasionally some Federal agency, because of some special activity or requirement on its part, may suggest the desirability of a survey in a given area. In general, the State soil-survey agency prepares a comprehensive program of survey several years in advance, and this program is followed in choosing the areas for coöperative surveys except where changes in relative importance of areas make deviation from the program desirable. The coöperative agreement provides for agreement in selecting the area, but the Federal Soil Survey, recognizing officially that the State soil experts are in the better position to determine the necessities, grants them substantial discretion about what areas are to be surveyed.

Ordinarily, the county is the unit of a survey project. In California, however, as in other mountainous States, because the topography varies and the counties usually comprise both fairly level agricultural valleys and steep nonagricultural mountain slopes, the unit commonly is an agricultural area rather than a county. Sometimes the survey area comprises parts of two or more counties.

In the selection of personnel, the Federal unit designates the man or men it will detail for a given survey, and the State agency does the same. A survey party usually consists of two men, one from each agency. Of the two, one is made the leader. In California, it has been the practice to rotate the leadership in successive projects, the leader of one survey becoming the assistant on the next, and vice versa. This presupposes two workers of somewhat equal ability and experience, as ordinarily is the case. Effort is made to designate two men who are mutually agreeable and can work together effectively. Where the breaking in of inexperienced youngsters is necessary, the party customarily is made up of more than two men.

Each agency pays the salary and subsistence expenses of its man or men. The costs of transportation within the area are shared equally by the two agencies.

The signed coöperative agreement provides for joint decision whether detailed survey or only reconnaissance of the area is required. The Department of Agriculture recognizes also that the State may want a map showing a greater degree of subdivision or differentiation of soils than would be needed by the Department. In such cases, the coöperative agreement provides that the State shall indicate the degree of subdivision held necessary, and that the map shall be made on that basis. The maps are published on a scale of 1 inch to the mile, unless some other scale is agreed upon. The Department agrees also that the State may use, on any copies of the maps furnished to it, any other system of soil nomenclature than that used by the Federal Soil Survey, provided the Survey's nomenclature is shown also at the same points on the map.

The leader designated is responsible for carrying the survey forward and preparing the report, with the help of the designated assistant. As noted above, these relative positions usually are rotated on successive surveys in California. Both the work of survey and of preparation of the report are supervised by officials representing the Federal and the State agencies. Preliminary inspection of the field work may be done by either or by both. Major problems, such as any modification of standard methods, are discussed in conference of field men and supervising officers. The Federal Soil Survey maintains one of its five district supervisors' offices in California. It is located in the post office building in Berkeley, only a few blocks distant from the division of soil technology of the University of California College of Agriculture, so that close contact between the two supervising agencies is unusually easy in this State. Another circumstance favorable to mutual understanding in California is the continuity of supervising personnel. Mr. Macy H. Lapham has been supervisor in charge of District 5 since the headquarters were established in Berkeley in about 1916, and Professor Charles F. Shaw has been in charge of the division of soil technology at the experiment station since the beginning of Federal-State coöperation in 1913.

In the coöperative agreement, the broader knowledge possessed by the Federal staff in the matter of soil nomenclature and correlation is recognized. The State agency also accepts the necessity of making the map of any soil area survey within its borders agree with the maps of other areas where the same soil types occur. This is especially important if such areas are contiguous or are near one another.

Preliminary interpretations and correlations are worked out, either in the field, or at Berkeley, or both, by the field men and the supervisors. Final recommendations are forwarded to the Soil Survey (Division) in Washington, with the manuscript and accompanying maps. The final decision on such interpretations rests with the correlation committee of the Bureau of Chemistry and Soils.

Manuscript copies of the field reports and maps are furnished to both coöperating parties as soon as completed. The division of soil technology of the College of Agriculture has typed the manuscripts of the reports and copied the field maps. Final editorial and cartographic work is done by the Bureau of Chemistry and Soils in Washington, wholly at Federal expense.

The coöperative agreement provides that publication may be by either party, and that the fact of coöperation shall be shown both on the report and on the accompanying maps. In California, however, the State has never published separately, and publication has been wholly by the U. S. Department of Agriculture. This is true in most other States, as well, and is due largely to the special Congressional provision for Federal publication, noted previously.

Under the terms of the coöperative agreement, the Bureau of Chemistry and Soils agrees to furnish 100 copies of the printed report to the California Agricultural Experiment Station, and to aid the station, as far as possible under the law, in "securing the publication of additional copies." The California Senators and Representatives usually place their total allotments with the division of soil technology, at the University at Berkeley, for distribution. This would give a maximum of 3000 copies, including the 100 copies from the U. S. Bureau, unless the area surveyed happened to lie in two Congressional districts, when the number would be increased to 5100 copies.

Each soil-survey report published by the U. S. Department of Agriculture, under authority of the legislation previously discussed, bears a declaration of the State coöperation on the outside of the front cover, together with the title of the report and the names of its authors. The statement of coöperation is repeated in different form on the inside of the front cover. The title of the report, with the names and titles of the authors, appears again at the top of the first text page. Facsimiles of the acknowledgments of coöperation on the report of one recently published California survey (31) are given herewith:

(Outside of Cover)

UNITED STATES DEPARTMENT OF AGRICULTURE
Bureau of Chemistry and Soils
In Coöperation with the University of California Agricultural Experiment Station

———

SOIL SURVEY OF THE SALINAS AREA, CALIFORNIA
BY
E. J. Carpenter, U. S. Department of Agriculture, in Charge
and Stanley W. Cosby, University of California

. . . .

(Inside of Cover)

BUREAU OF CHEMISTRY AND SOILS
Henry G. Knight, Chief
A. G. McCall, Chief, Soil Investigations
SOIL SURVEY
Curtis F. Marbut, in Charge
M. H. Lapham, Inspector, District 5

———

COÖPERATION
University of California Agricultural Experiment Station
E. D. Merrill, Director
Chas. F. Shaw, In Charge, Soil Survey

On the soil map itself, coöperation is shown by a repetition of most of the statements noted above as occurring on the inside of the front cover of the report. The major differences are the insertion of the words "U. S. Department of Agriculture" above "Bureau of Chemistry and Soils," and omission of the word "Coöperation" above the California statement. The layouts at the top of the map therefore are as follows:

U. S. Department of Agriculture
Bureau of Chemistry and Soils
Henry G. Knight, Chief
A. G. McCall, Chief, Soil Investigations
Curtis F. Marbut, In Charge, Soil Survey

University of California
Agricultural Experiment Station
E. D. Merrill, Director
Chas. F. Shaw, In Charge, Soil Survey

The name and title of the Inspector, District 5, and those of the authors are repeated at the bottom of the map.

Occasional coöperation has been had with other Federal agencies than the Soil Survey, when special needs have arisen in California. In 1914, formal coöperation, with a written memorandum of agreement, was effected with the Geological Survey of the Department of the Interior, for the preparation of their topographic map of the Santa Rosa Quadrangle. The University of California division of soil technology needed this topographic map in its soil investigations, but at that time the Geological Survey was not prepared to do the work. Consequently, by agreement, the University of California through its College of Agriculture contributed $1500 to the Geological Survey to enable them to undertake the work promptly. The Survey, in turn, furnished the College officials with copies of the field maps and notes promptly on their completion, and long before their final publication. The coöperation continued until 1916, when the work was finished.

In 1919, informal coöperation was arranged with the Bureau of Reclamation of the Department of the Interior, for a study of the soils of arid areas in southeastern California, including the Imperial Valley, the Chuckawalla Valley, and others. The program was arranged by correspondence and conference. The Reclamation Bureau obtained the loan of one soil expert from the U. S. Soil Survey, and another from the division of soil technology in the University of California, paying their salaries and expenses while they surveyed the high-line soils of the Imperial Valley. Professor Shaw of the division of soil technology conducted the surveys in the other areas at State expense, and also supervised both sets of operations. This work was done in connection with the proposed all-American canal for bringing water into the Imperial Valley.

Cost of coöperative soil surveys.—In California it appears that, in general, total expenses of the coöperative soil surveys, other than the expense of publication, are divided fairly equally between the State and Federal agencies. They share the field expenses. Each carries its own cost of administration and of field supervision of surveys. The State carries the total expense of laboratory studies of the soils mapped, and the Government carries the entire expense of editing the reports and of making the final maps. These two sets of separate expenses probably offset each other fairly well. Finally, the Government bears the cost of publication, under the Congressional Resolution quoted above, which makes the Federal share of the total expense appreciably larger than that of the State.

The Bureau of Chemistry and Soils has conducted soil surveys in California during thirty-two fiscal years, 1900 to 1931, inclusive.* The work was conducted independently during fourteen years, 1900 to 1913. It has been conducted coöperatively with California during eighteen fiscal years, 1914 to 1931. The Bureau estimates its total field expenses in California during the twenty-six fiscal years from 1906 to 1931 at $158,445, which would be at the rate of about $6100 per annum. This cost covers only the field expenses of the surveys, including field administration and supervision, but does not include either the editorial and cartographic expenses in Washington, or the cost of final publication. Of this total sum, approximately $50,000 were expended from 1906 to 1913, inclusive, before coöperation was effected.

The University of California through its division of soil technology has been conducting soil surveys in coöperation with the Federal Government for eighteen fiscal years, 1914 to 1931. It has compiled the field expenses as reported by both agencies during the seventeen-year period, 1914 to 1930. The total and average annual costs to each and both of the agencies during this period are tabulated in round numbers below:

Item	California	U. S. Bureau	Both Agents
Total cost......................	$94,390	$97,970	$192,360
Average annual cost.............	5,550	5,760	11,310

The State expenditures are said to cover field expenses and the cost of administration and inspection, but no charges for office supplies, stenographic assistance, miscellaneous help, or for the full cost of laboratory investigations. These extras are estimated at about $1000 per year. The Federal expenditures are understood by the State to cover all field expenses, including inspection, but not the cost of Bureau editing and map making, and administration, or the cost of printing. This latter is thought to amount to about $2000 per year.

The State estimates that the Federal government bears about 10

---

* Data for the fiscal year 1932 were not available when this chapter was written.

per cent more of the total expense than does the State. Federal figures compiled for twelve supposedly representative surveys in different States show that the field expenses, State and Federal, account for slightly more than 70 per cent of the total cost, and Washington expenses for slightly less than 30 per cent. The Washington expenses include map drafting, editing, typing, and Soil-Survey Division overhead, together comprising 13 per cent, and printing and lithographing, comprising 16.6 per cent, or exactly one sixth, of the total combined expense in field and Washington. It is not known just what State expenses were included in the Federal figures, by which the Federal overrun of 30 per cent of the total is determined. The actual figures may well be intermediate between the 10 per cent Federal overrun estimated by the State in California, and the 30 per cent estimated by the government for the country as a whole.

Approximately one half of the agricultural area of the State has been covered by either the reconnaissance or the detailed surveys. At the present rate of progress (1931), about seventeen years more will be required to complete the present program. The total cost of survey, including both Federal and State expenses, is estimated by the Federal Bureau at a fraction more than two cents per acre, for the United States as a whole. Naturally, in mountainous States such as California, with highly diversified soils, the cost per unit-area is higher than the average.

The final cost of any enterprise is conditioned, first, on its magnitude, and, secondly, on any future changes which may reasonably be expected in the expense per unit area. The present program is directed toward a survey of all the agricultural lands in the State. In general, perhaps one half of the total present agricultural area has been covered by one or another of the types of surveys. Part of the past surveys have been conducted by the reconnaissance rather than the detailed method. As the work progresses, these areas are being, and will continue to be, covered by the more detailed method of survey. As agriculture becomes more intensive and its industries more specialized, a demand for still more intensive surveys is likely to be created. This makes an estimate of the total final cost of soil surveys, even on the present agricultural areas, very difficult to construct.

Other factors enter into the situation. As time goes on, still other lands may become agricultural through the development of new industries, or the extension of reclamation enterprises over desert or swamp areas which either are not now farmed or provide only a sparse grazing. Then there is the growing recognition of the agricultural and commercial importance of the waste of our soil resources through uncontrolled erosion. California, with its large areas of relatively steep slopes and its general lack of snow cover or frozen soil during the season of precipitation, is peculiarly subject to such erosion. All of these conditions together are likely to cause an imperative demand for the continuation of special types of soil survey long beyond the time limits of the present program.

The great value of these surveys both to agriculture and to various industries is so well recognized, however, that their low cost, both per unit of area and per unit of resulting value, is generally appreciated.

California recommendations regarding procedure.—Professor Charles F. Shaw, Chief of the California Division of Soil Technology, has made some very interesting suggestions for the future betterment of this important coöperative enterprise. The paragraphs below summarize these in a form acceptable to him.

1. The coöperative soil survey in California has been very productive, both in the completion of surveys and in the developing of fundamental principles in soil morphology and taxonomy that are of worldwide application. Of the abilities, patience, and fine coöperative spirit of the Federal leaders, both in Washington and within the State, most hearty appreciation is expressed. The work has been almost entirely free from misunderstanding or controversy.

2. It appears desirable to increase the rate at which the program of soil survey is being accomplished. Maintaining two survey parties in the field, instead of one as now, would be merely going back to the prewar basis. It would double the speed of survey, but would make only a small increase in the cost of supervision. Other expenses by unit of area would remain approximately as now. The advantages would be a more prompt completion of important surveys, earlier revision of some of the old maps, and much more rapid availability of greatly needed information.

3. It seems highly desirable that the scope of the coöperative

work be enlarged to include reconnaissance soil surveys of the larger desert areas, a modified soil survey of the forest areas, and intensive studies of some of the more important California soils on a monographic basis.

4. The reports of the surveys should be published in larger editions than now are available. Under the present plan, some 3000 copies of each report are made available to members of Congress, who usually place their allotments with the Division of Soil Technology in the University of California for distribution. This is not a sufficient number, and no more are available from any source. The publications usually are out of print within eight or ten years, and long before the demand for them has ceased.

5. It is believed that the California agencies, namely, the State University, its College of Agriculture, and the college's Division of Soil Technology, get only a minor acknowledgment of credit for their share in financing this work. This condition might be remedied by printing the names of the agencies of the two governments in type of more nearly uniform size than is now employed, as noted in the example given. Another way to accomplish this would be to print a considerable part of the edition with a cover page showing the State as the principal agency and the Federal Bureau as being "in coöperation." As the great majority of the copies printed are used within the State, these recommendations seem only fair.

6. Most difficult, and sometimes threatening to harmonious progress, have been the final correlation of the soils and the decisions about the names in the series and the relations to other soils previously mapped. The Correlation Committee established for this purpose has been too much of a one-man committee in the past. The decisions of the Chief of the Soil Survey are final, and, although Dr. Marbut has a remarkably wide knowledge of the soils of the United States, it is impossible for one man to be conversant with all of the more than 1400 series now established. A true Correlation Committee with full and final authority should be made up of men thoroughly familiar with specific sections of the country. The Bureau inspector within his district and the State representative within his State should be more fully conversant with the intimate details of soil characteristics within their regions than any one

national representative. The conclusions of the State specialist and the district inspector of the Bureau should be overruled only after full field studies convince the committee that a change is warranted. Errors in judgment are much more serious to the State representative, for he must live within the State in close contact with the men who use these soils and the reports upon them. Where these experts have been overruled, time usually has proved the decisions to have been in error.

7. Another large difficulty is the long delay between completion of the survey and publication of the results. These delays frequently extend to more than four years, and sometimes to over five years. As areas are surveyed usually because of demands for information about their soils, it follows that such delays greatly decrease the usefulness of the results in the solution of initial problems, and tend to embarrass the State representatives. It is recognized that publication cannot be prompt, because the final interpretation of the work, the editing of the manuscript, the making of the complex map, and at last the typesetting, proofing, printing, and binding, all must follow in sequence. Two other causes of delay are avoidable to some extent. One is lack of funds for prompt printing, which can be remedied by more adequate appropriations. The other is the lack of such a Correlation Committee as has just been discussed. Some California survey reports have been held up for more than one year because of some debated point. The necessary correlations should have careful, wise, and prompt consideration, which can be had only when there is a real Correlation Committee with power to act.

Progress and Value of the National Soil Survey

Soil surveys were begun in this country in 1899, and consequently have been in progress for some thirty-four years. At first only the detailed surveys were made. Later, the preliminary or reconnaissance surveys were added. Some areas first covered by the reconnaissance survey have since been given detailed treatment. The totals of areas covered by each type of survey are stated cumulatively by decades and for the thirty-three-year period, 1899–1932, in Table 1. The data are taken from the annual reports of the Bureau of (Chemistry and) Soils for the years named.

In 1928 it was reported by the Federal Bureau that more than one thousand one hundred separate areas had been surveyed, exclusive of special surveys for the Forest Service, Bureau of Reclamation, and other Federal agencies. At the average rate of progress since that time, some two hundred additional areas should have been surveyed by the end of the fiscal year 1933. The total land area of the continental United States, exclusive of Alaska, is some 2,973,000 square miles. The totals given in Table 1 indicate, therefore, that approximately one half this area has been covered by

TABLE 1

Totals of Areas Covered by Detailed and Reconnaissance Soil Surveys,
Cumulated by 10-year Periods Ending in 1910, 1920, and 1930,
and for the 33-year Period 1899–1932

Year	Detailed Survey		Reconnaissance Survey		Data from Annual Report for
	Square Miles	Acres	Square Miles	Acres	
1910	360,000	230,000,000			1910:108
1920	547,733	350,549,120	516,286	330,423,040	1920:1
1930	798,638	511,128,320	608,610	389,510,400	1930:39
1932	859,462	550,055,680	628,354	402,146,560	1932:25

survey, somewhat less than two thirds of this one half being by detailed survey, and somewhat more than one third by reconnaissance survey.

The primary purpose of the soil survey is to give definite information to the agricultural officials, farmers, and business men of the area surveyed, as well as to those of the State and nation generally, regarding the included soil types, their agricultural values, and their proper utilization. These results are of particular value to the scientists of the State experiment station and the extension service, as well as to the county agricultural advisors and the farmers in the area surveyed. The reports have many and important uses, however, which reach far beyond the needs of these groups.

Many Federal agencies make large use of the soil surveys. In the U. S. Department of Agriculture, the Bureau of Agricultural Economics uses them in its farm management and land classification studies; the Bureau of Agricultural Engineering in many activities concerned with farm machinery and farm power, irrigation, drainage, water conservation, and erosion prevention; the Bureau of Entomology in studies of the distribution and destructiveness of soil-infesting insects; the Forest Service with regard to land classification, forest extension, and erosion prevention; the Bureau of Plant Industry in making crop recommendations; and the Bureau of Public Roads in highway location and construction.

In the Department of the Interior, the Geological Survey uses soil-survey reports in its work of land classification and in its mineral and water-resource surveys; the Bureau of Indian Affairs in extending both dry-land and irrigation farming on the Indian Reservations; and the Bureau of Reclamation in locating and developing irrigation projects. The Engineer Corps of the United States Army uses the survey reports in its operations for flood control.

In agricultural finance, the Intermediate Credit Banks and Federal Land Banks (formerly under the Federal Farm Loan Bureau of the Treasury Department but now comprised in the newly created Farm Credit Administration), and the Regional Agricultural Credit Corporation (formerly operating under the Reconstruction Finance Corporation), all make good use of these monographs on soil areas. So too does the Agricultural Adjustment Administration, which administers the recently passed Agricultural Adjustment (farm relief) Act.

Many State agencies other than the College of Agriculture use the soil-survey reports. Such officers and organizations as the commissioner of immigration, State land settlement board, State real estate commissioner, State bond commission, or their equivalents under different names, use them commonly in the conduct of their official business. And in similar ways, the officials of irrigation districts, drainage districts, levee districts, water conservation districts, and other such bond-issuing and tax-levying districts, use these scientific discussions of their soils.

Some of these State agencies use the soil-survey data effectively to prevent the development of fraudulent or unwise land development schemes and enterprises, thus saving millions of dollars to investors or to honest but uninformed organizers. Some of the projects thus prevented are very large, one of them being a $22,-000,000 enterprise. Perhaps of equal value to the actual moneys saved is the saving of men from the discouragement and misery that result from the manipulations of dishonest or uninformed promoters.

Many commercial agencies make continued use of the reports. Banks, mortgage companies, life-insurance companies, and other agencies loaning money on agricultural land make frequent use of them. Companies engaged in construction enterprises which require the penetrating or moving of the soil also find them of great occasional importance. One of the major oil companies of California used these data in locating the route of a new pipe line to avoid corrosive soils, where possible, and to insure knowing where to employ special preservative and protective coverings when such soils had to be crossed.

The long-continued depression in agriculture, beginning about 1920, makes a careful classification of agricultural lands more important than ever. This is especially true if there is to be any attempt at removing submarginal and marginal farm lands from competition with the better soils in crop production. The detailed soil survey is the first and fundamental step in the classification of land for agricultural and other purposes.

SPECIAL-PURPOSE SURVEYS AND CLASSIFICATIONS

The agencies concerned with soil survey frequently are asked by other governmental units, Federal, State, or intrastate, for aid in survey and classification of areas for special purposes. Some of these requests have to do with the location of institutions, such as agricultural schools, hospitals, etc., especially where the growing of crops or livestock is to be undertaken. Other requests relate to engineering projects, such as roads, irrigation structures, levees, and similar structures. Still a third group has to do with land classification for agricultural and forest lands, the differentiation of lands subject to homestead entry under various laws, and the determination of value for purposes of taxation and remuneration.

For Location of Institutions

In 1907 or thereabout, the Bureau of Soils coöperated with the States of Georgia and Alabama in selecting tracts of land for the location of an agricultural school in each Congressional District of these States. After approval of the sites by the State and local authorities, soil maps were prepared for each tract, usually of 200 or 300 acres (125—1907:438). Many cases of similar coöperation by State agencies with each other and with county or municipal agencies have occurred since the various States have developed highly trained soil-survey units.

With the entrance of the United States into the World War, the Bureau of Soils received numerous requests from the War Department for information concerning soils in specific localities where the establishment of camps, hospitals, munition depots, etc., was contemplated. Full coöperation was given in all such cases. Later developments showed that in some cases much fuller use could have been made of the existing information by the military authorities (82:104). Still earlier, the Bureau had aided the War Department in testing soils intended for use as parade grounds in the Philippine Islands.

In 1922 the Bureau was called upon by the Department of Justice for expert advice on the origin of certain soils in the bottom lands of the Red River in the vicinity of the Burkburnett oil fields on the boundary between Texas and Oklahoma. These had become the cause of a boundary dispute between the two States. The solution of the problem required detailed soils maps and more especially the profile maps of deep borings with mechanical analyses of the extracted soils (125—1922:5).

During 1930 and 1931, the Federal soil-survey unit was engaged in coöperation with the Treasury Department in studies antecedent to the location of institutions for the cure of drug addicts. Farm work by the addicts was part of the plan followed by the Bureau of Narcotics.

Several years ago the South Carolina Agricultural Experiment Station asked the help of the Bureau of Soils in locating a suitable "Sandhill Branch Experiment Station." This help was given and bureaus of the U. S. Department of Agriculture have since coöperated in experiments conducted on this branch station.

For Location of Engineering Projects

During the last several years the Federal Soil Survey has been coöperating with the highway engineers of the U. S. Bureau of Public Roads in a study of the soils composing the subgrade of highways in certain areas (125—1926:5; and 1930:37). Where sinking, swelling, or slipping of the subgrade soil occurs, very expensive injury may be done to a highway, as has happened in certain areas in California (26). A very good illustration of the important use made by highway engineers of soil-survey bulletins of the Bureau of Soils is given by the U. S. Bureau of Public Roads in a recent paper (92).

During the past thirty years, the Bureau of Soils and its successor have collaborated frequently with the Bureau of Indian Affairs and the Bureau of Reclamation (formerly Reclamation Service) of the U. S. Department of the Interior. The former has charge of the agricultural operations, both dry-land and irrigated, on the extensive Indian Reservations, and the latter is responsible for the location and development of the numerous reclamation projects of the Federal government. A knowledge of the soils is of great importance, especially in irrigation enterprises, where not only crop-producing ability but also the power of the soil to absorb and retain water, and its freedom from harmful alkalies, are vital to the success of the undertaking.

Special coöperation has been given the Bureau of Reclamation recently in a study of the soil problems involved in the construction of an aqueduct across southern California from Boulder Dam to the Metropolitan Water District centering on Los Angeles. Still more recently, similar service has been rendered in connection with the proposed transfer of water from the Sacramento Valley to the San Joaquin Valley in California, including a survey of the area of soils suitable for irrigation in both valleys (125—1930:40).

For the Engineer Corps of the Army, determinations have been made of the character of Mississippi flood-plain soils with reference to their use in building levees for control of floods (125—1922:10).

Before the War, when irrigation investigations were conducted by a section of the Office of Experiment Stations, in the U. S. Department of Agriculture, there was coöperation with the State of California in soil survey to classify land for irrigation purposes in the foothills of the Sierra Nevada. The work was done under two separate coöperative agreements between the Office on the one hand and the California State Department of Engineering and the

University of California Agricultural Experiment Station, respectively, on the other. Under the agreements, the study of soil conditions was made wholly by and at the expense of the division of soil technology at the California Station, while both Federal and State funds were applied to the irrigation studies. The results were prepared jointly and published by the California Station (91), the Federal author preparing the irrigation data and the State author those on soil conditions and crop adaptations.

Occasionally some special soil studies have been made in relation to coöperative irrigation investigations by the Division of Agricultural Engineering of the U. S. Bureau of Public Roads. Two such instances have occurred in California. In one case some properties of soils were concerned (10), and in the other case an improved method of taking soil samples (14), the coöperation being with the State Department of Public Works.

For Purposes of Land Classification

The soil survey is an important aid to land classification for various purposes, such as the application of the homestead laws, the segregation of forest and agricultural lands in the National Forests, suitability for the production of special crops, compensation under Federal purchase, and adjustment of tax rates.

For agricultural uses.—The Homestead Act of 1862 provided for homestead tracts of 160 acres each. Later, in portions of the semiarid West, Congress provided for homesteads of 320 and 640 acres, depending on the character of the land. The U. S. Department of the Interior, charged with the administration of the public domain, asked the coöperation of the U. S. Department of Agriculture in determining the applicability of the homestead laws in these areas and the Bureau of Soils and the Bureau of Plant Industry collaborated in the work, the former determining soil characteristics while the latter worked out both the probable productivity as indicated by the native vegetation and the type of farm management likely to be most successful.

In the administration of the national forests, the law provides that any portions of the areas better suited to agriculture than to forestry or watershed protection shall be segregated and opened for agricultural entry. Resultant decisions necessitate frequent cooperation of the Forest Service and the Bureau of Soils with the General Land Office of the Department of the Interior. In all this work the Geological Survey of the latter Department also coöperates in determining possible mineral deposits. There is coöperation also between the two Bureaus of the Department of Agriculture in regard to the relation of soil type to forest growth. The division of soils of the Minnesota Agricultural Experiment Station recently coöperated with the Forest Service in a study of the soils under aspen-birch stands with reference to conversion to more valuable forest species (4).

In California an extensive study of the relation of soil types to the destructive *Phylloxera* infestation of grape vines was made. The coöperation included the U. S. Bureau of Entomology, the Bureau of Soils, the State department of agriculture, and the horticultural commissioners of Fresno and Tulare Counties (86).

Determination of the suitability of an area for the production of crops, particularly certain special crops, is one of the services rendered frequently by the Soil Survey to other agencies. The Bureau of Indian Affairs of the Department of the Interior often asks assistance in determining the probable agricultural value of lands on the Indian Reservations, especially in relation to proposed irrigation projects. On the recent transfer of the Virgin Islands from the jurisdiction of the Navy Department to that of the Department of the Interior, the Office of Experiment Stations of the Department of Agriculture, which has charge of agricultural experimentation in the insular possessions, asked the Bureau of Chemistry and Soils for a soil survey in order to aid in determining possible agricultural readjustments, and a man was detailed for the purpose (125—1931 :41). Very recently, also, a soil survey has been made of the Yorktown National Monument for the National Park Service, and of the farm of the National Training School for Boys, near Washington, D. C., for the District of Columbia. Twenty-five years ago, the city authorities of Chicago received assistance in a soil survey of areas within one hundred miles of Chicago, with reference to the production of vegetables, berries, and other perishables. Soon after the Philippine Islands came under control of the United States, the War Department asked assistance of the Department of Agriculture in making a soil survey.

In 1923, the Department of Commerce asked the Department of Agriculture to coöperate in a study of certain soils in Central America, South America, the East Indies, the Federated Malay States, and India as part of an investigation of possible rubber production, and this study was continued during the two years following. Coöperation with the National Geographic Society enabled a study of cotton soils in Brazil and of wheat soils in Argentina at about the same time. Coöperation with the Tropical Plant Foundation gave similar opportunity for a study of sugar soils in Cuba. Just previous to the studies in tropical areas, the Bureau had sent a specialist to Europe to study and collect samples of the most important soils of that continent. These experiences abroad added to the ability of the Federal investigators to interpret soil conditions at home.

For purposes of valuation and taxation.—During the World War it was necessary for the War Department to acquire various areas for use as camp sites and for other special purposes. The terms of purchase could not always be adjusted easily, and the services of the Soil Survey of the U. S. Bureau of Soils were utilized in coöperative determinations of the value of the land taken. In cases of taking the question of proper compensation into the Federal courts, similar expert service was rendered to the Department of Justice. In the case of the camp site near Fort Bragg, California, the Bureau was credited with saving the Federal government some $500,-000 because of the reduced appraisals ordered by the Court after testimony by the Bureau (125—1922 :5).

The Army Engineer Corps of the War Department asked the Bureau for coöperation in making a soil survey to determine the value of the spillway strips required to be purchased by the proposed plan for flood control of the Mississippi River. A special appropriation of the War Department was transferred to the Bureau of Chemistry and Soils in 1930 and 1931 for this purpose.

Some years ago, land appraisers for banks, insurance companies, and other investing organizations asked the Iowa State College of Agriculture and the University of Nebraska to conduct special short courses for such appraisers, and the request was granted. The courses included a field study of soils, in which the U. S. Bureau of Soils coöperated (125—1926 :6).

In North Dakota, the regular coöperative soil survey conducted by the Federal Bureau and the State Agricultural College has just been used as a basis for determining the proper tax rate on agricultural lands. The State and the individual counties work out these details (125—1932:22).

Related to the special-purpose surveys are the mechanical analyses of soil samples made from time to time for many agencies of government, as well as for various colleges and universities. In the U. S. Department of Agriculture, frequent requests for such service come from such Bureaus as Entomology, Plant Industry, Public Roads, and the Forest Service. For the U. S. Geological Survey, the colloidal content of some fifty samples of deep-sea mud was determined, several years ago.

Recently the Division of Soil Investigations, of the Bureau of Chemistry and Soils, in collaboration with the Fertilizer and Fixed-Nitrogen Laboratory of the same Bureau, received the coöperation of the Navy Department in designing, constructing, and installing a supersonic driver and in furnishing other apparatus. The supersonic oscillator was used to determine the effect of high-frequency, high-intensity sound waves on the dispersal of soil materials, with special reference to the isolation of soil colloids (87).

For Study of Alkali and Peat Soils

Some of the earliest activities of the Division of Soils (advanced to Bureau in 1901) of the U. S. Department of Agriculture had to do with the survey and reclamation of alkali soils. At the request of the Federal Department, Professor E. W. Hilgard of the University of California published in its *Yearbook* for 1895 a general discussion of the origin, value, and reclamation of alkali lands (60). In 1906 the Bureau of Soils summarized the knowledge of alkali soils in the United States, with a review of the publications of the various States on the subject (41).

In the summer of 1899, the Division of Soils engaged in a study of the soils of Salt Lake Valley in coöperation with the Utah Agricultural Experiment Station. The results were published by the agencies separately, though more fully by the State, and with joint authorship in each case (49, 50). In the following winter the Division of Soils coöperated with the Arizona Station in a survey of the soils of the Salt River Valley. Both valleys, the Utah and the Arizona, were areas of alkaline soils. In 1901 the Division of Soils began, in coöperation with the Division of Alkali Investigation of the Bureau of Plant Industry, a study of the quantity of alkali which plants will tolerate (68). This collaboration included, also, in 1902, a study of alkali soils in Egypt by a Plant Industry representative from the Division of Seed and Plant Introduction (78).

In 1899, at the very beginning of the field study of soils, it was proposed to coöperate with a group of selected States in the reclamation of alkali lands. In May, 1902, shortly after the survey of the soils of Salt Lake Valley jointly with the Utah Station, the Bureau of Soils began coöperation with the station in the reclamation of the lands of that valley through systematically washing out the alkali with proper applications of irrigation water. The understanding was that the Bureau should have charge of the actual reclamation and that the station should carry out the subsequent growing of experimental crops (58). The experiments were continued for several years, to a successful conclusion (40, 42). Similar work was done later in several other States in coöperation with the owners of such land, but without actual coöperation with State agencies.

Beginning about 1925, the Office of Western Irrigation Agriculture of the U. S. Bureau of Plant Industry put a representative at the Arizona Agricultural Experiment Station to coöperate in a study of the nature of alkali soils and the factors of control of these soils. The coöperation continues and the results have been published in several of the *Technical Bulletins* of that station (17), and elsewhere. The unusual method of indicating the coöperative nature of the investigation and publication should be mentioned. The authors' names appear on the cover and at the top of the title page, but always unaccompanied by their scientific titles which would show their institutional affiliations. No mention of the coöperation has been noted in the foreword by the director, in any footnote from the authors' names, or in the text. The only recognition is on the inside of the front cover, where the names of the station staff are printed. From the name of the Federal representative is dropped a footnote reading "In cooperation with United States Department of Agriculture, Bureau of Plant Industry." This reference the average reader seems hardly likely to see.

More recently the Division of Agricultural Engineering of the U. S. Bureau of Public Roads, jointly with the Utah Agricultural Experiment Station, has made some studies of soil permeability in the course of a larger coöperation in irrigation and the reclamation of alkali lands (56).

Very recently the Bureau of Chemistry and Soils has worked with the Cornell Agricultural Experiment Station in a detailed survey and classification of the peat soils of New York State (125— 1931 :37). At the same time the uses of peat were investigated at the Arlington Experimental Farm in Virginia, near Washington, in coöperation with the Bureau of Plant Industry and the United States Golf Association.

The publications listed in the Literature Cited at the end of this chapter which have been cited in this subsection on Special-Purpose Surveys are Nos. 4, 10, 14, 17, 26, 40, 41, 42, 49, 50, 56, 58, 60, 68, 78, 82, 86, 87, 91, 92, and 125.

5. Soil Erosion and Soil Protection

BECAUSE OF ITS RELATIVE NEWNESS and unquestioned enormous importance, the erosion problem is presented somewhat fully and the coöperative attacks upon it are discussed in the succeeding sections on National Program and Coöperation in California.

THE PROBLEM

People are accustomed to thinking of geologic change in the earth's surface largely as the simple degradation or wearing down of mountain and foothill elevations and the consequent filling of the oceans and other waters bordering the degraded land areas. Little attention was paid to the effects of these destructive processes until increasing floods poured out vast quantities of soil, sand, rock, logs, and other mountain-side debris over the fertile farm and orchard lands and transportation lines in the valleys and plains below, or until rapidly growing gullies had ruined valuable cropping and grazing areas. These experiences, met with frequently in the progress of the national soil survey, led to careful consideration of the effects of this unending geologic process on the soil resources of the nation.

When the scope of the problem was first considered and estimates of the annual effect of the erosion processes were first made, the results were astounding. In 1907, the Federal Bureau of Soils, starting with some calculations made by the Army Engineer Corps about a half century before, estimated that fully 1,000,000,000 tons of soil were being carried out to sea annually by the river systems of the United States (125—1907 :440). One half of the enormous tonnage was credited to the Mississippi River system and the other half to all the other rivers combined. It was estimated also that fully 90 per cent of the tonnage was fertile soil, and that, as the plant-food content must be worth more than one dollar per ton of soil, the financial loss from that one source alone must exceed $1,000,000,000 annually.

Estimates by members of the U. S. Geological Survey, published in 1909, varied from 500,000,000 to 1,000,000,000 tons of soil transported annually to tidewater by the rivers (11). The Bureau of Chemistry and Soils in 1928 estimated that for every ton of material reaching the ocean at least two tons more, or 1,000,000,000 tons in all, were stranded annually somewhere between the point of origin and the mouths of the rivers. They admitted that the amount might be enormously greater. On the basis of the minimum estimates of 1,500,000,000 tons of solid matter moved annually, they estimated that 126,000,000,000 pounds of plant food are lost each year in this soil wastage by erosion, with a consequent annual loss of more than $2,000,000,000 (11). Other estimates place the quantities at double those mentioned. None of these writers appears to have noted that the billion tons of soil stranded en route one year might furnish the half billion tons carried out to sea the next year. This possibility, however, is of relatively small importance in view of the possibility that all the estimates are far short of the actual facts.

As the study of this problem progressed, the realization of the kinds and magnitude of the losses sustained became more and more disturbing. It was soon discovered that there were two somewhat different types of erosion, even on relatively level land. The first, known as gully erosion, was a familiar phenomenon. Drill-row or wheel-track rillways in sloping fields became small water-cut trenches or shoestrings, these grew into gullies or ravines, and these in turn into small canyons. In mountainous areas, the same processes are in operation on an even more obvious scale. Another phase of gully erosion is the undercutting and caving of river banks, through the constant shifting of the currents.

Additional research soon proved that from the surface of almost level land a steady movement of soil likewise was taking place, especially if, or when, that surface was unprotected. This latter type is known as sheet erosion. Some farm lands studied, which had a slope of 3.68 per cent, showed six-year average annual losses of 41.2 tons of surface soil per acre when plowed four inches deep. At this rate a seven-inch layer was being removed every 24 years. The removal of the same surface layer from a similar grass-covered acre would have required 3,547 years.

The ways in which these types of erosion cause injury and loss are much more numerous than was at first suspected. Among these may be named: (*a*) the removal of plant foods, of which it is estimated that 126,000,000,000 pounds, with a fertilizer value of some $2,000,000,000, are removed annually; (*b*) the loss of the friable and fertile surface soil; (*c*) the reduction of acreage through gullying and through the complete removal of surface soil and sometimes of subsoil also; (*d*) the increased difficulty of using machinery on gullied lands; (*e*) the reduction of crop production, including grazing; (*f*) the increase in cost of production per acre and per unit; (*g*) the silting of river channels, with hampering of navigation and increasing expense for levees; (*h*) the filling of reservoirs and ditches; (*i*) the increase of destructive floods; (*j*) the covering of low-lying fertile lands with sand, gravel, rock, and other debris; (*k*) the increased difficulty and expense of impounding water for irrigation and other prposes; and (*l*) the progressive reduction in the value of published soil-survey reports, due to the shifting of some soils and consequent exposure of others.

It must be remembered also that while the geologic processes have been going on since creation, the erosion problem as it affects soil resources is consequent largely to the disturbance of natural conditions by man in his various operations. The amount of precipitation to furnish the soil-carrying water has not increased, and continued degradation slowly reduces present elevations and gradients, thus slowing down the process. On the other hand, the breaking of the prairie sod, the tillage of fields, the cutting or burning of timber from forest-protected slopes, the burning of brush and chaparral areas, the overgrazing and trampling of both desert and forest range by livestock, the destruction of grass cover by rodents whose natural enemies man has reduced, the upheaval of the countryside in placer-mining operations, the ribbon gashes of highway construction, and the lethal effect of smelter smoke and fumes on vegetation, all have combined to expose the surface of both soil and rock more and more rapidly to destructive climatic influences.

Erosion prevention thus becomes a complex operation, requiring activities, either independent or coöperative, by many agencies. Besides the investigation of actual erosion or soil removal, it includes related studies on the transportation of soil, gravel, and boulders, by water; the silting of stream beds, valleys, deltas, and reservoirs; and the closely connected subjects of grazing control, forest management, reforestation of denuded areas, fire prevention in chaparral and forest, precipitation records, and percolation and runoff studies. Discussion of some of these activities belongs properly to the chapter on Forest Resources, and of others to the chapter on Water Resources.

NATIONAL COÖPERATIVE EROSION-PREVENTION PROGRAM

Some forty years ago, at about the time the Federal Division of Soils was established, the U. S. Geological Survey began to call attention to the economic features of soil erosion. Field geologists, accustomed to view land masses and geological processes in large perspective, naturally were the first to note the destructive effects of the erosion processes. In 1901 the U. S. Industrial Commission took cognizance of the problems in its hearings (146). As the national soil survey increased in geographic scope, the extent and character of the destructively eroded areas were increasingly revealed. In 1908 the conference of State governors, meeting at the White House, included the problem in their program (32). The Federal Bureau of Soils published an extensive bulletin on the subject in 1911 (77), and in the same year President Taft discussed conservation of the soil before the National Conservation Congress (109). Other publications followed, with increasing emphasis. In 1910 the Forest Service and the Weather Bureau began joint experiments on factors of streamflow in a forested area, one of the objectives being the determination of erosion effects (8; 9A; 9B). In 1914 the Division of Drainage Investigations in the U. S. Office of Experiment Stations began a study of erosion control through field terracing and gully damming. It seems probable that a comprehensive national program of research would have been formulated shortly had not the outbreak of the World War diverted official attention to other matters.

Wind erosion of soils also received attention. It had long been known that the movement of soil material by the wind was an important and continuing process, both in past geologic time and in recent years. The effects and prevention of wind, or eolian, erosion had been emphasized by many writers, but little research had been applied to the problem. In 1911, a monographic discussion of the subject was published by the U. S. Bureau of Soils (46), with an included bibliography covering ninety pages. During the years 1918 to 1923, the University of Wisconsin and the U. S. Weather Bureau coöperated in a study of the quantity and character of the dustfall at Madison, Wisconsin, resulting from wind erosion of soils elsewhere. Mechanical analyses were made by the Department of Soils and chemical analyses by the Department of Chemistry, while in the most recent dustfall the Department of Plant Pathology made examinations for plant-disease spores in the material (158).

With the close of the war came a period of readjustment. The Federal Division of Soil Survey was engrossed in the double problem of developing a satisfactory basis for soil classification and of enlisting State agricultural experiment stations in support of the evolutionary basis adopted and State coöperation in its application. Various States began to take up the twin problems of soil erosion and water conservation. A few instances will show the trend. While the war was still in progress, the Missouri Experiment Station began critical research on water loss and soil removal from fields under varying conditions of cover and slope. In 1921 the Legislature of California authorized an investigation of acute forest problems, including erosion damage within and without forested areas, and in 1923 a comprehensive report and bibliography was submitted and published (27; 84). Missouri published six-year results in the same year. In 1924 the Division of Agricultural Engineering in the Federal Bureau of Public Roads, comprising the engineering units formerly in the Office of Experiment Stations, began a long-time study of the engineering problems of terracing, in coöperation with the North Carolina Agricultural Experiment Station. In 1926 the Texas Station established extensive studies of erosion and runoff at its Spur Substation in the red lands of western Texas. This station was incorporated later in the series of stations comprising the Federal-State coöperative regional program.

In the meantime the steady progress of the Federal-State soil survey was revealing the enormous inroads on erstwhile agricultural lands which had been made by destructive erosion processes. Many counties were discovered in which 10,000, 20,000, or 30,000 acres had been rendered worthless, and a few counties in which destruction had overtaken as many as 60,000 and even 90,000 acres. The Forest Service and the Weather Bureau, which had been coöperating since 1910 in a study of cover, precipitation, runoff, and erosion at the Wagon-Wheel Gap Experiment Station in Colorado, published in 1921 and 1922 and again in 1928 (8; 9A; 9B); and the Forest Service had made similar studies at other points in the West. The Bureau of Plant Industry, in coöperation with the Arizona Agricultural Experiment Station, had made measurements of the silt carried by the Colorado River (16). The size and significance of the problem was becoming apparent to scientific and commercial groups alike. Then the Bureau of Chemistry and Soils and the Forest Service united in 1928 to present the erosion problem as a national menace (11). Both public and private agencies became aroused to the seriousness of the situation.

Because of the public interest awakened in this problem, the Congress in 1928 made available the sum of $10,000 for a reconnaissance survey of eroding areas throughout the country. The preliminary report showed eighteen separate agricultural areas or regions, characterized by different soil types and climatic conditions, in which destructive erosion was in progress and remedial measures were urgently needed. As a result, the appropriation bill providing funds for the work of the Federal Department of Agriculture for the fiscal year 1930 contained an item of $160,000 to enable an effective attack on the joint problem of erosion prevention and water conservation. The bill was formulated in the winter of 1928–29 and a portion of the fund was made immediately available on the passage of the bill and before the beginning of the fiscal year on July 1, 1929.

As the bill mentioned coöperation with other Federal units, State agencies, counties, commercial organizations, and individuals, the Department immediately created a coöperating committee of five, consisting of one representative each from the Bureau of Chemistry and Soils, the Forest Service, and the Division of Agricultural Engineering in the Bureau of Public Roads, and of the directors of the New Jersey and Texas Agricultural Experiment Stations, representing the land-grant college Association, to develop a program of coöperative research on the problem. The committee met on April 12, 1929, and rendered its first report on April 25. The program provided for the completion of the reconnaissance survey, a study of methods in use for erosion control and moisture conservation, laboratory studies of soil properties in relation to erosion, field and laboratory research on terraces, dams, drains, cultural operations, and all other effective methods of soil and moisture conservation, and, finally, research on vegetative cover and its effect on the two desired objects. The committee recommended that the funds provided in the pending bill be used in conducting research at erosion experiment stations to be established in eight of the eighteen eroding areas of agricultural lands, and at five stations in forest areas, all in coöperation with the State experiment stations and other State and commercial agencies (118: 252–69). A later supplemental report reviewed accomplishments and outlined further research.

In June, 1929, a Southwest Conference on Soil and Water Conservation was held at the Texas Agricultural College. It was a direct outgrowth of the interest aroused by the three-year results of the soil-erosion experiments at the red-lands station at Spur, Texas, and by the Federal-State program, and was sponsored by Texas members of the National Conservation Congress and of the

Federal-State Committee on Erosion. Representatives of the agricultural colleges, other State agencies, and many commercial organizations concerned with agriculture in the eight States of Missouri, Kansas, Colorado, Arkansas, Oklahoma, Louisian, Texas, and New Mexico were invited, as well as members of the Soil Survey and Irrigation Investigations Divisions and the Office of Experiment Stations of the Federal Department of Agriculture, and representatives of the Federal Land Bank system. In the published report it was brought out that in Texas the area terraced had increased from about 1,500,000 acres in 1926, when the Spur Station experiments were begun, to 2,800,000 acres in 1929; also that the Federal Land Bank of Houston employed a soil-conservation expert and wrote into its mortgages certain soil-protection requirements upon its borrowers (66).

The first major appropriation made by Congress for the Federal-State program of soil erosion research was $160,000 for the fiscal year 1930, of which $30,000 was allotted to the Forest Service and $65,000 apiece to the Bureau of Chemistry and Soils and the Division of Agricultural Engineering. For the fiscal year 1931 the total amount was increased to $185,000, with an allotment of $30,000 to the Forest Service and $77,500 to each of the other units. For 1932 a further increase brought the total to $330,000, of which $100,000 went to the Forest Service and $115,000 each to Chemistry and Soils, and Agricultural Engineering, the latter being made an independent Bureau at the beginning of the year. The soil-erosion item also was transferred from the appropriation for the Bureau of Chemistry and Soils to the miscellaneous items of the Secretary of Agriculture. As a result of the economy program, the $230,000 allotted to Soils and Engineering was cut to $200,000, and the other $30,000 impounded as savings (72). For the fiscal year 1933, the total amount appropriated was $289,160, of which $89,160 was allotted to the Forest Service and $100,000 each to the Bureaus of Chemistry and Soils and of Agricultural Engineering. No deduction was made from these amounts.

With the large funds provided, the reconnaissance survey was continued and the establishment of a series of experiment stations for studies on soil erosion and water conservation was begun. The plan of the Federal-State committee was to place a station in each of the eighteen chief eroding agricultural regions and others at strategic points in the forested areas. By 1932 there were eight in operation in agricultural areas, as follows: Guthrie, Oklahoma (the first one established) ; Temple, Texas; Hays, Kansas; Tyler, Texas; Bethany, Missouri; Clarinda, Iowa; Statesville, North Carolina; and Pullman, Washington. In addition, the soil-erosion station established independently in 1926 by the State at the Spur Substation, in Texas, was made a part of the coöperative program. Under the survey in Texas, a reconnaissance erosion survey was made of the drainage area of the Brazos River, in coöperation with the Brazos River Conservation and Reclamation Commission and the Texas Agricultural Experiment Station, the work being completed in 1930 (125—1931:44).

In every case the coöperation of the State agricultural experiment station was obtained, and as a result the land for the soil-erosion experiment stations was made available to the Federal government without cost. It was estimated that the total contributions of the States in rentals, purchases, laboratory facilities, etc., had then amounted to about $84,000. From the Federal end the stations are established, equipped, and conducted jointly by the Bureaus of Chemistry and Soils and Agricultural Engineering, the former being responsible for soil problems and the latter for engineering problems. In the case of the Red Plains Soil-Erosion Experiment Station at Guthrie, Oklahoma, the first one of the series to be established, the Oklahoma Agricultural Experiment Station makes the analyses of rainwater, runoff water, eroded material, and cotton seed (89). By the end of 1932, the establishment of two additional stations was under way, one at La Crosse, Wisconsin, and one near Zanesville, Ohio, the States furnishing the land in both instances.

Already the results of the erosion stations are becoming apparent, although the work is just getting under way. Papers are appearing in technical journals and in the series published by State and Federal agencies. The problem is being attacked from every angle. In Kansas, the State and Federal representatives at the Hays Erosion Station, which is also a State agricultural substation, devised a new type of tillage implement on which a special set of shovels leaves alternating holes and heaps of soil. This condition slows down runoff and increases water absorption. Highly satisfactory results have been obtained from its use (125—1932: 26).

Several Federal agencies are intimately concerned with the problem, while several others are less closely interested. The Bureau of Chemistry and Soils is officially charged with knowledge of soil properties, including erodability, and with responsibility for soil conservation. Recently it has published on the physical and chemical characteristics of the soils from the erosion experiment stations (120A—316). The Bureau of Agricultural Engineering, formerly a Division of the Bureau of Public Roads, is charged with research in terraces and dams through its Division of Structures, with study of terracing and tilling machinery through its Division of Mechanical Equipment, and with field station research through its Division of Drainage and Erosion Control. Its Division of Irrigation Investigations also coöperates largely with the Forest Service in common problems of water conservation in relation to erosion prevention. The Forest Service holds responsibility for the protection of watersheds, water supplies, and water-carrying structures from the effects of erosion, including erosion caused by overgrazing on watershed lands. The Weather Bureau is interested from the standpoint of precipitation and wind as erosion causes. All these agencies are in the Department of Agriculture. In the Department of the Interior, the Bureau of Reclamation, the Office of Indian Affairs, and the National Park Service all have responsibilities for the protection of the land areas under their charge, and also for water conservation, while the Geological Survey has interest both in land classification and in water supply. The various land-mortgage agencies of the new Farm Credit Administration are interested from the standpoint of land protection as a basis of mortgage security.

Within the several States, several different agencies, likewise, are concerned with the erosion problem. Chief of these is the State college of agriculture with its agricultural experiment station, in which the soils, forestry, agricultural engineering, and irrigation units will be chiefly concerned. Other State agencies will be those that contain the State forester and the State engineer, where these are separate from the experiment station. Many counties, numerous conservation and irrigation districts, and some municipalities have a direct interest in this problem, and several coöperate in the activities discussed.

The publications listed in the Literature Cited at the end of this chapter which are cited in this subsection on National Erosion-Prevention Program are Nos. 8, 9A, 9B, 11, 16, 27, 32, 46, 66, 72, 77, 84, 89, 109, 118, 120A, 125, 146, and 158.

COÖPERATION IN EROSION PREVENTION IN CALIFORNIA

It is desirable to list the various official agencies coöperating in the study of erosion problems in California, to present briefly the history of the development of their relationships, and to explain those relations in the problems and projects on which the agencies are engaged in common.

Agencies and Joint Committees

The principal Federal agencies are the Forest Service and the Bureau of Agricultural Engineering, both in the U. S. Department of Agriculture. The most important State agencies are the University of California and the State Departments of Natural Resources and of Public Works. In addition, both counties and municipalities take official part in the program.

The Forest Service formerly took part through its Branch of Grazing or Branch of Operations, but now coöperates with other agencies almost entirely through its California Forest Experiment Station which, in spite of its name, is wholly a Federal organization. This experiment station is one of several, geographically distributed, and the only one bearing the name of a single State. By invitation of the College of Agriculture of the University of California it occupies a suite of twenty-six rooms in the new Giannini Hall (A. D. 1930) on the University campus. The forest station is furnished with free light, heat, water, and janitor service by the University. The station estimates that it would cost at least $3,000 per annum to obtain similar adequate quarters elsewhere. It has been granted also the free use of laboratories in certain divisions of the College of Agriculture, such as the laboratory of soil technology. In addition, the University of California furnishes to the forest experiment station plots of land in Strawberry

Canyon and on the Oxford Street tract, and has provided certain equipment used in the experiments. This will be discussed more fully in presentation of the research projects.

The Bureau of Agricultural Engineering is represented chiefly by its Division of Irrigation, which has its national as well as its western headquarters in the post office building in Berkeley, only a few blocks from the University of California. Both Federal agencies and this State agency, therefore, are very near each other. The Division is interested in the erosion problem primarily from the standpoint of water conservation, but in all the West these two problems are inseparably linked.

The most important State agency is the University of California, through its College of Agriculture, of which the California Agricultural Experiment Station is a part. The College divisions of soil technology, forestry, and irrigation investigations and practice all are officially concerned in the joint conservation of soils and water. In the State Department of Natural Resources, the division of forestry, of which the State forester is executive officer, has a large interest in the problem. In the State Department of Public Works the division of water resources, of which the State engineer is chief, is concerned with soil erosion from the standpoint of water supplies. These two State departments are at Sacramento, the capital.

Local governments which are taking part in the program of erosion prevention are those of Los Angeles, Orange, San Bernardino, San Diego, and Santa Barbara Counties, and the municipalities of San Bernardino and Santa Barbara.

For the planning and coördination of the programs in forest research, including erosion studies, there are two coöperative coordinating committees in California. One is the Regional Committee for Region 5 of the Forest Service, this region comprising California and a small part of southwestern Nevada. In the personnel of this committee are Professor Walter Mulford, head of the division of forestry in the California Agricultural Experiment Station, and Dr. A. W. Sampson, plant ecologist of this division. For the California Forest Experiment Station of the U. S. Forest Service, the Secretary of Agriculture appoints an advisory council, of which the President of the University of California and the head of its division of forestry are members. The University, on the other hand, gives to Director E. I. Kotok of the California (U. S.) Forest Experiment Station an appointment as consulting forester in the Agricultural Experiment Station.

History of Erosion Activities and Relationships

The Forest Service of the U. S. Department of Agriculture has been interested in the subject of soil erosion in the national forests for more than twenty-five years. In 1909, some observations were made on the effect of sheep-grazing on erosion. In 1910, these observations were continued, and meteorological stations were established in the Cleveland, Angeles, and Santa Barbara National Forests, others being established later. Apparently various observations were continued irregularly from 1912 to 1919, but no definite research projects on erosion were under way. In the latter year, mention was made of the effect of chaparral cover on soil erosion.

In 1920, separate studies of erosion were made on the Angeles, California, and Shasta forests, and a direct relation established between lack of cover and the amount of soil eroded from slopes. In 1921, coöperation was first established with the State Board of Forestry, and erosion and stream-flow studies were begun thereunder by E. N. Munns, then of the Forest Service. Plans for erosion control on the smelter-damaged area at Kennett also were made.

In response to a joint resolution of the California Legislature, in 1921, a very comprehensive survey was made of the influence of forest and brushland treatment on erosion and stream flow. Mr. Munns left the Forest Service to carry on this survey for the State, but there is no indication of any active coöperation in the survey. The treatments affecting erosion included the results of hydraulic mining, smelter fumes, overgrazing, burning, and lumbering. The results were published in 1923 by the State Board of Forestry (84). No further work appears to have been done before 1927. In the meantime, the division of forestry at the California Agricultural Experiment Station began, in 1922, its observations and studies on the relation of cover type to runoff and erosion, and the converse relation of erosion to plant succession.

In 1925, the California State Board of Forestry recommended

and the State legislature made available an appropriation of $15,-
000 to the State forester for coöperation with the U. S. Forest
Service in research in California forest problems. The regional
investigative committee of the Forest Service stated that the outstanding forest problems of the State were the relation of forest
and brush cover to water, in southern California, including both
stream flow and erosion. The committee felt, however, that unless
$50,000 a year were available, no attack should be attempted on
this comprehensive problem. Owing to failure of the Federal Congress to appropriate funds at that time for the establishment of a
forest experiment station in California, the Forest Service was not
able to begin the work, and the State bill, therefore, was vetoed
by the Governor.

In 1926, the California (U. S.) Forest Experiment Station was
established by the Forest Service. In 1927 the California Legislature again appropriated $15,000 to the State forester for use dur-
ing the ensuing biennium in research coöperative with the Federal
forest station. Some objection was made by the University to the
appropriation of State funds for forest research to the State forester rather than to the division of forestry at the Agricultural Experiment Station. In the autumn of 1927 the "forest influence"
project was initiated by the California (U. S.) Forest Experiment
Station, through the establishment of two studies in erosion and
runoff, under the project title "Relation of Brush Cover to Stream
Flow and Erosion." In 1928, the project was enlarged to cover all
forest influences, under the name, "Influence of Vegetation and
Soil Profile on the Water Cycle and Erosion." The plan of attack
also was changed in an attempt to isolate variables under experimental control, then to trace their operation from effects in instruments to the immediate complexes of plots of ground, and finally
into the larger complexes of watersheds.

In the spring of 1929 the Legislature of California increased the
biennial appropriation for coöperative forest investigations to
$25,000, and again made it available through the State forester.
At that time, Professor Mulford, head of the division of forestry
in the experiment station, was a member of the State Board of
Forestry, and therefore not in a position to object to a State appropriation to the State forester, instead of to the University

forestry agencies. In August of 1929, a joint conference redefined the objectives of this research, and reoutlined the methods to be employed. The four projects finally recognized were:

1. Water-cycle and erosion studies, by tank experimentation.
2. Surface runoff and erosion studies, by plot experimentation.
3. Watershed studies, by general surveys and on specific watersheds, including duplicate or paired watersheds.
4. Water-soil-plant relations, studied by various experimental methods, including laboratory and field installations.

In 1931, the State appropriation of $25,000 for the biennium was renewed, but was made to the University of California instead of to the State forester. Under agreement with the University, $23,500 of this amount is allotted to the California (U. S.) Forest Experiment Station, and $1,500 to the California office of the Division of Forest Insects, of the U. S. Bureau of Entomology.

In addition to these quarters, services, equipment, and funds made available from State sources, appropriations, or their equivalent in personnel and field expenses, have been made available for Federal coöperation by certain counties and municipalities in the southern part of the State. These funds were provided primarily for water-conservation studies; but, as pointed out, it is impossible to separate completely the water-runoff and soil-erosion experimentation, and a portion of these contributions therefore must be regarded as applying to erosion studies.

Coöperative Research on Erosion Prevention

It will be remembered that in 1929 the program of coöperative research was reviewed by a joint committee and redrafted to include tank experimentation under controlled conditions, plot experiments, and watershed studies, with a fourth project on the interrelations of soil, water, and plant. Some coöperative work is being done in all these fields. Under Federal and State appropriations, as noted above, the principal agencies now operating are the U. S. Forest Service through its California Forest Experiment Station, and the division of forestry at the California (State) Agricultural Experiment Station. Other agencies, as noted, are the U. S. Bureau of Agricultural Engineering, the State forester, the State engineer, the divisions of soil technology and irrigation investigations at the

California Station, and various counties and cities of southern California.

Experiments in tanks under controlled conditions.—These experiments are conducted in three series of soil tanks, installed on the Oxford Street Tract belonging to the University of California, just northwest of the University campus. They are designed to permit the application of water to the contained soils in a form imitating rains, the durations and intensities of which are subject to accurate control. Studies are made on the effects of natural rainfall, also. The tanks are equipped with apparatus for determining the rate and amount of runoff and percolation, and the rate and amount of erosion of the soil. The experiments are coöperative between the California (U. S.) Forest Experiment Station and the division of forestry in the State agricultural experiment station, though the resulting papers do not always mention the fact.

The first series of eight tanks was installed by the University of California division of forestry, in the autumn of 1927, at a cost of $1000. They originally contained two types of mountain soil (Aiken and Holland) and one type (Altamont) from the Berkeley hills, and are used to compare the effects of water on soil covered with forest litter, as compared with soil from which the protective litter has been burned. The second series, consisting of five tanks, all having the same Altamont soil, was installed by the University of California in 1928, at a cost of $1200, and is used to obtain the same experimental data from soil unprotected, soil protected by litter, and soil protected by each of two grasses, *Hordeum murinum* and *Bromus hordeaceus*.

The third series of these tanks, five in number, was supplied by the Forest Service in 1929, at a cost of $1200. This series was installed in coöperation with the minor-roads section of the Branch of Operations of the Forest Service, to obtain data needed in road and trail construction in the national forests. These tanks are adjacent to the other series, and originally were filled with the same soil (Altamont) as series 2. They are used to determine the effect of gradient of bare soil on surface runoff and erosion. The change of gradient is accomplished by tilting the tanks to slopes varying from 5 to 20 per cent. The soil now being tested is the Aiken, from near Placerville, derived from serpentine rocks.

Plot experiments on runoff, percolation, and erosion.—In the following discussion it is to be understood, unless otherwise stated, that the experiments were installed by the California (U.S.) Forest Experiment Station of the U. S. Forest Service with the funds noted above as provided by both Federal and State appropriations. A part of southern California comprises one of the eighteen destructively eroding areas for which the establishment of an erosion-experiment station was recommended by the Federal-State Committee appointed by the U. S. Department of Agriculture. This area has not yet been reached in that program. However, the problems in this area had become so acute several years ago that Federal and State forest agencies united to attempt their solution. Here also the problems of soil erosion and water conservation are inseparably linked.

In 1927, the forest experiment station equipped two pairs of runoff plots (Barranca Installation) at an elevation of 3000 feet in Devil Canyon, San Bernardino County, in southern California. Records began in 1928. Each plot has an area of 1000 square feet. The plots were equipped with automatic measuring devices for runoff water, percolated water, and the sediment carried off as a result of erosion. The purpose was to determine percolation, runoff, and erosion from a mountain soil, in the one case covered with chaparral and, in the other, burned clean. The vegetation was allowed to return rapidly on the burned plots, annuals becoming most conspicuous in the first year, and perennials developing in the second year. The cost of installation was $4500. The work was done in local coöperation with the county and city of San Bernardino. A multiple electric-contact recorder has been installed since, to synchronize the records from the two pairs of plots. There was coöperation also with the division of irrigation engineering in the State Experiment Station, which constructed a dam at a cost of $2500. Another similar installation (Panorama) was made in the same canyon in 1928, and equipped with a multiple recorder in 1929.

In 1929, a similar series of experiments was installed at North Fork, in the foothills of the Sierra, in the transition zone between the foothill chaparral and the western yellow pine. The plots were $\frac{1}{40}$th acre in extent, being 10 feet wide and approximately 115 feet long, on a 26–per-cent slope. The cost of installation was $1500.

Here again the chaparral was burned from some plots, and allowed to remain on others. A third pair of plots was added in September, 1930, making a standard installation of this type. One pair of burned plots will be allowed to return to equilibrium through the natural succession of vegetation, and one burned pair will be maintained in a bare condition during the life of the experiment. No local coöperation in this experiment is recorded.

In February, 1930, the Federal Forest Experiment Station installed a series of plots in the San Dimas Canyon, Los Angeles County, and runoff and erosion records have been obtained for all storms since that time. The slope of the plots is 40 per cent, one of the steepest in the series of experiments. The installation is made possible through the coöperation of a private landowner; the Department of Conservation of the Los Angeles Chamber of Commerce, which supplied funds for equipment; the Los Angeles County Department of Forestry, which furnished labor and supervision in burning slash; the San Dimas Water Company, which furnished attention for the instruments; and the Los Angeles National Forest, labor and supervision for cleaning the ground.

The Forest Experiment Station also laid out and equipped, about 1930, a series of small plots in Strawberry Canyon in the Berkeley hills, on the upper part of the University campus. The equipment consists of large lysimeters, with self-recording apparatus for measuring the water which runs off and that which percolates, together with the amount of soil moved. The total cost of equipment was $5200. The soil type is the Altamont, which is used also in some of the tank experiments on the Oxford Street tract near the lower end of the campus. Some of the plots are brush-covered, some grass-covered, and some burned bare. Only natural precipitation is employed in this series of experiments. Although the Federal Forest Experiment Station is quartered in University buildings and the plots are on University land, the experiments are not considered coöperative.

The division of forestry in the State Agricultural Experiment Station also is conducting plot studies in Strawberry Canyon, although in a different part. Three series of grass-covered plots, each plot $\frac{1}{40}$th of an acre in size, were located in 1931 on a slope of 38 per cent; on the Olympic soil series, a type very closely related to the Altamont, previously mentioned. All the plots are provided with silt traps and with tanks for the collection of runoff water, this installation having been made at a cost of about $1000. After this study of runoff and erosion caused by individual storms of different durations and intensities, a study of the effects of cover and of cover management in preserving the soil profile will be begun. The first series of plots will be planted with native shrubs. The second series will remain in the present grass cover, which will be grazed at different intensities. The third will remain in the present grass cover, without grazing. The study of erosion under these different covers and cover treatments will be continued, and the water requirements of the plants in each cover and cover treatment also will be determined. This study is wholly independent of the similar Federal project nearby.

Field and watershed studies of erosion.—For several years the division of forestry in the California State Agricultural Experiment Station has conducted studies in Mendocino and Humboldt Counties, to determine the effect of different methods of managing chaparral, or brush-forest type, on the erosion of the supporting soil. No instruments are installed, but quadrats and transects are established, and steel pegs driven deeply into the soil serve as a basis for measuring the soil erosion caused by precipitation and by wind. The study has proved that burning the chaparral is destructive wherever the slope is in excess of 20 per cent, regardless of the depth or the fertility of the original top-soil layer. Apparently this work is done independently.

The California (U. S.) Forest Experiment Station, in its project on forest influences, also has begun studies on erosion in selected watersheds. A preliminary erosion survey of the southern part of the San Joaquin Valley has been completed and prepared for publication. In this survey, there has been some informal coöperation with the division of soil technology at the State Agricultural experiment Station. A state-wide survey, especially as to how conditions are affected by grazing, is under way, to determine erosion damages and necessary control measures. Plans are well under way for much more intensive study of selected watersheds, with instrument equipment, and a study of erosion and runoff in paired canyons, one brush-covered and one denuded by burning.

The division of soil technology in the California Station has been conducting experiments in soil erosion and water runoff in the vicinity of Riverside, California, since 1929. The work is done in informal coöperation with the Division of Irrigation, Bureau of Agricultural Engineering, of the U. S. Department of Agriculture. The coöperation is the result of personal agreement between the administrative representatives of the two research units, and is subject to change or termination at any time. There is informal coöperation, also, with the division of orchard management at the California Citrus Experiment Station at Riverside. There are two principal lines of investigation conducted, namely, the measurement of the volume of eroded soil, and the measurement of water runoff.

Determination of soil erosion is made by measuring the volume of silt collected from the runoff water of a 12-acre field after each precipitation and each irrigation, and from the storm-drainage system of the experiment station property. The division of soil technology pays the citrus experiment station for cleaning out the silt accumulations from the division's apparatus at the 12-acre field under its control. The citrus experiment station, through its division of orchard management, furnishes the soil technology division with rainfall records from the station rain recorder, and with the measurements of the quantities of silt collected from the station storm-drainage system, on the station property.

Runoff measurements also are made on the 12-acre field after each precipitation and each irrigation. Similar measurements are made at the storm-drainage system at the lower end of the experiment station property. In each case, the runoff studies are correlated with the precipitation records determined by an automatic or self-recording rain gage belonging to the citrus station. The automatic water-stage recorders used are the property of the California Agricultural Experiment Station, but are operated by representatives of the Federal Bureau, and their records made available to both parties. The Parshall flumes used are the property of the Federal Bureau of Agricultural Engineering.

Neither the California Station division of soil technology nor the Federal Division of Irrigation keeps a representative stationed at Riverside for this investigation, though personnel from both units visit the location from time to time. Both precipitation and irrigation are seasonal, and more or less intermittent, so that permanent and continuous supervision is not required. The Citrus Experiment Station has the resident staff to look after the instruments and their records. This informal coöperation of the three agencies therefore enables obtaining a maximum of results with a minimum of expense.

Interrelations of soil, water, plant.—The division of forestry in the California Agricultural Experiment Station and the California (U. S.) Forest Experiment Station, both on the campus of the University of California at Berkeley, are coöperating in studying the problem of soil erosion also from the standpoint of the relative productivity of top soil, subsoil, and unweathered parent material, and the effect of erosion on plant succession (99). In surface or sheet erosion, the top soil, or horizon A, is the first to go; the subsoil, or horizon B, follows; and eventually the parent material, or horizon C, may be eroded. The producing capacity of these three successive horizons for grazing crops, chiefly grasses, has been determined by pot experiments on the Oxford Street Tract, in Berkeley, using three of the important and extensively distributed soil types of California. Two of these, the Holland and Aiken series, are typical of the Transition life zone in the Sierra Nevada mountains. The third, the Olympic series (closely related to the Altamont), is representative of the Upper Sonoran zone, which is typical of the woodland-savannah type, represented by the Berkeley hills. All three represent important grazing areas in California.

6. SUMMARY OF COÖPERATION

WIDESPREAD COÖPERATION, both informal and formal, exists among Federal units and between Federal and State agencies in soil and fertilizer research. In 1884 Federal and State chemists founded the Association of Official Agricultural Chemists and began their long-continued coöperation in methods of analysis. In 1889 a joint Federal-State committee on uniform fertility experiments was created by the Federal Department and the State stations. Since 1894 coöperation has developed successively and rapidly in the fields of soil fertility, soil survey, and soil-erosion prevention.

SOIL FERTILITY AND SOIL AMENDMENTS

Soil fertility.—The present Division of Soil Fertility Investigations is a unit assigned successively to the Division of Chemistry (1894), and the Bureaus of Soils (1907), Plant Industry (1915),* and Chemistry and Soils (1927). It has received the increasing collaboration of other Federal units and of the State agricultural experiment stations in assembling soil samples for pot tests of fertility; in checking the results of long-established State soil-fertility plots by the rapid wire-basket method; and in testing the relations of sources, materials, combinations, ratios, concentrations, and times and methods of application of fertilizers, and the relations of harmful ingredients, to the quantity and quality of product and the development of disease in many and diverse crops over a period of 35 years or more.

Soil microbiology.—Conducting mostly independent laboratory work, the Division collaborates with other Federal units in studies of special groups of organisms. Coöperation with State experiment stations includes studies of soil bacteria, especially legume inoculants; supplying State institutions, on request, with living type cultures of organisms; and supervising, under law, the State institutions and commercial firms producing crop inoculants. There is minor interstate collaboration.

Fertilizer resources.—In 1911 the Bureau of Soils and the Geological Survey were jointly charged by Congress with a national survey of natural fertilizer resources. There was minor coöperation with State agencies, especially with California in the study of kelps as potash sources. During the World War, Federal agencies, sometimes working with the States, exercised large control over manufacture, distribution, and prices of fertilizers. The Departments of War and Agriculture coöperated intensively in developing processes for the fixation of atmospheric nitrogen and in testing the resulting products. After the War, there was extensive Federal-State coöperation in testing new types of fertilizers. The use of certain potash fertilizers containing boron having injured crops, widespread Federal-State tests were made of boron tolerance by various crops. Eight contiguous States also conducted a remarkable joint attack on the boron problem.

---

* Retransferred to Plant Industry in 1934.

SOIL SURVEY AND CLASSIFICATION

This comprises both the nation-wide detailed and reconnaissance soil surveys and the many special surveys of restricted areas for special purposes. Both include much coöperation.

National soil survey.—The necessity of Federal-State coöperation to insure a single unified system for the whole country was recognized from the start. The Bureau of Soils began survey in 1899, largely in coöperation with State experiment stations, geological surveys, and boards of agriculture, and has so continued. At first, agreements were for individual surveys but since about 1910 a continuing systematic program has been arranged. In practice the State agencies select the areas for survey, both agencies provide personnel, the leadership usually alternating, and expenses for subsistence, travel, supervision, and report are shared fairly equally. The States usually provide laboratory facilities and help with the manuscript. Congress provides for Federal publication of coöperative surveys, though States may publish independently.

Special soil surveys.—These are to locate various institutions and engineering projects; to aid land classification for homestead entry, for valuation and for taxation, and for crop adaptation at home and abroad; and to ascertain areas of alkali and peat soils. There is widespread coöperation between different Federal agencies, between Federal and State agencies, and sometimes between these and district, county, and municipal units.

Uses of soil surveys.—Large numbers of Federal, State, and local official units, as well as commercial agencies, make use of the soil surveys in agricultural education, farm management, farm finance, land classification, plant and insect distribution, crop adaptation, forest extension, disease prevention, drainage, water conservation, irrigation, flood control, highway construction, pipe-line location, and other engineering enterprises.

SOIL EROSION PREVENTION

Federal surveys of areas, losses, and causes of erosion were conducted from 1900 to 1911, mostly in connection with soil survey. Field experimentation, Federal interbureau, Federal-State, independent State, and State-local, increased steadily from 1910 onward. In 1929, after a nation-wide reconnaissance survey of erosion, Congress provided large annual appropriations for erosion investigation and control. A Federal-State Committee on Erosion recommended the establishment of regional erosion stations in the eighteen rapidly eroding agricultural areas, and others in affected forest areas. Already ten have been established in agricultural areas under coöperative control of the Federal Bureaus of Chemistry and Soils and Agricultural Engineering and the respective State agricultural experiment stations, which have contributed the land and some equipment and services, with help from commercial bodies. On forest lands the U. S. Forest Service and Bureau of Agricultural Engineering, in coöperation with the Weather Bureau and other Federal units, State forest and soil agencies, county and city authorities, and commercial organizations, are expanding activities in erosion control. California is especially prominent in this movement because of the large areas of forest and chaparral involved.

7. Literature Cited

1. Agnew, Mary A. Workers in subjects pertaining to agriculture in State agricultural colleges and experiment stations. U. S. Dept. Agric., Misc. Publ. 154:1–133, 1933.

2. Allison, F. E., J. M. Braham, and J. E. McMurtrey, Jr. Field experiments with atmospheric-nitrogen fertilizers. U. S. Dept. Agric., Dept. Bul. 1180:1–44, pls. 1–14, 1924.

3. Allison, F. E., E. B. Vliet, J. J. Skinner, and F. R. Reid. Greenhouse experiments with atmospheric nitrogen fertilizers and related compounds. Jour. Agric. Research 28:971–76, pl. 1, 1924.

4. Alway, F. J., and Joseph Kittredge, Jr. The forest floor under stands of aspen and paper birch. Soil Science 35:307–12, 1933.

5. Association of Official Agricultural Chemists. Proceedings of the ———— Annual Convention of the Association of Official Agricultural Chemists. [These Proceedings of the Second to the Twenty-ninth Annual Conventions were published in] U. S. Dept. Agric., (Division and) Bur. Chemistry, Buls. 7, 12, 16, 19, 24, 28, 31, 35, 38, 43, 47, 49, 51, 56, 57, 62, 67, 73, 81, 90, 99, 105, 116, 122, 132, 137, 152, and 162. 1885–1912.
   The first four of these had different titles and the next two had subtitles of the same sort.

6. Balch, David M. On the chemistry of certain algae of the Pacific Coast. Jour. Indus. and Engin. Chem. 1(12):777–87, December, 1909.

7. Barnette, R. M., and J. B. Hester. Influence of inorganic nitrogen compounds on reaction and replaceable bases of Norfolk sand. Soil Science 30:431–37, 1930.

8. Bates, Carlos G. First results in the stream-flow experiment, Wagon Wheel Gap, Colorado. Jour. Forestry 19:402–08, 1921.

9A. Bates, Carlos G., and A. J. Henry. Streamflow experiment at Wagon Wheel Gap, Colorado. Preliminary report on termination of first stage of experiment. Mo. Weather Rev. Suppl. 17:1–55, figs. 1–41 (incl. 2 maps and 9 half-tones), front., 1922.

9B. Bates, Carlos G., and A. J. Henry. Forest and stream-flow experiment at Wagon Wheel Gap, Colorado. Final report, on completion of the second phase of the experiment. Mo. Weather Rev. Suppl. 30:1–79, figs. 1–43 (incl. 4 maps and 20 half-tones), front., 1928.

10. Beckett, S. H. The use of highly viscous fluids in the determination of volume-weight of soils. Soil Science 25:481–83, 1928.

11. Bennett, H(ugh) H., and Chapline, W. R. Soil erosion a national menace. Part. 1. Some aspects of the wastage caused by soil erosion, by H. H. Bennett, pp. 1–22. Part 2. Soil erosion on western grazing lands, by W. R. Chapline, pp. 24–35. U. S. Dept. Agric., Circ. 33:1–36, April, 1928.

12. Bennett, Hugh H., and M. A. Crosby. Soils of the prairie regions of Alabama and Mississippi and their use for alfalfa. Part I. Houston clay and associated soils, by Hugh H. Bennett, pp. 5–31. Part II. Alfalfa on the Houston clay: its culture and management, by M. A. Crosby, pp. 32–48. U. S. Dept. Agric., Rept. 96:1–48, figs. 1–4, pls. 1–7, 1911.

13. Blair, A. W., and B. E. Brown. The influence of fertilizers containing borax on the yield of potatoes and corn, season 1920. Soil Science 11:369–83, pls. 1–4, 1920.

14. Blaney, H. F., and C. A. Taylor. Soil sampling with a compressed air unit. Soil Science 31:1–2, pl. 1, 1931.

15. Brandt, R. P. Potash from kelp: early development and growth of the giant kelp, *Macrocystis pyrifera.* (With Introduction by J. W. Turrentine) U. S. Dept. Agric., Dept. Bul. 1191:1–40, figs. 1–16, December, 1923.

16. Breazeale, J. F. A study of the Colorado River silt. Ariz. Agric. Exp. Stat., Tech. Bul. 8:165–85, 1926.

17. Breazeale, J. F., and P. S. Burgess. The reaction between calcium sulphate and sodium carbonate, and its relation to the reclamation of black alkali lands. Ariz. Agric. Exp. Stat., Tech. Bul. 6:125–39, 1926.

18. Briggs, Lyman J., C. A. Jensen, and J. W. McLane. The mulched-basin system of irrigated citrus culture and its bearing on the control of mottle-leaf. U. S. Dept. Agric., Dept. Bul. 499:1–31, pl. 1, February, 1917.

19. Brown, B. E. Effect of borax in fertilizer on the growth and yield of potatoes. U. S. Dept. Agric., Dept. Bul. 998:1–8, fig. 1, pls. 1–4, 1922.

20. Brown, B. E., and F. V. Owen. Concentrated fertilizer for potatoes in Aroostook County. Maine Agric. Exp. Stat., Bul. 350:1–44, figs. 1–7, 1929.

21. Brown, B. E., and F. V. Owen and E. R. Tobey. Sources of nitrogen for potato fertilizers in Aroostook County. Maine Agric. Exp. Stat., Bul. 354:1–38, figs. 1–9, 1930.

22. Brown, Frederick W. Importance of developing our natural resources of potash. U. S. Dept. Agric., Yearbook 1916 (Sep. 717):301–10, pl. 67, 1917.

23. Burd, John S. The economic value of Pacific Coast kelps. Calif. Agric. Exp. Stat., Bul. 248:181–215, 3 unnumbered figs., February, 1915.

24. Caffey, Francis G. A brief statutory history of the United States Department of Agriculture. 26 p. October 23, 1916. [Reprinted from *Case and Comment* 22(9–10):723–33, 850–56; February and March, 1916]

25. California Department of Agriculture. Agricultural statutes of the State of California. Part Four, Chemistry, corrected to June 30, 1931. (Sacramento: State Printing Office, 1932), 27 p., 12mo.

This publication consists of ten parts, by subjects, separately paged and issued, but also issued as a single bound volume.

26. California Department of Public Works. Division of Highways. Biennial Report of California Highway Commission, 1921/22–1931/32. (Sacramento: State Printing Office, 1922–32)

27. California State Board of Forestry. Report to the Legislature on Senate Concurrent Resolution No. 27 (Legislature of 1921) by the California State Board of Forestry. (Sacramento: State Printing Office, 1923), 165 p., 44 figs., 3 maps. (Bibliography of soil erosion, pp. 123–24) (See Entry No. 84.)

28. Cameron, Frank K. Possible sources of potash in the United States. U. S. Dept. Agric., Yearbook 1912 (Sep. 611):523–36, 1913.

29. Cameron, Frank K., *et al.* A preliminary report on the fertilizer resources of the United States. (With Appendices A–T.) U. S. Cong., 62d, 2d sess., Doc. 190:9–290, figs. 1–3, pls. 1–19, maps 0–18. [Maps and plates grouped at end of Document.] (Washington: Government Printing Office, 1912) (Report by Cameron, pp. 9–48; Appendices A–T, pp. 49–290.) (See Entry Nos. 38, 76, 97, and 113.)

30. Cameron, Frank K., et al. Potash from kelp. U. S. Dept. Agric., Rept. 100:1–122, figs. 1–2, pls. 1–40 (following p. 122). Maps in portfolio. April 10, 1915.

31. Carpenter, E. J., and Cosby, Stanley W. Soil Survey of the Salinas area, California. U. S. Dept. Agric., Bur. Chem. and Soils, Series 1925, No. 11:1–80. Map. 1929.

32. Chamberlin, Thomas Chrowder. Soil wastage. *In* U. S. Congress, 60th, Second Session, House Doc. 1425:75–83, 1909.

Proceedings of the Conference of Governors on the Conservation of Natural Resources, held in the White House, Washington, D. C., May 13–15, 1908.

33. Colby, George E., *et al.* Commercial Fertilizers [1922]. Calif. Dept. Agric., Special Publ. 35:1–36, 1923. (Contribution from Bureau of Chemistry.)

34. Cook, F. C. Boron: Its absorption and distribution in plants and its effect on growth. Jour. Agric. Research 5:877–90, 1916.

35. Cook, F. C., R. H. Hutchison, and F. M. Scales. Experiments on the destruction of fly larvae in horse manure. U. S. Dept. Agric., Dept. Bul. 118:1–26, pls. 1–4, 1914.

36. Cook, F. C., and J. B. Wilson. Effect of three annual applications of boron on wheat. Jour. Agric. Research 10:591–97, 1917.

37. Cook, F. C., and J. B. Wilson. Boron: Its effects on crops and its distribution in plants and soil in different parts of the United States. Jour. Agric. Research 13:451–70, 1918.

38. Crandall, W. C. Appendix N. The kelps of the southern California coast. U. S. Cong., 62d, 2d sess., S. Doc. 190:209–13. Maps 9–18 [in the back of the volume]. 1912. (See Entry No. 29.)

39. Dore, W. H. Commercial Fertilizers, 1919–20. Calif. Agric. Exp. Stat., Bul. 327:93–127. [1921]

40. Dorsey, Clarence W. Reclamation of alkali soils. U. S. Dept. Agric., Bur. Soils, Bul. 34:1–30, pls. 1–4, 1906.

41. Dorsey, Clarence W. Alkali soils of the United States: A review of literature and summary of present information. U. S. Dept. Agric., Bur. Soils, Bul. 35:1–196, figs. 1–13, 1906.

42. Dorsey, Clarence W. Reclamation of alkali land in Salt Lake Valley, Utah. U. S. Dept. Agric., Bur. Soils, Bul. 43:1–28, pl. 1, figs. 1–2, 1907.

43. Eisenhower, M. S., and A. P. Chew. The United States Department of Agriculture: its growth, structure, and functions. U. S. Dept. Agric., Misc. Publ. No. 88:i–iv, 1–147, 21 charts (unnumbered). September 1, 1930.
This publication was prepared "with the assistance of officials in all the Bureaus and Offices of the Department."

44. Ellett, W. B., and W. G. Harris. Coöperative experiments for the composting of phosphate rock and sulfur. Soil Science 10:315–25, 1920.

45. Ewell, Ervin E. The fertilizing value of street sweepings. An investigation made under the direction of H. W. Wiley, Chief Chemist. U. S. Dept. Agric., Div. Chem., Bul. 55:1–19, 1898.

46. Free, E. E. The movement of soil material by the wind, with a bibliography of eolian geology by S. C. Stuntz and E. E. Free. U. S. Dept. Agric., Bur. Soils, Bul. 68:1–272, pls. 1–5, figs. 1–2, 1911. (Bibliography, pp. 174–263)

47. Free, E. E. Report of a reconnoissance of the Lyon nitrate prospect near Queen, N. Mex. U. S. Dept. Agric., Bur. Soils, Circ. 62:1–6, figs. 1–5, 1912.

48. Gardner, Frank D. Fertility of soils as affected by manures. U. S. Dept. Agric., Bur. Soils, Bul. 48:1–59, figs. 1–5, 1908.

49. Gardner, Frank D., and John Stewart. The soils of the Salt Lake Valley, Utah. U. S. Dept. Agric., Div. Soils, Circ. 4:1–11, fig. 1, 1900.

50. Gardner, Frank D., and John Stewart. A soil survey of Salt Lake Valley, Utah. Utah Agric. Exp. Stat., Bul. 72:77–114, figs. 6–10, pls. 10–20, 4 maps (col.), 1900.

51. Gates, Otis H. [compiler]. Sections 10, 128, and 450, pp. 6, 52–53, and 241, *in* Laws applicable to the United States Department of Agriculture, 1923. iv, 897 p. (Washington: Government Printing Office, 1924)

52. Gillespie, Louis J., and Lewis A. Hurst. Hydrogen-ion concentration—soil type—common potato scab. Soil Science 6:219–36, figs. 1–3, 1918.

53. Goldenweiser, E. A. A survey of the fertilizer industry. U. S. Dept. Agric., Dept. Bul. 798:1–29, fig. 1, pl. 1 (map), October, 1919.

54A. Greathouse, Charles H. [compiler]. Historical sketch of the U. S. Department of Agriculture: its objects and present organization. U. S. Dept. Agric., Div. of Publ., Bul. 3:1–74, front. and 2 pls., 9 unnumbered figs. (halftones), 1898; rev. ed., same paging, 1898. (Soils Division, p. 38.)

54B. Greathouse, Charles H. [compiler]. Historical sketch of the U. S. Department of Agriculture: its objects and present organization. U. S. Dept. Agric., Div. of Publ., Bul. 3, 2d rev. ed. 1–97, front. and 2 pls., 9 unnumbered figs. (half-tones), 1907. (Bureau of Soils, p. 51)

55. Handy, R. B., and Minna A. Cannon. List by titles of publications of the United States Department of Agriculture from 1840 to June, 1901, inclusive. U. S. Dept. Agric., Div. Publ., Bul. 6:1–216, 1902. (Division of Soils, pp. 169–72)

56. Harris, A. Evan. Effects of replaceable sodium on soil permeability. Soil Science 32:435–46, figs. 1–3, 1931.

57. Hays, W. M. Report on statements of Dr. Cyril G. Hopkins relative to Bureau of Soils. U. S. Dept. Agric., Off. Secy., Circ. 22:1–12, 1907.

58. Heileman, W. H. Reclamation of alkali land near Salt Lake City, Utah. U. S. Dept. Agric., Bur. Soils, Circ. 12:1–8, fig. 1, 1904.

59. Hilgard, E. W. The agriculture and soils of California. U. S. Dept. Agric., Rept. Commr. 1878:477–507, 1878.

60. Hilgard, E. W. Origin, value, and reclamation of alkali lands. U. S. Dept. Agric., Yearbook 1895 (Sep. 35, pt. 2):103–22, figs. 3–7, pl. 2, 1896.

61. Hoagland, D. R. Organic constituents of Pacific Coast kelps. Jour. Agric. Research 4:39–58, April 15, 1914.

62. Hopkins, Cyril G. The duty of chemistry to agriculture. Ill. Agric. Exp. Stat., Circ. 105:1–27, 1906.

63. Houghland, G. V. C., and J. A. Schricker. The effect of potash on starch in potatoes. Jour. Amer. Soc. Agron. 25:334–40, 1933.

64. Hunt, Mabel G. List of publications of the United States Department of Agriculture from January, 1901, to December, 1925, inclusive (compiled by comparison with the originals). U. S. Dept. Agric., Misc. Publ. 9:i–vi, 1–182, 1927. (Bureau of Soils, pp. 144–63.)
"Supplementary to Bulletin No. 6, Division of Publications, issued in 1902, but duplicating that list for months of January-June, 1901."

65. Hunt, Mabel G. List of publications of the United States Department of Agriculture from January, 1926, to December, 1930, inclusive, compiled by comparison with the originals. U. S. Dept. Agric., Misc. Pub. 153:1–46, 1932. (Bureau of Soils, pp. 37–46.)

66. Jackson, A. D. [secretary]. Report of proceedings of the first session of the Southwest Conference on soil and water conservation, held at the Agricultural and Mechanical College of Texas, College Station, Texas, June 20 and 21, 1929. 64 p., 1 folded map. College Station, Texas [1929].

67. Karraker, P. E. Notes on the Conference on elementary soil teaching, held at Lexington, Kentucky, June, 1920. Soil Science 10:247, 1920.

68. Kearney, Thomas H., and Frank K. Cameron. Some mutual relations between alkali soils and vegetation. U. S. Dept. Agric., Rept. 71:1–78, 1902.

69. Kelley, W. P., W. H. Dore, and S. M. Brown. The nature of the base-exchange material of bentonite, soils, and zeolites, as revealed by chemical investigation and X-ray analysis. Soil Science 30:25–56, pls. 1–5, 1931.

70. Lee, Daniel. The study of soils. U. S. Dept. Interior, Report of the Commissioner of Patents for the year 1850, Part II, Agriculture, pp. 25–81, 1851.

71. Leonard, Lewis T. A failure of Austrian winter peas apparently due to nodule bacteria. Jour. Amer. Soc. Agron. 22:277–79, 1930.

72. Lipman, J. G. A quarter century progress in soil science. Jour. Amer. Soc. Agron. 25:9–25, 1933.

73. Lipman, C. B., P. S. Burgess, and M. A. Klein. Comparison of the nitrifying powers of some humid and some arid soils. Jour. Agric. Research 7:47–82, 1916.

74. Lipman, C. B., and D. D. Waynick. A detailed study of the effects of climate on important properties of soils. Soil Science 1:5–48, pls. 1–5, 1916.

75. McBeth, I. G. Fixation of ammonia in soils. Jour. Agric. Research 9:141–55, fig. 1, 1917.

76. McFarland, Frank M. Appendix M. The kelps of the central California coast. U. S. Cong.; 62d, 2d sess., S. Doc. 190:194–208. Maps 4–8 [in the back of the volume]. 1912. (See Entry No. 29.)

77. McGee, W J. Soil erosion. U. S. Dept. Agric., Bur. Soils, Bul. 71:1–60, pls. 1–33, figs. 1–3, 1911.

78. Means, Thomas H. Reclamation of alkali lands in Egypt as adapted to similar work in the United States. U. S. Dept. Agric., Bur. Soils, Bul. 21:1–48, pls. 1–8, figs. 1–6, 1903.

79. Mehring, Arnon L., and Glenn A. Cumings. Factors affecting the mechanical application of fertilizers to the soil. U. S. Dept. Agric., Tech. Bul. 182:1–96, pls. 1–18, figs. 1–26, 1930.

80. Mehring, A[rnon] L., and G[lenn] A. Cumings. Effects on cotton of irregular distribution of fertilizers. Jour. Agric. Research 44:559–70, figs. 1–4, 1932.

81. Merritt, Dixon. The United States Department of Agriculture: what it is and how it serves. U. S. Dept. Agric., 47 p., mim., 8½″ × 11″, [about 1920]. (Bureau of Soils, pp. 20–22)

82. Merritt, Dixon. Department of Agriculture in the War. U. S. Dept. Agric., Press Service, 208 p., mim., 8½″ × 11″ [about 1920]. (Bureau of Soils, pp. 104–6)

83. Moss, E. G., J. E. McMurtrey, Jr., W. M. Lunn., and J. M. Carr. Fertilizer tests with flue-cured tobacco. U. S. Dept. Agric., Tech. Bul. 12:1–58, figs. 1–9, pls. 1–3, 1927.

84. Munns, E. N. Erosion and flood problems in California. Pp. 9–165. *In* California State Board of Forestry, Report to the legislature on Senate Concurrent Resolution No. 27 (Legislature of 1921). 165 p., 44 figs., 3 maps. (Sacramento, State Printing Office, 1923) (See Entry No. 27.)

85. Neller, J. R., and W. J. Morse. Effects upon the growth of potatoes, corn, and beans resulting from the addition of borax to the fertilizer used. Soil Science 12:79–131 (incl. pls.), pls. 1–13, 1921.

86. Nougaret, R. L., and Macy H. Lapham. A study of *Phylloxera* infestation in California as related to types of soils. U. S. Dept. Agric., Tech. Bul. 20:1–38, figs. 1–6, February, 1928.

87. Olmstead, L. B. Dispersion of soils by a supersonic method. Jour. Agric. Research 42:841–52, figs. 1–3, 1931.

88. Parker, E. G., and Lindemuth, J. R. Analyses of certain of the Pacific Coast kelps. Jour. Indus. and Engin. Chem. 5(4):287–89, April, 1913.

89. Phillips, S. W. Soil rebuilding at the Red Plains Erosion Station. Jour. Amer. Soc. Agron. 25:346–50, 1933.

90. Robbins, William J., and E. C. Lathrop. The oxidation of vanillin to vanillic acid by certain soil bacteria. Soil Science 7:475–85, fig. 1, 1919.

91. Robertson, Ralph D., and Nelson, J. W. Irrigation and soil conditions in the Sierra Nevada foothills of California. Calif. Agric. Exp. Stat., Bul. 253: 321–74, figs. 1–26, map, May, 1915.

92. Rose, A. C. Field methods used in subgrade surveys by the U. S. Bureau of Public Roads on the Pacific Highway, Washington. Public Roads 6:93–101, 115–16, figs. 1–4, July, 1925.

93. Schreiner, Oswald. Fertilizer in small bulk being tested. U. S. Dept. Agric., Yearbook 1926:355–58, 1927.

94. Schreiner, Oswald, B. E. Brown, J. J. Skinner, and M. Shopavalov. Crop injury by borax in fertilizers. U. S. Dept. Agric., Dept. Circ. 84:1–35, figs. 1–25, February, 1920.

95. Schreiner, Oswald, and Howard S. Reed. Some factors influencing soil fertility. U. S. Dept. Agric., Bur. Soils, Bul. 40:1–40, pls. 1–3, 1907.

96. Scofield, C. S. Effect of farm manure in stimulating the yields of irrigated field crops. Jour. Agric. Research 15:493–503, 1918.

97. Setchell, William Albert. Appendix K. The kelps of the United States and Alaska. U. S. Cong., 62d, 2d sess., S. Doc. 190:130–78, pls. 9–19 [in the back of the volume]. 1912. (See Entry No. 29.)

98. Shaler, Nathaniel Southgate. The origin and nature of soils. U. S. Dept. Interior, Geol. Survey, Ann. Rept. 12 (1890–91):213–345, pls. 2–31, figs. 1–27, 1891.

99. Sinclair, Jesse D., and Arthur W. Sampson. Establishment and succession of vegetation on different soil horizons. Hilgardia 5(7):155–74, figs. 1–9, January, 1931.

100. Skinner, J.J., and F. E. Allison. Influence of fertilizers containing borax on the growth and fruiting of cotton. Jour. Agric. Research 23:433–44, pls. 1–4, 1923.

101. Skinner, J. J., and J. H. Beattie. City street sweepings as a fertilizer. U. S. Dept. Agric., Bur. Soils, Circ. 66:1–8, figs. 1–2, 1912.

102. Skinner, J. J., B. E. Brown, and F. R. Reid. The effect of borax on the growth and yield of crops. U. S. Dept. Agric., Dept. Bul. 1126:1–31, pls. 1–11 (1 col.), 1923.

103. Skinner, J. J., and J. B. Demaree. Relation of soil conditions and orchard management to the rosette of pecan trees. U. S. Dept. Agric., Dept. Bul. 1378:1–16, pls. 1–8, 1926.

104A. Skinner, J. J., and H. B. Mann. Effect of synthetic nitrogen and concentrated fertilizers on cotton and sweet potatoes. N. C. Agric. Exp. Stat., Bul. 266:1–40, figs. 1–6, 1929.

104B. Skinner, J. J., C. B. Williams, and H. B. Mann. Fertilizers for sweet potatoes based on investigations in North Carolina. U. S. Dept. Agric., Tech. Bul. 335:1–46, figs. 1–14, 1932.

105. Skinner, J. J., and C. F. Noll. Botanical composition of a permanent pasture as influenced by fertilizers of different compositions. Soil Science 7: 161–79, figs. 1–4, pls. 1–2 (col.), 1919.

106. Snyder, A. H., and C. L. Cook. Fertility studies on Wooster Soil. Ohio Agric. Exp. Stat., Bul. 167:87–119, October, 1905.

107. Stewart, Guy R. Availability of the nitrogen in Pacific Coast kelps. Jour. Agric. Research 4:21–38, April 15, 1915.

108. Stuntz, Stephen Conrad. Reference list on the electric fixation of atmospheric nitrogen and the use of calcium cyanamid and calcium nitrate on soils. U. S. Dept. Agric., Bur. Soils, Bul. 63:1–89, 1910.

109. Taft, William H. Conservation of the soil. U. S. Dept. Agric., Off. Secy., Circ. 38:1–8, October 10, 1911.
Address before the National Conservation Congress, Kansas City, Missouri, Sept. 5, 1911.

110. Thom, Charles, and James N. Currie. *Aspergillus niger* group. Jour. Agric. Research 7:1–15, 1916.

111. Thorp, James. The effects of vegetation and climate upon soil profiles in northern and northwestern Wyoming. Soil Science 32:283–301, figs. 1–6, pls. 1–2, 1931.

112. True, Rodney H., Otis F. Black, and James W. Kelly. Ash absorption by spinach from concentrated soil solutions. Jour. Agric. Research 16:15–25, figs. 1–2, 1919.

113. Turrentine, J. W. Appendix Q. The technology of the seaweed industry. U. S. Cong., 62d, 2d sess., S. Doc. 190:232–62, 1912. (See Entry No. 29.)

114. Turrentine, J. W. The composition of the Pacific kelps. Jour. Indus. and Engin. Chem. 4(6):431–35, June, 1912.

115. Turrentine, J. W. The occurrence of potassium salts in the salines of the United States, with analyses by Ross, Gardner, Merz, and Cullen. U. S. Dept. Agric., Bur. Soils, Bul. 94:1–96, figs. 1–3, 1913.

116. Turrentine, J. W. Nitrogenous fertilizers obtainable in the United States. U. S. Dept. Agric., Dept. Bul. 37:1–12, 1913.

117. U. S. Congress, House, Committee on Mines and Mining. Hearing on S. 3047, June 3, 1924, authorizing joint investigation of Geological Survey and Bureau of Soils to determine location and extent of potash deposits or occurrence in the United States and improved methods of recovering potash therefrom. 2 pts. 47 p. (Washington: Government Printing Office, 1924)

118. U. S. Congress, Senate. Agricultural appropriation bill for 1932. Hearings before the Subcommittee (on Agriculture) of the Committee on Appropriations, United States Senate, Seventy-first Congress, Third Session on H. R. 15256: Bill making appropriations for the Department of Agriculture for the fiscal year ending June 30, 1932, and for other purposes. 305 p. (Washington: Government Printing Office, 1931) (Soil erosion data, pp. 252–69)

119. U. S. Department of Agriculture. Report of the (Commissioner) Secretary of Agriculture for the year ———. 1862–.

Report of the Commissioner, 1862–88: Report of the Secretary, 1889–. From 1862 to 1920, inclusive, and for 1922 and 1923, the reports of Chiefs of Offices, Divisions, and Bureaus are included with the report of the Secretary in a consecutively paged volume. From 1921 and 1924 to date, all these reports are issued separately each year, with separate paging.

120A. U. S. Department of Agriculture. Technical Bulletins 1–, 1927–.

120B. U. S. Department of Agriculture. List of technical workers in the Department of Agriculture and outline of Department functions, 1931. U. S. Dept. Agric., Misc. Publ. 123:1–165, 1931. (Bureau of Chemistry and Soils, pp. 61–66)

121. U. S. Department of Agriculture. Washed soils: how to prevent and reclaim them. U. S. Dept. Agric., Farmers' Bul. 20:1–22, 1894.

122. U. S. Department of Agriculture. Coöperative laboratory (of Mackay School of Mines, U. S. Bureau of Soils, and U. S. Geological Survey) at Reno, Nev., for the examination of potash-bearing materials. U. S. Dept. Agric. (undesignated publ.), 4 p., 1912.

123. U. S. Department of Agriculture, Office of the Secretary. Method of sale of nitrate of soda to farmers by the United States Government. U. S. Dept. Agric., Off. Secy., Circ., 78:1–11, January, 1918.

124. U. S. Department of Agriculture, Bureau of Plant Industry. Report of the Chief of the Bureau of Plant Industry for ———. 1916–27.

125. U. S. Department of Agriculture, (Division and) Bureau of Soils. Report of the Chief of the (Division) Bureau of Soils for ———. 1894–.

Division of Agricultural Soils, 1894–96; Division of Soils, 1897–1901; Bureau of Soils, 1902–27; Bureau of Chemistry and Soils, 1928–. The report for 1921 was not published, and that for 1928 was mimeographed.

126. U. S. Department of Agriculture, (Division and) Bureau of Soils. Bulletins 1–96, 1895–1913. 8vo.

Bulletins 1–5, 1895–96, were issued by the Division of Agricultural Soils; Nos. 6–18, 1897–1901, by the Division of Soils; the remainder by the Bureau of Soils. On June 30, 1913, all Bureau series of publications were discontinued, and thereafter all appeared in series of the Department as a whole.

127. U. S. Department of Agriculture, (Division and) Bureau of Soils. Circulars 1–7, 1894–1913.

128. U. S. Department of Agriculture, Bureau of Soils. Legal authority for the work of·the Bureau of Soils. 45 p., mim., 8½″ × 11″, U. S. Dept. Agric., Bur. Soils. 1907.

129. U. S. Department of Agriculture, Bureau of Soils. A report on the retail prices of nitrate of soda and acid phosphate as of May 1, 1919. U. S. Dept. Agric., Dept. Circ. 39:1–15, May, 1919.

130. U. S. Department of Agriculture, Bureau of Soils. A report on the retail prices of unmixed fertilizer materials as of June 1, 1919, with comparative prices for May 1. U. S. Dept. Agric., Dept. Circ. 57:1–11, July, 1919.

131. U. S. Department of Agriculture, Fixed Nitrogen Research Laboratory. Annual report of the Fixed Nitrogen Research Laboratory. 1922–26.

The report for 1925 was not published. The report for 1927 is in that of the Bureau of Soils, and those for 1928 to date in the annual reports of the Bureau of Chemistry and Soils.

132. U. S. Department of Agriculture, Office of Experiment Stations. Co-operative field experiments with fertilizers. U. S. Dept. Agric., Off. Exp. Stat., Circ. 7:1–39, March, 1889.

Contains the proceedings of a conference of the representatives of the various stations, held at the U. S. Department of Agriculture on March 5 and 6, 1889.

133. U. S. Department of Agriculture, Office of Experiment Stations. Explanations and directions for soil tests with fertilizers. U. S. Dept. Agric., Off. Exp. Stat., Circ., 8:1–11, March, 1889.

134. U. S. Department of the Interior, Patent Office. Report of the Commissioner of Patents for the year ————. 1839–48; Report . . . Part II, Agriculture. 1849–61.

During the years 1839–48, the Patent Office was in the State Department. For the years 1853–61, the words "Part II" were omitted.

135A. Vanick, J. S., W. W. de Sveshnikoff, and J. G. Thompson. Deterioration of steels in the synthesis of ammonia. U. S. Dept. Commerce, Bur. Standards, Technologic Papers 361:199–233, figs. 1–17, 1927.

135B. Voorhees, Edward B., and Jacob G. Lipman. A review of investigations in soil bacteriology. U. S. Dept. Agric., Off. Exp. Stat. Bul. 194:1–108, 1907.

136A. Waggaman, W. H. A review of the phosphate fields of Idaho, Utah, and Wyoming, with special reference to the thickness and quality of the deposits. U. S. Dept. Agric., Bur. Soils, Bul. 69:1–48, pl. 1 (map), 1910.

136B. Waggaman, W. H., C. R. Wagner, and R. P. Gardiner. Analysis of experimental work with ground raw rock phosphate as a fertilizer. U. S. Dept. Agric., Dept. Bul. 699:1–119, 1918.

137. Walling, William English, and Harry W. Laidler. State Socialism: pro and con. Official documents and other authoritative selections—showing the world-wide replacement of private by governmental industry before and during the war. With a chapter on municipal socialism, by Evans Clark. 649 p. (New York: Henry Holt & Co., 1917) (Soils, pp. 168–72)

138. Walton, George P. Rabbit's-foot oil and organic ammoniate fertilizer. Western Rabbit Magazine 1(8)5–6, 9, 11–14, July, 1926.

139. Weber, Gustavus A. The Bureau of Chemistry and Soils: its history, activities, and organization. Institute for Government Research, Service Monograph 52:i–xi, 1–218 Baltimore. (The Johns Hopkins Press, 1928.)

140. Whitney, Milton. (Assisted by Janette Steuart) Catalogue of the four thousand samples in the soil collection of the Division of Soils. U. S. Dept. Agric., Div. Soils, Bul. 16:1–145, 1899.

141. [Whitney, Milton] Announcement [of organization of the Division of Agricultural Soils.] U. S. Dept. Agric., Weather Bur., Div. Agric. Soils, Circ. 1:1–3, [1894].

142. Whitney, Milton. Division of Soils. U. S. Dept. Agric., Yearbook 1897 (Sep. 119):122–35, 1898.

143. Whitney, Milton, et al. Field operations of the Division of Soils, 1899. U. S. Dept. Agric., Rept. 64:1–198, maps, 1900.

144. Whitney, Milton, et al. Field operations of the (Division) Bureau of Soils, 1900–1922. U. S. Dept. Agric., (Div.) Bur. Soils, Field Operations, 1901–28.

145. Whitney, Milton. Soil investigations in the United States. U. S. Dept. Agric., Yearbook 1899 (Sep. No. 169) :335–46, 1900.

146. Whitney, Milton. Exhaustion and abandonment of soils. U. S. Dept. Agric., Rept. 70:1–48, 1901.

147. Whitney, Milton. The work of the Bureau of Soils. U. S. Dept. Agric., Bur. Soils, Circ. 13:1–13, 1904; rev. ed., 15 p., 1905.

148. Whitney, Milton. Soils of the United States, based upon the work of the Bureau of Soils to January 1, 1908. Part I. Results of recent soil investigations. Part II. Classification of the soils of the United States. U. S. Dept. Agric., Bur. Soils, Bul. 55:1–243, figs. 1–7, pls. 1–2 (maps), 1909. (California soils, pp. 192–205; area surveyed, pp. 208–10)

149. Whitney, Milton. Fertilizers for corn soils. U. S. Dept. Agric., Bur. Soils, Bul. 64:1–31, 1910.

150. Whitney, Milton. Fertilizers for cotton soils. U. S. Dept. Agric., Bur. Soils, Bul. 62:1–24, fig. 1, 1909.

151. Whitney, Milton. Fertilizers on soils used for oats, hay, and miscellaneous crops. U. S. Dept. Agric., Bur. Soils, Bul. 67:1–73, 1910.

152. Whitney, Milton. Fertilizers for potato soils. U. S. Dept. Agric., Bur. Soils, Bul. 65:1–19, 1910.

153. Whitney, Milton. Fertilizers for wheat soils. U. S. Dept. Agric., Bur. Soils, Bul. 66:1–48, figs. 1–28, 1910.

154. Whitson, A. R., and H. B. Kendrick. Extension courses in soils. U. S. Dept. Agric., Dept. Bul. 355:1–92, 1916.

155. Wiest, Edward. Agricultural organization in the United States. xxiii, 618 p. University of Kentucky, Lexington, 1923. (The University of Kentucky: Studies in Economics and Sociology, vol. 2.) (Bureau of Chemistry, pp. 129–41; Bureau of Soils, pp. 142–47)

156. Wiley, H. W. Historical sketch of the Association of Official Agricultural Chemists. *In* Proceedings of the Sixteenth Annual Convention of Official Agricultural Chemists. U. S. Dept. Agric., Bur. Chem., Bul. 57:16–49, 1899.

157. Wilson, Woodrow. General regulations governing the importation, manufacture, storage, and distribution of fertilizers and fertilizer ingredients. U. S. Dept. Agric., Off. Secy., Circ. 145:1–4, Nov. 7, 1919.

158. Winchell, Alexander N., and Eric R. Miller. The dustfall of February 13, 1923. Jour. Agric. Research 29:443–50, figs. 1–2, 1924.

159. Young, G. J. Potash salts and other salines in the Great Basin Region. U. S. Dept. Agric., Dept. Bul. 61:1–96, figs. 1–8, pls. 1–6, 1914.

Chapter IV: AGRICULTURAL CHEMISTRY

[Because each chapter covers a different subject and therefore will be used chiefly by a different constituency, it seems desirable to make each one complete and self-contained. For this reason, among others, a complete table of chapter contents is placed at the beginning of each chapter, rather than at the front of the volume. A list of all literature cited in the chapter will be found at the end of the chapter and the numbers in parentheses in the text refer the reader to the corresponding entries in the list. All entry numbers occurring in each major section of a chapter also are listed in numerical sequence at the end of that section, thus forming what is in effect a section list of literature cited. These features all should prove of great convenience to readers.]

CHAPTER CONTENTS

Chapter IV

AGRICULTURAL CHEMISTRY

1. Introduction

AGRICULTURAL CHEMISTRY has an exceedingly wide and varied scope. Starting with the chemical composition of soils, fertilizers, crops, and domestic animals, it gradually has developed into wider fields. For many years the major part of its work has been concerned with the chemistry of the products of agriculture after they had become articles of commerce, as in the case of foods and drugs. Other parts of the work lie in the fields of industrial or engineering chemistry, as in the former testing of materials for highway construction and the continuing work on dust explosions and the utilization of agricultural wastes.

Agricultural chemistry is so closely connected, both historically and from the standpoint of national organization, with the subject of soils and fertilizers that this chapter logically is placed immediately after that on soils, which included soil fertility also. In recent subject matter it relates more largely to the composition of plants and animals and their products, and therefore may be placed properly before the chapters devoted to Animal Industries and Plant Industries, respectively.

2. Historical Development

THE BACKGROUND OF RESEARCH in agricultural chemistry in America was formed in the early years of our national history. It lies in the observations and experiments of Sir Humphrey Davy in England, republished in this country in 1815; in those of Thomas Taylor and Edmund Ruffin in Virginia, whose first publications appeared soon after Davy's and whose writings were expanded and revised for many years; in the work of Samuel Dana, whose published papers appeared from 1838 onward; and in the epochal studies of Liebig in Germany, made public in 1840.

Official Federal attention to the chemistry of agriculture apparently dates from the instructions given by the House of Representatives in 1830 to the Secretary of the Treasury to prepare a manual on sugar culture and sugar refining, which was done in 1833. From

[267]

about 1839 to 1861, the Agricultural Division of the Patent Office was the official agency for this work. It was a part of the State Department until 1849, when the Department of the Interior was created and the Patent Office transferred thereto. During this period considerable attention was given to numerous chemical problems relating to crops, soils, fertilizers, and plant and animal products, but there seems to have been no particular development of coöperative relations between official agencies. Within the several States, the State departments, or boards, of agriculture became widely established before the Civil War, and gave attention to the chemistry of soils and fertilizers, as well as other agricultural materials.

The Civil War focused national attention on food problems for almost the first time. This resulted, in 1862, in the enactment of three far-reaching laws. The first created the United States Department of Agriculture, effective July 1, 1862, which took over the Agricultural Division of the Patent Office in the Interior Department. The second act (Morrill Act) provided for grants of land to aid in establishing a college of agriculture and mechanic arts in each State. These colleges gradually became the seats of extensive research in agricultural chemistry. The third act was the Homestead Act, under which hundreds of thousands of persons have become the owners of farm land taken from the public domain. This gave the Federal government a vital and continuing connection with agricultural population and problems.

The act creating the Federal Department of Agriculture specifically authorized the employment of chemists, among other scientists. A Chemical Division was created in 1862, one of the first divisions of the new Department, and a chemist was appointed in the same year. Chemical investigations, already important in the Agricultural Division of the Patent Office, steadily increased in number and scope, as indicated by the succeeding annual reports (50).* For many years, there was relatively little collaboration with other Federal units, or with State agencies. Some minor instances occurred at intervals, however, as related by Weber (76: 15, 17). In the fiscal year 1865, postage stamps and cancelling inks were examined for the Post Office Department, a forerunner of

---

* Numbers in parentheses refer to the Literature Cited, at the end of the chapter.

similar and more extensive studies a third of a century later. In 1868 a study of cereals was begun on several hundreds of samples obtained through various State agricultural societies.

Following the Civil War, various other official agencies besides the U. S. Department of Agriculture gradually developed increasing investigation in the province of agricultural chemistry. The State boards and departments of agriculture were given more and more authority in the regulation of commercial fertilizers and other commodities. State and municipal boards of health were increasingly concerned with the quality of milk and other food stuffs. The departments of chemistry of the rapidly developing agricultural colleges began studies in numerous fields. Finally, the Hatch Act, passed by the Federal Congress in 1887, provided for the establishment of an agricultural experiment station in each State, and appropriated $15,000 annually for its support.

As agricultural chemistry became more and more concerned with regulatory activities, and its findings were used as evidence in legal cases, the necessity grew rapidly for more uniform methods of analysis and for more exact results. This more and more insistent necessity led inevitably to the formation of an organization of chemists from the various official agencies.

ASSOCIATION OF OFFICIAL AGRICULTURAL CHEMISTS

The formation of this Association grew out of previous conventions of agricultural chemists, both official and commercial. Two such meetings were held in 1880, the first at the U. S. Department of Agriculture; a third was held in 1881, and two more in 1884. The second of those last mentioned, held in September, 1884, effected a permanent organization of the official chemists, under the name, "Association of Official Agricultural Chemists," which resolved itself into the first annual meeting of the Association (64—57; 80). In regulatory matters the official and the commercial chemists often had standpoints somewhat opposed in character, whence the necessity, if the association were to be harmonious, of restricting its membership to official chemists. From 1885 to 1892 it met regularly in Washington, D. C. Of these early meetings, some were held at the buildings of the U. S. Department of Agriculture and others at the U. S. National Museum.

In the early years of this movement, both before and after the founding of the Association, those who attended were concerned almost exclusively with the regulation of commercial fertilizers. Those who formed the new Association were, largely, fertilizer chemists. By 1890 foods and feeding stuffs, dairy products, fermented liquors, and sugars also were being considered. The scope of the work has grown steadily. By 1920 their published methods of analysis covered many groups or classes of agricultural products. There has been similar growth in the scope of the membership. At first the membership came from the U. S. Department of Agriculture, the State boards and departments of agriculture, and the State agricultural colleges. In 1885, municipal chemists having regulatory or inspectional duties were admitted to the Association. In 1887 the constitution was amended to allow membership to official chemists not necessarily concerned with regulatory activities, including those of the U. S. Department of the Treasury. The development of State agricultural experiment stations in the agricultural colleges after 1887 greatly expanded the numbers of chemists.

The Association was a large-scale coöperative enterprise from its very inception. It was composed of official chemists from the three levels of government, Federal, State, and municipal. Its main purpose was to develop, provisionally approve, thoroughly test, and officially adopt more and more accurate methods for the determination of the chemical composition of agricultural products and accessories. When a new or modified method was proposed and provisionally approved, numerous coöperative tests of the accuracy, economy, and reliability of the method were made immediately by all the institutions concerned with its particular field. In this important activity the Association operated through a series of committees and later through referees, each charged with developing methods of analysis for one substance or group of substances. By this close-knit organization, what otherwise could have been accomplished only after much effort and delay in arranging a coöperative program was done year after year as a matter of course by the many agencies involved.

There also was coöperation of other agencies with the Association. The U. S. Department of Agriculture and other Federal agencies, such as the U. S. National Museum, provided rooms and facilities for many of the meetings, especially in the early years. The annual volume of *Proceedings* of the Association was published by the U. S. Department of Agriculture for twenty-eight years, covering the second to the twenty-ninth annual meetings, 1885 to 1912, inclusive (6; 64). The voluminous compilations of the official methods of analysis, too, were published by the Department of Agriculture throughout the twenty-eight-year period. From 1884 to 1894 they were included in the *Proceedings*. From 1895 to 1908 they were published in separate bulletins of the Bureau of Chemistry (64—46, 65, and 107, and revisions). From 1903 to 1912 the changes only were published annually in the circulars of the Bureau (65). Beginning in 1920, the Association published the revisions itself, in a comprehensive volume, and has revised it at five-year intervals.

The Chief of the Federal Division of Chemistry, Dr. Harvey W. Wiley, who also was secretary of the Association for many years from 1889 onward, recommended in 1899 and again in 1900 that Congress recognize the Association as the official advisor of the government in the field of agricultural chemistry. Congress took such action finally, and the recommendations of the Association, when approved by the Secretary of Agriculture, became official for the Department. Most of the States also recognized the Association findings as official. Chemical results obtained by these officially approved methods became accepted as final in courts of all levels of jurisdiction in cases involving the institutions comprising the Association membership.

Specific investigations, especially those concerning methods of analysis of new substances, were initiated from time to time by one or another of the institutions represented in the Association, and presently these were made a part of the coöperative program of research. If the study started in the Federal agency, then—often— the final results were published in the series of circulars of the Bureau of Chemistry (65).

DIVISION AND BUREAU OF CHEMISTRY

The Division of Chemistry, as noted at the beginning of this section, was established in the newly created Department of Agriculture in 1862. It remained a division, often called the Chemical Division, until its promotion to be a Bureau of Chemistry on July

1, 1901. In 1927 it was combined with the Bureau of Soils and the Fixed-Nitrogen Research Laboratory to form the present Bureau of Chemistry and Soils. The history of the Division and Bureau may be gleaned from many sources. The annual reports of the Secretary of Agriculture (50) and the chief of the Bureau (61) present current activities and organization. An annual publication shows personnel of the U. S. Department of Agriculture arranged by organization units and subunits (54). Another annual Federal publication gives similar information regarding the personnel of the State agricultural experiment stations (1). Publications especially prepared by the Bureau (62; 79; 81) and by the Department (19; 25; 38; 39; 49; 51; 52; 53) give history, activities, and organization as of their periods. Several private publications devote space, varying from paragraphs to chapers, to the Federal Bureau (75:181–85; 76; 77; 78:129–41). No attempt is made to present a history here, except as it becomes apparent in the discussions of the development of coöperative relations which follow.

Certain publications either dealing with the laws under which the Bureau has operated, or listing the publications it has issued, should be noted here. The principal ones containing laws or parts of laws affecting the Bureau are four in number (13A; 24; 76; 77). Those listing the publications, in full or in part, are for periods ending in 1901 (26; 63), in 1902 (72), in 1904 (63; 65—14), in 1925 (27), and in 1930 (28).

OTHER CHEMICAL AGENCIES

One of the most striking trends in the history of agricultural chemistry is the continued and steady increase in the number of units devoted to chemical research. This has been coincident, of course, with the broadening of the field in which chemistry is applied. For many years after the creation of the U. S. Department of Agriculture in 1862, all chemical studies related to agriculture were made in its Division of Chemistry. It is shown later in this chapter that for some years the Bureau of Chemistry contained a Contracts Laboratory for examination of articles to be purchased by Federal establishments. Gradually, however, with the expansion of the Federal structure, the major agencies each provided its own laboratory for testing materials for its own use.

Within the Department of Agriculture itself the same development took place. The Bureau of Animal Industry, created by Congress in 1884, soon established a Biochemic Division. A typical example of its recent chemical work is represented by the publication on the chemical and physical control of cresol solutions (55—1308). The Bureau's Dairy Division also began chemical studies in its Dairy Research Laboratory at an early date. In the field of plant studies, the Division of Vegetable Physiology and Pathology made experiments in the chemical purification of water supplies even before the Bureau of Plant Industry was created in 1901. Since that time chemical investigation in the Bureau has increased steadily. The former Division of Plant Physiology and Fermentation Investigations (which had several different names and is now discontinued) and the present Division of Drug, Poisonous, and Oil Plant Investigations (which also has had several names) are conspicuous examples. They have investigated and published in collaboration with the Bureau of Chemistry, as noted above, and also independently in increasing volume.

The Plant Industry unit charged with horticultural investigations developed also a chemical and physiological laboratory, early, in connection with its work on fruit and vegetable utilization and storage. After about 1920, its contributions were numerous in this field (55—1022, 1025, etc.) The Division of Tobacco Investigations (now Division of Tobacco and Plant Nutrition) has done the same thing, as did also the Bureau of Soils when it began the study of tobacco quality in relation to soil type and curing processes. In more recent years other units, e.g. the Divisions of Cereal Investigations, Sugar-Plant Investigations, Egyptian Cotton Breeding, and others concerned with crop-plant production and protection, have developed their own chemical studies to a greater or lesser extent.

The Bureau of Soils always has had its own independent unit for investigations in soil chemistry (55—1311). This has been concerned solely with soils, and has no connection with the larger chemical units concerned with soil fertility or with the manufacture of synthetic nitrogen products, which have had varying organizational affiliations. The Bureau of Agricultural Economics has developed a Milling, Baking, and Chemical Laboratory in its

Grain Division, and Cereal Investigations in Plant Industry has collaborated with it in some studies, as well as with the Bureau of Chemistry. The Bureau of Home Economics, dating from 1923, conducts extensive chemical research, especially in foods, vitamins, etc.

The publications listed in the Literature Cited at the end of this chapter which have been cited in this section on Historical Development are Nos. 1, 6, 13A, 19, 24, 25, 26, 27, 28, 38, 39, 49, 50, 51, 52, 53, 54, 55, 61, 62, 63, 64, 65, 72, 75, 76, 77, 78, 79, 80, and 81.

3. Governmental Interunit Chemical Services

Chemistry is a highly specialized science. Intensively trained personnel and expensively equipped laboratories are necessary antecedents to efficient investigation of chemical problems. Agricultural operations present an infinite variety of such problems, concerned with the continued improvement of soils and of plant and animal products. The U. S. Department of Agriculture, the State boards and departments of agriculture, and the State colleges of agriculture and their agricultural experiment stations, naturally, have established chemical divisions and supplied them with the personnel and equipment essential to research. Chemical problems arise, however, in many different units of government, in relation to the supplies and materials used by them. It is only natural, therefore, that the established chemical units should be called upon to render frequent services to the many other units in their own level of government, whether Federal, State, or local. On the other hand, the chemical unit itself occasionally must ask reciprocal services from other governmental units in working upon its own problems.

It is quite impossible to draw a hard and fast line between tests and studies made for other government units and those made as part of the normal research program of the chemical unit itself. Some studies begun primarily as services become broadly investigational, and some begun as definite investigations result in services later. Still others remain in an intermediate status and might properly be classified with either group.

FEDERAL INTERUNIT CHEMICAL SERVICES

The Division of Chemistry of the U. S. Department of Agriculture, as noted previously under Historical Development, rendered various services to units of other Departments, and to other Divisions of the Department of Agriculture, almost from its beginning in 1862. About fifty years ago the demand for such services began to increase rapidly. This was fairly coincident with the opening of the regulatory period, the second of the three periods in the development of the Department. This period began, roughly, in 1889, when Agriculture became a full-fledged Department with a Secretary who was a cabinet officer. It was coincident also with the focusing of national attention on the wholesale adulteration of manufactured articles and the enactment of laws to prevent such fraud. There arose also many questions of the relative quality of different brands of articles not deliberately adulterated, and the relative economy of the purchase of a given quality for a given use. The answering of these and similar questions greatly increased the work of chemical units in government agencies. For nearly a score of years this was true in the Federal government, and finally led to the establishing of one central agency for the chemical testing of government supplies and materials.

Contracts Laboratory for Federal Purchases

The steady increase in the number of requests for chemical service made to the Division of Chemistry of the U. S. Department of Agriculture led its chief, Dr. Wiley, to recommend repeatedly the establishment of a Contracts Laboratory in the Division. In it all tests of materials to be purchased by agencies of the government would be made without imposing undue burdens on laboratories charged with other specific duties. Such a laboratory was established, finally, on July 1, 1903. At the end of the first year it was recorded (61—1904:216–19) that it had handled samples of fuels, lubricants, waters, fabrics, papers, inks, adhesives, disinfectants, typewriter ribbons, etc., as well as food and forage for the military establishments. Within a short period there had been added colors, paints and varnishes, soaps, oils, fats and waxes, tars and turpentines, paper pulps, ink pads, and many and varied other articles of common use by government agencies.

Early in 1903, just before the Contracts Laboratory was officially established, the Bureau of Chemistry published methods for the examination of canceling and stamping inks (65—12). In 1907 the Bureau published a discussion of the examination of many kinds of paper, including those used by various other governmental agencies (65—34). After five years of this enlarged service there was published in 1908 a comprehensive paper on the technical methods of testing supplies (64—109), of which a revised edition was published in 1910.

Gradually, as the government establishments grew in size and scope, operations required to be speeded up, and units became separated by increasing physical distances, it was only natural that they should tend to become more and more self-sufficient through the establishment of their own technical laboratories. For instance, the Bureau of Engraving and Printing established its own chemical laboratory for testing inks, dyes, etc., and obtained from the Bureau of Chemistry one of the men who previously had done that work for it and for other agencies. In the same way the Forest Service established its Forest-Products Laboratory in 1905, and the Grain Investigations Division of the Bureau of Agricultural Economics gradually added chemists to its Milling and Baking Laboratory. The Divisions which now comprise the Bureaus of Plant Industry, Dairy Industry, and Agricultural Engineering set up their own chemical laboratories at varying dates.

Interdepartmental Relations

It is possible to present here only the more readily noted examples of services rendered by the Bureau of Chemistry to other Departments of the Federal government, and by them to it. Many other similar instances doubtless have occurred of which no published mention has been made. These have been gleaned from the annual reports of the Bureau (61), and from publications descriptive of its work (62). For convenience of reference the Federal departments served are arranged in alphabetical order, followed by various independent administrative establishments, including the Congress.

Department of Commerce.—The only item of chemical service noted for this Department was an examination of life preservers.

Discussion of assistance given to the Bureau of Fisheries and the Coast and Geodetic Survey, and toward the establishment of a Bureau of Standards, all units which later were made parts of the Department of Commerce, will be found under the discussion of the Departments of the Interior and the Treasury, respectively.

Department of the Interior.—Water samples were analyzed for the U. S. Commission of Fish and Fisheries (after 1903 the Bureau of Fisheries) as early as 1899 (61—1899 :334), and this was continued at intervals for several years. In 1905, the Bureau of Chemistry coöperated with the Bureau of Fisheries in tests of American and Norwegian cod-liver oils (61—1905 :510). Still later, analyses were made of samples of air, water, and fish foods, in a single year. In 1899, for the Office of Indian Affairs, an analysis was made of a sample of lemon extract which had caused the death of an Indian, in order to determine whether it contained methyl alcohol (61— 1899 :32). In the same year tests were begun on numerous samples of mineral waters from the springs in the Hot Springs Reservation in Arkansas. The work was completed in three years and published as Senate Document No. 289 (61—1902 :142). Analyses also were made of disinfectants, lubricating oils, and coals for the National Hospital for the Insane, and of papers and soil samples for the Geological Survey (61—1903 :180).

Department of Justice.—The Division and Bureau of Chemistry in the Department of Agriculture has been called upon to perform many services for the Department of Justice. During the years from 1899 to 1903, it made tests of shellac to determine if the alcohol was sufficiently denatured to prevent re-use as a beverage, and analyses of beers, malt extracts, and other beverages to determine if they were of legal composition for sale to Indians.

An important and long-continued coöperative study had to do with smelter fumes. From 1904 to 1912 the Bureau coöperated with the Department of Justice and the Forest Service in a widespread investigation of injury to forests and to farm and orchard crops alleged to have been caused by smelter smoke and fumes, and by the pouring of smelter tailings into streams, whence they flowed into irrigation ditches. This work was begun in 1904 with an investigation of injury to Federal forests, and some three hundred determinations of sulphur dioxide were made in a space of three months (61—1904 :220). A graphic picture of the devastation wrought by smelter fumes in three areas of California is given both by the California State Board of Forestry (13B :25–31) and the U. S. Bureau of Chemistry (64–89).From 1907 to 1910, these investigations were continued in the vicinity of Ducktown, Tennessee, and New Anaconda, Montana, and covered not only the amounts of sulphur dioxide injurious to trees, farm crops, and farm and game animals, but also the effects of smelter tailings on irrigation water (21 :64–113). The facts finally presented to the Department of Justice led it to compel smelters both in the South and in the Northwest to condense their fumes in order to prevent injury to forests, crops, livestock, and irrigation waters. In the meantime the Bureau assisted the smelter companies in developing methods of condensation by which the sulphur fumes could be converted into sulphuric acid and a harmful product turned into a profitable fertilizer (61—1907–12). A similar study in a recent case having international complications is discussed under the Department of State.

Post Office Department.—From 1899 onward the Division and Bureau of Chemistry collaborated with the Post Office Department in three lines of investigation, namely : determinations of the quality of supplies to be purchased by the Department; tests of articles likely to be dangerous, corrosive, or explosive in the mails; and studies of articles to determine if fraudulent advertising were being admitted to the mails. In the first line of inquiry, tests were made of the quality of pulps for postcards and envelopes, paper, envelopes, adhesives, glycerin, soaps, lubricating oils and linoleum, inks and ink pads used, the latter involving critical tests of the inks used in cancelling stamps, and of cancelled stamps themselves, to determine whether the ink could be removed without destroying the color or texture of the stamp. Methods for the investigation of stamping and cancelling inks were published in 1903 (65—12). The second group included a wide variety of articles, chiefly liquids or powders. The third line of investigation involved determinations of the composition of many manufactured articles, chiefly chemicals, drugs, and medicines, where there was indication of fraudulent advertising, and the Post Office Department sought evidence on which to decide whether fraud orders should be issued against the manufacturers. Even refrigerating machines were included in the latter group.

Department of State.—The Bureau of Chemistry entered into extensive collaboration with the State Department in tests of the quality of exported and imported articles of which complaints were made. As early as 1899, tests were made of exported butters against which the recipients had lodged complaints. In the same year (61—1899:31–34), similar tests of the quality of imported oleomargarines and fertilizers were made. In this work the consular officers of the State Department coöperated extensively in obtaining declarations of foreign exporters regarding the origin and character of food products offered for export to the United States (61—1904:209). Tests were made also of papers, ink, typewriter ribbons, carbon papers, etc., for the State Department and others where permanence of records is important.

In 1930 the Bureau of Chemistry assisted the State Department in making a study of the influence of smelter fumes on crop plants in northeastern Washington, the alleged source of the injury being a Canadian smelter near the international boundary (61—1930: 37). Previous similar studies are discussed under Department of Justice.

Department of the Treasury.—Two major lines of coöperation with the Treasury Department are mentioned in the years from 1899 onward. The first was the testing of the quality of the supplies which the Treasury Department contemplated purchasing, including ice, water, dyes, oils, glue, soap, steel, and miscellaneous supplies used by the Bureau of Engraving and Printing in the manufacture of currency and postage stamps. The second was the determination of the purity, quality, and origin of foods and food products on which the Treasury Department was required to collect customs duties, through its Bureau of Internal Revenue. From 1899 on, these included alcohols, butters, fruits, fruit juices, pineapples (*Journal of the American Chemical Society,* March, 1903), saccharin, sugars, Sicilian sumac imported for tanning purposes, and numerous and varied other articles.

In 1901 the Bureau of Chemistry was officially designated by the Department of the Treasury to be supervisor of sugar polarization for the Treasury appraisers at Philadelphia, New York, and Boston (61—1901 :102), although the Department of Agriculture still bore the expense. Effective January 1, 1905, this coöperative supervision was transferred to the Department of Commerce and Labor, at the request of the Secretary of the Treasury. In 1900 Congressional authorization was given for the inspection of the quality of imported foods, with coöperation required from the customs officers of the Treasury Department in obtaining samples (61—1900 : 22). In the agitation and discussion which resulted in the enactment of the national Food and Drugs Act (Pure Food Law) in 1906, the Secretary of Agriculture was specifically authorized, by act of July 1, 1903, to inspect food products offered for entry and to determine any adulteration or misbranding in respect of character, quality, or origin. Collaboration with the Treasury Department was provided, under which samples were collected from the invoices received. The Secretary of the Treasury, also, was designated to refuse entry of products subject to exclusion under the law (61—1904 :209). Further discussion of this subject will be found below under United States Congress.

In 1899 petroleum was refined for the use of the Coast and Geodetic Survey, then in the Treasury Department. In 1900, a comprehensive brief for a national standardizing bureau was drawn up by the Division of Chemistry, at the request of the Secretary of the Treasury (61—1900 :24). This movement culminated in the creation of the Bureau of Standards in 1901.

Departments of War and Navy.—Most of the collaboration of the Division of Chemistry with the Departments of War and Navy had to do with tests of the quality of materials which those agencies contemplated purchasing. As a result of the Spanish War food scandals in 1898, the Department of Agriculture was asked to examine numerous samples of army and navy food materials of many kinds, including especially the canned meats, with respect to nutritive qualities, the use of preservatives, etc. (61—1899 :30–34). Thereafter, the inspection was extended to include the chemical and physical qualities of the cloth used in uniforms. Similar collaboration existed with the Navy Department, but on a somewhat smaller scale. During the World War, these services to the military departments were renewed on a large scale in the way of tests and standards for materials (39 :96–97).

Independent establishments and the Congress.—Examinations were made of the qualities of supplies purchased by various independent boards, commissions, and offices of the Federal Government. For the Government Printing Office, papers, gums, oils, glues, and alloys were tested. Tars and turpentines were studied for the Isthmian Canal Commission, and samples of pipes were investigated for the White House.

For the Congress the Division of Chemistry examined several hundred food samples purchased on the open market by the Senate Committee on Manufactures, which was engaged for nearly a year in a study of the question of food adulteration (61—1899 :34; 77 :8). This coöperation was continued, and the results largely influenced the introduction of the Food and Drugs Bill and its favorable consideration by committees of the House and Senate (61—1900 :24).

Interbureau Relations in Department of Agriculture

The difficulty of distinguishing between more or less routine service of the Bureau of Chemistry for other Bureaus and investigations conducted coöperatively by two Bureaus is much greater than in cases of relations with other Departments. These services are continued until the present time. For example, in 1931 the Bureau of Biological Survey published on the wild-duck foods of North Dakota Lakes (56—221). The bulletin contains (pp. 5–9) the analyses of the waters from seventy-five different lakes, made by the Bureau of Chemistry. Frequently the casual service to a related Bureau later developed into a coöperative study. Only two Bureaus have had a sufficient volume of service to be mentioned under unit names.

Bureau of Plant Industry.—The Division of Chemistry had performed a multitude of analyses for the various Divisions which now comprise the Bureau of Plant Industry, and the two Bureaus have maintained the same relations since 1901, when both were established. The chemical service has included miscellaneous analyses of cereals, forages, fruits, vegetables, drug plants, and poisonous plants. The more systematic and extensive relations in these fields will be discussed under the research program in the next section. Analyses made for Plant Industry also have included such special plant organs as honey glands and raphidian crystals. Plant Industry units have reciprocated by testing the vitality of the lots of seed of sugar beets and other plants distributed by the chemical unit, and the seeds of the crop plants used in the pot and plot experiments with fertilizers. Plant Industry also has aided in obtaining both seeds and plant materials desired by Chemistry.

Bureau of Public Roads.—The Bureau of Chemistry made an investigation of methods of testing road materials for the Office of Public Road Inquiry as early as 1900 (61—1900:25). The Secretary then established a Testing Laboratory in the Bureau in cooperation with the Office. This became known as the Division of Tests and was transferred to the Bureau of Public Roads on July 1, 1905 (61—1905:505). Results of the coöperative tests were published by Chemistry (64—79) in 1903, and in the *Journal of the American Chemical Society* for 1901, 1902, and 1903.

FEDERAL-STATE SERVICE INTERRELATIONS

Federal chemical agencies render few services to State agencies, because the latter are fully equipped to handle their own problems, which, naturally, are more local in character than are the Federal. On the other hand, in much of the early investigation of the Federal chemical unit the States, through their agricultural experiment stations, rendered much routine service to the Federal Division or Bureau of Chemistry by supplying it with samples of soil, fertilizer, seeds, crops, and animal products, or by growing material which it wished to analyze. Further mention of some of these activities will be made under the discussion of coöperative chemical research, in the next section of this chapter.

INTRASTATE SERVICE ACTIVITIES

Within the various States much the same types of service relations exist, though on a somewhat smaller scale, as have been described for the Federal units. Divisions or laboratories devoted to chemistry in the agricultural colleges and experiment stations, or in State boards of agriculture, render more or less routine services to the other units of their level of government. To a smaller extent the same holds true of municipal chemical agencies. At times, again, definite testing agencies, similar in work to the former Contracts Laboratory in the Federal Bureau of Chemistry, have been set up to pass on materials purchased for State or municipal use.

The publications listed in the Literature Cited at the end of this chapter which have been cited in this section on Governmental Interunit Chemical Services are Nos. 13B, 21, 39, 56, 61, 62, 64, 65, and 77.

4. CHEMICAL RESEARCH

INVESTIGATIONS in the province of agricultural chemistry were the first duty of the Federal Division of Chemistry and of the chemical departments and divisions in the State agricultural colleges and their experiment stations. For a time, as noted previously, services to other units increased rapidly and sometimes interfered with the investigational program. Then the number of chemical units was increased, the service duties more widely distributed, and the research programs greatly expanded, in the last twenty years.

So far as chemical investigation was a matter of laboratory analysis, there was little need or opportunity for coöperation with other agencies, except in obtaining material. Many of the early interrelations were of this nature. When field cultures became necessary to the investigation, the chemical units naturally were obliged to ask the coöperation of other agencies. Field experiments on State agricultural experiment stations and substations, as well as on Federal field stations and experiment farms, were conducted chiefly by units representing plant industries and animal industries. Naturally, therefore, the major part of the coöperation of the chemical units was with these two groups. The research is subdivided here by subject-matter groups rather than by the kinds or levels of the agencies concerned with it.

As pointed out previously, no sharp line of demarcation can be drawn between service activities and research operations. Some of the coöperative relations discussed below might have been placed with almost equal propriety under the services discussed earlier.

SOILS AND FERTILIZERS

The volume of research on the chemistry of soils and fertilizers has been enormous and still remains so. It need have but brief mention in this chapter, however, for two reasons. An earlier chapter has been devoted to soils and, because of the intimate relation between the two classes of materials, the problems of soil fertility and the use of fertilizers were treated fully in that chapter. In the second place, the actual analysis of either soils or fertilizers usually has not been a coöperative enterprise. In the Federal organization, the Bureau of Soils has carried its own work in soil chemistry for the last thirty years, and the same has been largely true in the State units. A brief review of the development of this line of investigation, therefore, is sufficient here.

Agricultural chemistry had its origin primarily in the study of soils and fertilizers, as pointed out in the Section on Historical Development. Much attention to the composition of both these classes of substances was given by the Agricultural Division of the Patent Office for many years before the creation of the Federal Department of Agriculture in 1862, but it involved little or no coöperation with other official agencies. The same was true of the Chemical Division of the new Department of Agriculture, which devoted increasing attention to both groups. The first extensive official coöperation in this field was that developed by the Association of Official Agricultural Chemists from its organization in 1884 onward to the present time. This covered the coöperative testing of methods of analysis, as discussed earlier in this chapter.

A Division of Agricultural Soils was established in the Weather Bureau of the Department of Agriculture in 1894. An act passed by the Congress in the same year provided, among other things, for the determination of the chemical character of different soils. This portion of the work was assigned to the Division of Chemistry. In 1901, when the Division became the Bureau of Chemistry, seven laboratories were established, two of which were charged with the investigation of soils and fertilizers, respectively. In the meantime the expanding Division of Soils, which also became a Bureau in 1901, had gradually increased its activities to include the chemistry of soils. In 1900 the two Divisions had coöperated in soils analysis, a chemist from the Soils Division being given laboratory facilities in the Division of Chemistry for the purpose. In 1904 the Soils Laboratory of the Bureau of Chemistry was transferred to the Bureau of Soils. In the ten-year period from 1894 to 1904, while the work was in the chemical units, however, certain interrelations had developed.

Soon after the authorization of 1894, the Division of Chemistry, through the coöperation of the various State agricultural experiment stations, obtained numerous samples of typical soils and determined their chemical composition. The same samples were used also in a series of greenhouse pot experiments in which the removal of plant foods from these soils by different crops was ascertained (76:23). In 1902 the new Bureau of Chemistry began another series of experiments in coöperation with about half of the State stations. While primarily concerned with crops, the studies involved the shipment of quantities of soils to the Bureau, their chemical analysis, and the determination of plant foods withdrawn from them by crops (65—9 and 11). As recently as 1926 the Bureaus of Chemistry and Soils collaborated in developing an improved method for the determination of phosphoric acid in fertilizers (71—1926:9).

In collaboration with some of the larger cities of the United States, chemical studies were made of the composition of street sweepings, municipal garbage, and sewage, from the standpoint of their agricultural value as fertilizers (76:24). The Division of Chemistry had given attention to this phase of soil fertility as early as 1872 in collaboration with cities in the United States and abroad (12), but apparently no analyses were made at that time.

PLANT CHEMISTRY

In the Federal Bureau of Chemistry many successive and contemporary units have been charged with chemical studies on plants and their products. A Plant-Analysis Laboratory was established in the Bureau in 1904, when the Soil and Fertilizer Laboratories were transferred to the Bureau of Soils. In 1907 this was abolished and a Section of Vegetable Physiological Investigations was established. This in turn gave way to units of other names, such as Plant Chemistry, Crop Chemistry, etc. In recent years the work has been distributed among several units in at least two divisions of the Bureau. In the Food Research Division are the Sections of Cereal Chemistry, Fruit and Vegetable Chemistry, Bacteriology and Microchemistry, Plant Products, and Phytochemistry. In the Industrial Farm Products Division is the Section of Agricultural By-Products. In the Bureau of Plant Industry nearly every Division is interested in the chemistry of the crops on which it works, and at some time or other collaborates in chemical studies. Most instances relate to specific crops and will be discussed under the crop groups. A few deal with general plant chemistry.

During the first two decades of the present century, when agriculture was spreading rapidly over the semiarid and arid lands of the West, the question of the indicator value of native vegetation with reference to the agricultural value of such lands was pertinent and led to studies. One of these studies, in which three Offices of the Bureau of Plant Industry took part, was chemical from the standpoint of alkali indicators (32). A recent contribution on vitamin-like substances in plant nutrition, published in 1927, resulted from coöperation between the Bureau of Plant Industry and the Arizona Agricultural Experiment Station (10). It is one of those curious instances where the only clue to the coöperation is a footnote from the author's name in the list of Station staff on the inside of the bulletin cover page.

Cereals and Forages

The cereals always have been important crops in the United States. Forages, also, have been tremendously important in this livestock-producing country, but relatively they have been greatly neglected because not originally comprising crops of recognized high commercial value.

A large volume of collaboration on cereals developed between the Bureau of Plant Industry and the Bureau of Chemistry during the first decade of the present century. This was coincident with a considerable expansion in plant-industry activities, including world-wide exploration for cereal and forage crops abroad, the establishment of numerous field stations in arid and semiarid areas, the starting of new crop industries under untried environments, and the gradual development of Federal grain standards. All these required knowledge of the chemical composition of the materials imported, produced, and sold. That this collaborative work was not regarded by the Bureau of Chemistry as service tests for Plant Industry, but as coöperative investigation, is shown by their publication, in 1909, of the feeding value of cereals as calculated from chemical analysis (64—120). In the Letter of Transmittal, this is stated to be a collaboration of the Cattle-Food and Grain Laboratory, Miscellaneous Division, Bureau of Chemistry, and the Office of Grain Investigations, Bureau of Plant Industry.

The appropriation act for the fiscal year 1901 provided for an investigation of the cause of deterioration of gluten content in the wheat of the Pacific Coast and elsewhere, and of methods of increasing the content of valuable food constituents in wheat and other cereals (76:31). For the fiscal year 1903, appropriation was made to the Bureau of Chemistry to study, in collaboration with the Weather Bureau and the State agricultural experiment stations, the influence of environment upon the composition of wheat and other cereals, with special reference to the gluten content, and including the quality of barley for brewing and other purposes (76:31–32; 82). This authorization was repeated for several years. As most of the work was done with wheat, the most important crop, the coöperative procedure and results will be discussed under that special crop.

In 1902, the Bureau of Chemistry began coöperation with some twenty-five or more State agricultural experiment stations, including California, in determining the chemical composition of four cereal crops. Seed of wheat, oats, barley, and rye, furnished uniformly to each station, was sown in selected plots, and the resulting crops harvested and sent to the Bureau of Chemistry for analysis. All results from all stations were furnished to each coöperating station. In addition, samples of the soil from these plots, before seeding, were sent to the Bureau, the same crops grown in them in a series of pot experiments, the crop composition ascertained, and these determinations also sent to the stations. This work was continued and a similar study of oats, clover, cowpea, and corn was carried on for at least two years (61—1902:144; 61—1904: 225; 62).

The Laboratory of Vegetable Physiological Investigations, like the Plant-Analysis Laboratory which it replaced in 1907, was established specifically to work in collaboration with the Bureau of Plant Industry on problems of common interest. For some years it was concerned chiefly with cereals, especially with the effect of climate on newly introduced varieties, the effect of different environments on composition, with chemical changes during growth, and with the chemical changes in aging flour (61—1907 :308). In 1907 it was recorded by the Bureau of Chemistry that 567 samples of domestic and imported cereals were analyzed for feeding value, in coöperation with the Office of Grain Investigations, and also 187 samples of malts and barleys for beer production (61—1907 :391). By 1908 the samples numbered 850, on which 9000 separate determinations were made for the Offices of Grain Investigations, Grain Standardization, Dry-Land Agriculture, and Seed and Plant Introduction, all of the Bureau of Plant Industry (61—1908 :484). This work was continued in large volume for several years (61—1910 : 107). The feeding values of introduced varieties of oats and barleys also were determined. The special work with wheats is discussed separately under that heading.

In or about 1922 a collaborative study was begun on the protein chemistry of the cereal kernels. This was done under a coöperative agreement between the Office of Cereal Investigations and the Office of Plant Physiology and Fermentation Investigations, both of the Bureau of Plant Industry. The former provided certain funds for personnel services and the latter provided trained personnel and laboratory facilities. Five papers resulted (30). The results from the study of wheat kernels were published in the *Journal of the American Chemical Society* in 1923 and those on oats in the *Journal of the Franklin Institute* in 1924. The other three papers, covering results obtained in the studies of the kernels of maize, rye, and rice, respectively, appeared in the Journal of Agricultural Research in 1925 and 1927 (30). The coöperation was shown in the scientific titles of the authors at the beginning of each paper.

The chemical study of forages, from the results previously stated, has not been extensive, and the coöperative examples are still fewer. A little work was done in connection with agricultural changes in the semiarid West, it being recorded that the Bureau of Chemistry analyzed some fifty-seven samples of forage plants collected by the Office of Farm Management (61—1907 :391). In the next year a study of locoweeds, poisonous forage plants from the western ranges, was made in coöperation with the Bureau of Plant Industry (61—1908 :474). In a study of the relation of curing practices to the quality of alfalfa hay, conducted by the

Division of Agronomy of the Nebraska Agricultural Experiment Station, in coöperation with the Federal Bureaus of Plant Industry and Agricultural Economics and published in 1931, the Department of Chemistry of the University of Nebraska made the protein determinations (56—235).

Wheat.—Of all the commercial crops wheat has been the most important, with corn (maize) ranking next. Naturally, therefore, the earliest commercial studies were made on these two crops. Some relations in wheat studies have been given in the preceding pages, as a part of general cereal studies. Special wheat studies follow.

In 1883 and 1884, the Chemical Division of the U. S. Department of Agriculture published two comprehensive reports containing extensive analyses of samples of wheat and maize (64—1 and 4). Most of the samples were obtained from farmer coöperators of the Department, but the Agricultural Colleges of Colorado and Michigan and the State University of Ohio grew wheats primarily for these tests, Professor Blount, the wheat breeder of Colorado, being especially interested (82). This was before the agricultural experiment stations were established with Federal aid.

In 1899, the Soil and Fertilizer Laboratory of the Division of Chemistry began the first of a notable series of studies on the composition of wheat, in coöperation with various units of what became, in 1901, the Bureau of Plant Industry, and with varying numbers of the State agricultural experiment stations. The studies were directed toward the problem of deterioration of wheat quality, and its improvement by chemical methods. Arrangements were made in that year with the Stations in California, Colorado, Indiana, Kentucky, Maryland, Michigan, and Missouri, to grow portions of a uniform lot of wheat seed to be furnished by the Division, which made all the analyses (61—1899:38; 82). This work was continued and expanded to include other cereals in 1900, and still other crops in 1901, as noted in the discussion of cereals (65—9 and 11).

In 1900, the Office of Grain (Cereal) Investigations (after 1901, of the Bureau of Plant Industry) of the U. S. Department of Agriculture began the introduction and testing of durum wheats, which provide the semolina used in the manufacture of the edible pastes such as macaroni, spaghetti, and vermicelli. The coöperation in the agronomic field will be discussed under Plant Industries, but the relations in chemical studies are pertinent here. The Division of Chemistry and the Office of Grain Investigations coöperated at the beginning in this phase of the work (14; 61—1901: 102). Soon afterwards, the Office of Cereal Investigations employed its own physiological chemist and published a comprehensive bulletin (15) in 1904, containing a mass of chemical data. The chemist-author was transferred to the Bureau of Chemistry some three years later when the Laboratory of Vegetable Physiological Investigations was established there in 1907. In 1900, also, coöperative experiments were begun with the South Dakota Agricultural Experiment Station in both agronomic and chemical tests of these wheats and were continued for several years (47).

In 1905 a coöperative agreement was made by the Bureau of Plant Industry and the California Agricultural Experiment Station for the improvement of wheat and other cereals. The work was primarily agronomic but the plan provided for chemical studies by the experiment station, which was represented by its Division of Chemistry as well as by crop specialists, the Federal agency being the Office of Cereal Investigations. The formal coöperation lasted only two years, but informal coöperation continued. The State published limited chemical data in 1907 (45), giving the history of the experiment and the content of the agreement.

The year 1905 saw also the beginnings of coöperative experiments in exchange of seed to determine the influence of climate on the composition of wheat. These were conducted by the Laboratory of Vegetable Physiological Chemistry (Bureau of Chemistry), the Office of Grain Investigations (Bureau of Plant Industry), and the Divisions of Agronomy and Chemistry at the California Station. They were part of what was designated as trilocal experiments because conducted in three States simultaneously. Two varieties of wheat were used. In 1905, the wheat grown in one of these States was sent to each of the other two for sowing. In 1906 and each year thereafter the wheat thus grown in each State was sown again in that State and sent as well to each of the others for sowing. Thus three plats of a given variety were grown in each State each year, one from home-grown seed and the other two from seed home grown in the other States. Kubanka durum wheat was grown in

South Dakota, Kansas, and California, while Crimean hard red winter common wheat was grown in Kansas, Texas, and California. Three State Experiment Stations took part in the two trilocals, the Texas agency being a Federal field station. The Federal Bureau of Chemistry published results in 1910 (35), stating the coöperation of the two Federal bureaus in the Letter of Transmittal and in the Introduction, and naming the States involved but not specifically stating the coöperation.

In 1907, a coöperative bilocal experiment in the exchange of soil between States was begun. The same Federal and California agencies were concerned, together with the Kansas station. Soil from a small plat at the California Station at Davis was taken up in six-inch layers and shipped to the Hays Branch Station at Hays, Kansas, from whence similar quantities of soil were sent to Davis. Each soil was laid down in the other State, to replace that shipped. One half of each plot was sown with home-grown seed of wheat and the other half with seed from the State where the soil originated. In 1908 a new trilocal experiment involving exchange of soil was begun. The same Federal agencies and the California and Kansas Stations again took part, with the Maryland Agricultural Experiment Station as the third point in the triangle. The chemical data from these wheat experiments have been published by California (46), and by the U. S. Department of Agriculture (36), both making minor reference to the coöperation, in the text.

In recent years the Office of Cereal Crops and Diseases of the Federal Bureau of Plant Industry has conducted extensive milling and baking experiments with wheat, involving some chemical determinations, especially of nitrogen. The greater part of this work has been done in coöperation with the Milling, Baking, and Chemical Laboratory of the Grain Division of the Federal Bureau of Agricultural Economics, the Cereals Division furnishing technical personnel for the work (55—1183). At times similar arrangements have been made with the Division of Cereal Chemistry of the Federal Bureau of Chemistry, so far as nitrogen determinations were involved. For a time (1915–17), also, coöperative arrangements were maintained with the milling section of the Division of Chemistry in the North Dakota Agricultural Experiment Station (55—1183).

The publications listed in the Literature Cited at the end of this chapter which are cited in this portion devoted to Cereal and Forage Crops in the subsection on Plant Chemistry are Nos. 10, 14, 15, 30, 32, 35, 36, 45, 46, 47, 55, 56, 61, 62, 64, 65, 76, and 82.

Sugar and Sirup Plants

One of the first investigations in chemistry ever undertaken by the Federal government had to do with sugar. In 1830 the House of Representatives requested the President to obtain sugar cane, among other agricultural products, and directed the Secretary of the Treasury to prepare a manual on the culture of sugar cane and the refining of sugar. The task was confided to Professor Silliman of Yale University in 1832, and the manual was prepared and published in 1833, the work having been done in coöperation with various other chemists. As sugar was in growing demand and was wholly imported, the Patent Office gave a good deal of attention to the problems of sugar production from 1839 up to the transfer of its agricultural activities in 1862. The sugar beet was introduced in about 1830. The Federal distribution of seed of the sorgos or sirup sorghums was begun in 1855 with the Chinese Amber variety, and in 1857 with the South African imphees. Distribution was through State agricultural agencies and also direct to farmers. Sugar cane and even the sugar maple were not forgotten. Beginning in 1841, the Patent Office gave much attention to the possibility of obtaining sugar from the stalks of maize or Indian corn (76:8–9).

The creation of the U. S. Department of Agriculture in 1862 and the establishment of a Chemical Division in the same year made for increased attention to the culture of sugar plants and the manufacture of sugar. No experiment stations were established but much work was done in the field through coöperation with commercial sugar growers and makers. The investigations (76:25–29) proceeded along three major lines, namely, the possibility of producing sugar from sorghum and maize, the determination of where and how the sugar beet might be profitably grown, and improvements in sugar-cane culture, cane-sugar making, and sirup manufacture. Some collaborative relations developed in each of these fields, though mostly minor in scope.

Sorgo for sugar.—The Agricultural Section of the Patent Office in the U. S. Department of the Interior began the distribution of the seeds of sorgo or sweet sorghum as early as 1855, and continued it vigorously with both Chinese Amber and African imphees until interrupted by the Civil War. The Division of Chemistry of the U. S. Department of Agriculture took up the work after the War and continued it until about 1893. The object was the production of sirup north of the sugar-cane belt, and the possible establishment of a new sugar industry. In the distribution of seeds and the testing of varietal adaptations, the Federal agencies collaborated with the State agricultural societies, agricultural colleges, and agricultural experiment stations, as these successively developed.

The question of sugar production from sorghum was always coming up, and the chemical problems involved were studied from time to time. Similar studies were made on corn stalks. Intensive experiments in the making of sorghum sugar were conducted by Dr. Peter Collier, Chemist of the Department of Agriculture (50), in the years from 1878 to 1883, but ceased with his resignation. Little or no coöperation was involved. Interest was revived by Dr. Wiley and a review of the entire sugar industry in America (cane, beet, sorghum, and maple) was published in 1885 (64—5). Experiments were begun on improved chemical processes in 1885 and one bulletin (or more) issued on the annual experiments from 1885 to 1893 (64—6, 14, 17, 18, 20, 26, 29, 34, 37, and 40). Starting in a small way, these experiments gradually covered many States from New Jersey to Kansas and southward, but finally became concentrated at points in Kansas. Most of the work was done in private sugar factories, by Federal chemists detailed for that purpose during the crushing season. In some cases the Division provided equipment. Later, it built one or more small plants, because of the difficulty of exact control of experimental operations in commercial plants. Some of the commercial factories with which the Division collaborated were enabled to keep going through sugar bounties provided by State or local government agencies.

There was only minor and sporadic coöperation with any official agencies in the sorghum sugar experiments. In 1890, selected Kansas sorghum seed was sent to the Mississippi Station, which grew and analyzed the resulting crop, the Division furnishing the Station a hand mill for the grinding (64—29). In 1892, sorghum seeds were sent from the Department's plots at Sterling, Kansas, to thirty-two State experiment stations for growing, but only a few definite reports were received (64—37). At the close of the experiments it was proposed to furnish seed of pure lines of the various improved varieties to the State agricultural experiment stations, if they would agree to keep them pure from admixtures (64—40). The necessity of purifying the varieties and the hope of developing still better sugar-producing varieties led the Division of Chemistry to establish breeding plots as early as 1889. For the most part these were on land leased from farmers near the sugar-making plants, the areas gradually increasing until 173 acres were so used at Sterling, Kansas, alone, in 1892. Some of this work, also, was done in coöperation with the Louisiana Station at its Kenner Sugar Experiment Station, beginning in 1889.

Sugar beet.—In about 1888, the Division of Chemistry began to give attention to the sugar beet in its study of all possible sources of sugar production in America (64—3 and 5). The first endeavor was to promote beet growing in the North Central States. Having no field stations of its own, the Division asked State experiment stations to coöperate by growing beets from seed furnished by the Department. The first comprehensive Federal publication (64—27), appearing in 1890, reviewed the history of the sugar beet in Europe and America, and noted the results of experiments in 1888 and 1889 by State Stations in Indiana, Iowa, Michigan, Nebraska, South Dakota, and Wisconsin, those in Wisconsin being coöperative wth the Division. Four successive additional bulletins (64—30, 33, 36, and 39) presented the results of experiments conducted in 1890, 1891, 1892, and 1893, respectively. Tons of selected German seed were distributed to farmers, from whom samples for analysis were obtained; the coöperation with Wisconsin Station was expanded (64—33 :90–111) ; and tillage and rotation experiments were begun in 1891 on leased land at Schuyler, Nebraska, thought to be representative of a large area in several States. At the end of 1893 all the experiments were discontinued by order of Secretary Morton.

Investigation of sugar-beet production was reëstablished along two separate lines by order of Secretary Wilson, in 1897. Coöperative studies with the State agricultural experiment stations were begun by the Federal Division of Chemistry. The Secretary appointed the Directors of the various State stations to be special correspondents of the Department with the use of the franking privilege in distributing beet seeds to farmers and in assembling the mature beets for analysis. If seeds were distributed by a State, analyses were made by the State station and the results communicated to the Division as well as published by the State itself. The Division published these coöperative State results for 1897 in a comprehensive bulletin (64—52:56–125), which also appeared in House Document 396 of the second session of the 55th Congress. Special experiments in seed production were conducted by the Division in coöperation with the State Stations in Indiana, Iowa, Kentucky, New York, Tennessee, and Wisconsin. In 1899 the Division of Chemistry obtained some twenty tons of high-grade sugar-beet seed in Europe and distributed it largely to and through the State experiment stations (61—1899:29). The resulting samples of beets were analyzed by the Division.

In 1900, the Division of Chemistry began a rather comprehensive study of the influence of environment, chiefly climate and soil, upon the composition and yield of the sugar beet. Identical lots of seed from specially selected beets were grown, on request of the Division, at a group of State agricultural experiment stations chosen because of their climatic and soil environments. Samples for analysis, taken weekly over a period of several weeks, were forwarded to the Division in Washington, and in many cases a corresponding sample was analyzed at the State station. Samples of the soil from the beet plots were forwarded to Washington for chemical analysis. The Bureau of Plant Industry helped to obtain and test the seed and also grew beets in its plots near Washington. Meteorological data for each station were obtained through coöperation by the Weather Bureau, the length of the day at each station was computed by the Naval Observatory, and the data on altitude and latitude of each station were contributed by the Coast and Geodetic Survey, then of the Treasury Department. In the appropriation bill of the Department of Agriculture for the fiscal year 1903, the Bureau of Chemistry was specifically authorized to collaborate with the Weather Bureau and the State agricultural experiment stations in studies of the effect of environment on the chemical composition of sugar-producing plants (76:29). Previously the work had been done under the general authorization and funds of the Bureau. These studies were continued during a period of five years (1900–1904) and the Bureau published the results annually in its series of *Bulletins* (64—64, 74, 78, 95, and 96), the fifth and last containing a summary of the five-year study.

Coöperation was indicated plainly and with unusual frequency in this series of publications. On the front cover, and again on the title page, of each bulletin appear the words, printed in small capitals, "In collaboration with the Weather Bureau and the Agricultural Experiment Stations of ———" [names of the States]. This probably is the earliest instance of this plain and prominent statement of coöperation on the covers and title pages of publications. The coöperation of the Weather Bureau and the State stations was acknowledged again in the Letter of Transmittal of the bulletins. The coöperating State stations were named in the introductory paragraphs. The Table of Contents showed the coöperation plainly by the entries, "Experiments conducted by ——— [State] Station," and this was repeated, or at least the name of the station was, as a bold-face center heading in the text, under which the State data appeared. The collaboration of the Coast and Geodetic Survey and the Naval Observatory was acknowledged in the Letters of Transmittal of three of the five bulletins, and as footnotes to the tables in two of them. This series must be regarded as an early and gratifying example of unusually prominent and frequent posting of the coöperative relations.

The States coöperating in 1900 were Indiana, Iowa, Kentucky, Michigan, New York (both stations), North Carolina, Utah, and Wisconsin. During some part of the five-year period, California, Colorado, New Mexico, Oregon, Virginia, and Wyoming also took part. The results from analyses of beets grown in each State were published by the Division under the State name, whether the analyses were made by the State station or by the Bureau, or both.

Miscellaneous analyses made in the years from 1905 to 1910, apparently involving no collaboration with official agencies, are reported in Bureau of Chemistry *Bulletin* 146 (64—146).

In the meantime a commercial and agricultural study of sugar-beet production in the United States was being made by a special agent appointed by and directly responsible to the Secretary of Agriculture. He prepared annual reports on the progress of the sugar-beet industry for the years from 1897 to 1909, inclusive, except 1903. Each was issued in the year following that covered by the contents. Those for 1897, 1898, and 1899 were published in the unnumbered Special Reports of the Department of Agriculture (26:14), whereas those for 1900 to 1909, excluding 1903, were published in the series of numbered Reports of the Department (59—69, 72, 74, 80, 82, 84, 86, 90, and 92). In most cases (1897–99) they were published by or under direct annual authorization of the Congress, as noted on or in the volumes, and by Gates (24:130). These reports well illustrate the gradual transition of the functions of the Division of Chemistry from field experiments in the culture and improvement of crops to the more restricted field of chemical analysis only, coincident with the creation of the Bureau of Plant Industry in 1901 and its subsequent rapid development. These annual progress reports had to do with all the agricultural phases of the beet industry, as well as the commercial progress. The first four, 1897–1900, inclusive, were joint products of the Secretary's special agent and the Division of Chemistry, each part, however, under separate authorship. They contained also brief annual summaries of the work of the State stations on sugar beets, including some chemical data, communicated by the several directors. Those from 1901 to 1907 were similar joint products of the agent and the Bureau of Plant Industry, the latter at first limited to discussions of seed and diseases, but including fertilizers from 1904 and all cultural phases from 1906. No State experiment station data were included, except briefly in 1905. In 1902 the Congress had specifically authorized the Secretary of Agriculture to continue inquiry on the progress of the beet-sugar and sorghum-sugar industries, but the item was under the Bureau of Plant Industry (76:29). From 1906 onward the reports were transmitted to the Secretary by the Bureau of Plant Industry rather than by the special agent.

Sugar cane.—In 1830 the Congress directed the Secretary of the Treasury to prepare a manual on the culture of sugar cane and the refining of sugar, which was done in 1833. Sugar-cane growing and cane-sugar making had become thoroughly established industries, long before the Chemical Division was created in the U. S. Department of Agriculture in 1862. For many years, therefore, the Division gave its attention to the newer and promising sugar crops, sorgo (saccharine sorghum) and sugar beets. Out of the sorghum experiments, however, was developed the diffusion process for extraction of sugar which caused the Division to begin experiments in the making of cane sugar.

In 1884, the Division of Chemistry installed a complete sugar laboratory at the Cotton States Exposition at New Orleans, and exhibited also its small diffusion battery used in 1883. In 1884, also, the Division began experiments in the chemical control of sugar manufacture at the Magnolia plantation of Governor Warmoth at Lawrence, Louisiana. From this beginning was developed an extensive coöperation with commercial sugar factories in Louisiana, including the Des Lignes plantation at Baldwin and the Calumet plantation at Pattersonville. In 1886 some 150 tons of cane were shipped to a sorghum-sugar factory in Kansas and extracted by the diffusion process, which resulted in its commercial adoption in Louisiana, beginning with the Magnolia plantation in 1887 (64—21).

In 1885, or possibly in 1884, experiments were begun by the Division at the Kenner Sugar Experiment Station, Louisiana, in coöperation with the Louisiana Agricultural Experiment Station. Reports on the collaborative experiments and those conducted in commercial factories were published from time to time (64—22 and 23).

About 1902, under direct authorization from Congress, the Bureau of Chemistry began a series of experiments in Georgia on the production of table sirup from sugar cane (64—75, 93, and 103). Apparently these were wholly independent of any State coöperation. More than twenty years later, the Bureau of Chemistry again collaborated in studies of sugar-cane sirup manufacture. The resulting publication (55—1370) contained chapters by that Bureau, the Bureau of Plant Industry, and the Sugar Experiment Station of the Louisiana Agricultural Experiment Station.

Fruit Juices and Fruits

For more than thirty years the Bureau of Chemistry has been conducting studies on the composition of fruit juices and on their fermentations, as well as on the fruits from which such juices are obtained. Some of this work has been coöperative with State or Federal agencies and some has been wholly independent. Apparently the work with juices was the first to be undertaken.

Fruit juices.—About 1901 the Bureau of Chemistry of the U. S. Department entered into a coöperation with the Virginia Agricultural Experiment Station whereby Prof. W. B. Alwood of that Station was appointed a special agent to undertake extensive studies on the composition of apples and of the apple pomace and must resulting from expression for cider making (64—88). This project, later, was expanded to include analyses of American fruits generally in reference to the manufacture of wine, cider, and vinegar, and to include a study of organisms causing the fermentation of such fruit juices (61—1902:146). Such studies were called enological-chemical investigations and were carried on for several years. New equipment for this research was furnished by the Bureau in 1907 (61—1907:400). Not long thereafter, however, the laboratory was removed from the Virginia Station and established at Charlottesville, but apparently entirely independently of any other institution. From this as a base, studies were conducted in various States, mostly without coöperation. In 1916, on the other hand, the Bureau published an extensive study of the composition of American grapes (55—452) conducted in several States and coöperative in North Carolina with the State Board of Agriculture, which provided quarters in its chemical laboratory at Raleigh and directed the superintendent of its Pender Experiment Farm to aid in collecting samples in the State (*op. cit.*, p. 3).

In about the year 1906 the Bureau began to develop fruit-juice studies in its own laboratories, in coöperation with the horticultural experts of the Bureau of Plant Industry. The results of a study of unfermented apple juice were published in 1908 (64—118), Plant Industry having selected and supplied the materials (*op. cit.*, p. 11). Other studies followed in rapid succession. Two published in 1910 included the cold storage of apple cider (65—

48) and the value of peaches as vinegar stock (65—51), in which Plant Industry aided by inoculating certain lots of fruit with a pure culture of Monilia. In 1915 appeared the results (55—241) of a four-year study on fruit juices derived from the pineapple and from various berries and citruses. Plant Industry collaboration is acknowledged in selecting the localities and obtaining the samples of the different fruits (*op. cit.*, p. 1).

Fruits.—In 1903, the Division of Foods of the Bureau of Chemistry, with the collaboration of the Microchemical Laboratory of the same Bureau, began a study of the chemistry of fruits, with special reference to storage, in collaboration also with the Bureau of Plant Industry, all of the U. S. Department of Agriculture. This was continued for several years. The Office of Pomological Investigations of the latter Bureau, in charge of Wm. A. Taylor, arranged to obtain and select the samples of fruits to be studied, arranged for their transportation to and storage in Washington, supplied pomological data on the material, and aided in planning and interpreting the experiments, as stated in the various letters of transmittal for publication. From 1924 to 1926 the Office of Horticultural Crops and Diseases, Bureau of Plant Industry, and the Food, Drug, and Insecticide Administration investigated the effects of the frozen-pack method of preserving berries in the Pacific Northwest and published jointly (56—148) in 1930. The Western Washington Experiment Station at Puyallup, a branch of the State Station, furnished office and laboratory facilities for the work.

The first study, published in 1905, covered the chemistry and physiology of apples, with examinations of the starch grains (64—94). The second study, also published in 1905, covered similar investigations of peaches (64—97). In a chemical study of the processing of persimmons to render them nonastringent, published in 1911, the Bureau of Industry not only selected the fruits to be tested, but suggested the lines of investigation most likely to prove of value to persimmon growers. An extensive review of the persimmon industry (*op. cit.*, pp. 5–9) was contributed by David G. Fairchild, Chief of the Office of Foreign Seed and Plant Introduction, in the Bureau of Plant Industry (64—141). A second contribution, in which the Bureau of Plant Industry again collaborated, discussed large-scale processing of persimmons (64—155). Coöperative experiments were conducted also on the preparation of sugared, dried pineapples (65—57). In 1911, also, there were published the results of experiments on the respiration of fruits, again in coöperation with the Bureau of Plant Industry (64—142).

In about 1914 the question of alleged toxicity of spray residues on American fruits became important to export trade. Accordingly, extensive investigations were conducted during 1915 and 1916. The Bureau of Chemistry (Insecticide and Fungicide Laboratory, Miscellaneous Division) made chemical analyses of samples of seven different kinds of fruits and three kinds of vegetables which had been sprayed by the Bureau of Entomology (Fruit Insects) and the Bureau of Plant Industry (Fruit Diseases). A full discussion of the results wes published in 1922 (55—1027), accompanied by an extensive bibliography (pp. 58—66). Other noncooperative studies followed. From 1925 to 1929 the Division of Fruit Insects of the Bureau of Entomology, coöperating with the Maine Agricultural Experiment Station and the State Department of Agriculture on the control of the blueberry maggot in Maine, received also the coöperation of the Federal Bureau of Chemistry in analyses of the arsenical residues (56–275).

In 1924, the Bureau of Plant Industry published on the Chinese jujube (55—1215), to which the Laboratory of Fruit and Vegetable Chemistry of the Bureau of Chemistry contributed a chapter on chemical composition (pp. 24—29).

For many years the Bureau of Plant Industry has been investigating bud variation in the citrus fruits: lemons, oranges, and grapefruits (70). After numerous favorable and unfavorable variants had been isolated and propagated, it became desirable to determine the inheritance of chemical composition in fruits from such vegetative reproduction. Coöperative arrangements were made between the Bureau of Chemistry, represented by its Laboratory of Fruit and Vegetable Chemistry at Los Angeles, and the Bureau of Plant Industry, represented by its field station of horticultural crops and diseases located in coöperation with the State Citrus Experiment Station at Riverside, California. The study was begun in 1919, Plant Industry furnishing the selected material. The first publication by the Bureau of Chemistry covered a four-

year study of lemons (55—1255). An introduction was written by
Plant Industry, and a footnote gives credit to the Scripps Institution of the University of California for advice and coöperation.
A second study covered oranges (56—163), and was published in
1930. All fruits were selected by Plant Industry, the progeny trees
being grown on the Citrus Experiment Station at Riverside.

Vegetables

Relatively little coöperative study has been devoted by the Bureau
of Chemistry to the chemistry of vegetables. One of the projects
started under the general investigation, begun in 1901, on the influence of environment on the composition of crops, was a study
of muskmelons. This included the Agricultural Experiment Stations of Arizona, California, Colorado, Delaware, Indiana, Kentucky, Maryland, New Jersey, North Carolina, and Texas (61—
1902:142). Apparently the results were not published in the
Bureau series.

About 1905, there arose the question of poisonous qualities in
certain cassava varieties introduced by the Bureau of Plant Industry of the Department. The two Bureaus coöperated in a study.
Plant Industry grew the material at its Gulf Coast field station
and also contributed the botanical descriptions of the varieties, as
stated in the Letter of Transmittal. The Bureau of Chemistry determined the hydrocyanic acid and other constituents and published the results in 1907 (64—106). The cover and title pages bear
the words, "In Collaboration with the Bureau of Plant Industry."

As part of the study of the influence of environment on crop composition, a four-year study of sweet corn was begun in 1905, after
the conclusion of the similar studies on sugar beet. The results were
published in 1909 (64—127). The Letter of Transmittal says that
the collaboration included the Bureau of Plant Industry and the
Agricultural Experiment Stations of Connecticut, Florida, Maine,
Maryland, New Jersey, and South Carolina. A chemist from the
Bureau went to each coöperating station to make the analyses.
Plant Industry aided in growing the crops and in the interpretation of the results of breeding and adaptation.

In the course of nutrition studies conducted by the Office of Home
Economics of the States Relations Service, U. S. Department of

Agriculture, collaboration was effected with the Bureau of Plant Industry in ascertaining the digestibility of the dasheen. The publication of results (55—612) in 1917 showed that the material was grown and shipped by Plant Industry (p. 2).

About 1920 the Bureau of Chemistry collaborated with the Maine Agricultural Experiment Station in determining possible poisoning of potato plants by soils where potatoes had been sprayed with copper solutions (17). According to a statement in the text, the tests were conducted at the Aroostook Farm of the Maine Station.

In an investigation of the possibility of obtaining sirup from sweet potatoes, considerable collaboration was developed. The Laboratory of Fruit and Vegetable Utilization of the Bureau of Chemistry obtained the use of a commercial oil plant in Georgia for the manufacturing operations, and the Office of Development Work of the same Bureau designed and installed the equipment needed. The coöperation of the Federal States-Relations Service and of several State agricultural extension services was enlisted for testing the quality of the sirups (55—1158).

Recently a minor collaboration of the Offices of Vegetable and Forage Diseases and Fruit Diseases, in the Bureau of Plant Industry, and the University of Chicago, which furnished laboratories, studied injury to onions and fruits caused by exposure to ammonia (42).

Miscellaneous Crops

The multiplying of chemical laboratories in different official agencies in recent years has made collaboration on many miscellaneous problems unnecessary. A few instances of relations in the plant field may be cited, however, some of which are recent.

In 1896 the Office of Experiment Stations of the U. S. Department of Agriculture published a comprehensive treatise of some 430 pages on the cotton plant, including its history, botany, chemistry, enemies, and uses (68—33). The chapter on chemistry was contributed by the Division of Chemistry. In 1921, a compilation of cotton-seed analyses made by commercial crushers was issued as a joint contribution of the Bureau of Markets and the Bureau of Chemistry, both in the Federal Department of Agriculture (55—948). Other chemical studies on cotton are discussed under

Attractants, in the Section on Insecticides, Repellents, and Attractants, later in this chapter.

From 1914 to 1916 the Office of Cereal Investigation in the Bureau of Plant Industry was making an intensive study of varieties of flax. Chemical studies of the resulting linseed oil were highly important and were obtained through a coöperative arrangement with the Office of Drug, Poisonous, and Oil Plant Investigations of the same Bureau (55—883).

Tobacco.—Tobacco quality is more directly and profoundly influenced by soil characters than is that of most crops. It probably was only natural, therefore, that tobacco investigations should have originated in the Division of Soils rather than in a plant-industry unit. However, coöperative relations were quickly effected between the Division of Soils and the Office of Vegetable Physiology and Pathology, one of the units which soon after became a component of the Bureau of Plant Industry. A fermentation specialist (Oscar Loew) was detailed from the latter agency to the Soils Division, and a study of the relation of tobacco fermentation processes to the soils was made (50—1899 and 1900). Three special publications (59—59, 65, and 68) were issued in 1899, 1900, and 1901, respectively. The Division of Chemistry collaborated in the analyses. The Connecticut Agricultural Experiment Station assisted in conducting the experiments in that State (71—1900:78).

The investigation of tobacco always has entailed chemical and physiological studies, so much so that the Office of Tobacco Investigations soon was enlarged in name to Tobacco and Plant Nutrition Investigations. Many of the coöperative investigations of this Division might be cited under agricultural chemistry, but it seems preferable to discuss them under plant industry, where their major emphasis lies. A few instances will serve to show the recent chemical outreach. The Tobacco Division and the North Carolina Department of Agriculture established a Branch Tobacco Station in that State. The results of a coöperative study of a tobacco chlorosis, due to magnesium deficiency, and the relation of potassium compounds to the disease were published in 1923 (22). In 1930 two coöperative papers appeared (23A; 23B). They discussed the relation of magnesium, calcium, and chlorine to tobacco nutrition, and represented coöperation of the Division with the North Carolina Department of

Agriculture, the Georgia State College of Agriculture, and the Agricultural Experiment Stations of Connecticut, Maryland, and North Carolina.

Forest Products

Relations under this heading belong properly to the chapter on Forests, in the volume on Natural Resources, and will be presented fully there. Only early or unusual relations need brief mention here.

As early as 1900, the Division of Chemistry began to work with the Division of Forestry in chemical tests of woods and barks, and provided space for an investigator from the Division of Forestry (61—1900:25). In 1902 a Dendro-Chemical Laboratory was established in the Bureau of Chemistry in coöperation with the Bureau of Forestry (76:46), to correlate and continue the collaboration of the two units in chemical studies of woods, wood pulp, papers, tanning materials, distillates, chemical killers for inferior timber growth, and other chemical and histological studies in forests and forest products (61—1902:140).

On July 1, 1904, the Dendro-Chemical Laboratory was discontinued as such, and a Leather and Paper Laboratory established in the Bureau of Chemistry. In 1905, the Forest-Products Laboratory was established in the Forest Service, and the coöperation of the two Bureaus ceased. The work on tanning materials and naval stores (rosin, turpentine, etc.) remained permanently in the Bureau of Chemistry.

During the World War, the Bureau of Chemistry and the Bureau of Mines collaborated with the War Department in extensive tests of charcoal materials and charcoal manufacture in connection with the development of the justly famous American gas masks (39: 100).

In 1921 the Bureau of Chemistry of the U. S. Department of Agriculture and the Department of Forestry of the University of Idaho issued a joint publication (55—1003) under joint authorship, on the distillation of logging wastes and stumpwood of western yellow pine, the result of collaborative investigation. The U. S. Bureau of Mines, through its station at Salt Lake City, coöperated in testing the resulting oils for use in the flotation of ores in smelting.

The publications listed in the Literature Cited at the end of this chapter which are cited in this subsection on Plant Chemistry are Nos. 10, 14, 15, 17, 22, 23A, 23B, 24, 26, 30, 32, 35, 36, 39, 42, 45, 46, 47, 50, 55, 56, 59, 61, 62, 64, 65, 68, 70, 71, 76, and 82.

ANIMAL CHEMISTRY

Relatively little coöperative investigation has been made in animal chemistry. Important instances may be cited, however, under the problems of dairy products, fish and meat composition, animal nutrition, and leather quality. The cited instance of coöperation in animal nutrition is remarkable for its duration, and for the prominent and consistent display of the coöperative relations in the series of publications.

Dairy Products

Extensive investigation of the adulteration of dairy products, such as milk, butter, and cheese, was begun by the Division of Chemistry as early as 1883, when Wiley became its chief (76:37). These studies soon were extended to cover meats, meat products, lard, etc. Apparently there was no particular coöperation in these early years. In 1884 Congress created the Bureau of Animal Industry, which resulted in the gradual transfer of the studies on animal and dairy products to that Bureau. By 1901, however, and perhaps earlier, collaboration between the Division of Chemistry and the Bureau of Animal Industry had begun through a chemical study of dairy products, especially cheese (61—1900:24, and 1901:102). In 1902, and for some years thereafter, the Congress provided for an investigation by the Bureau of Chemistry, in collaboration with the Dairy Division of the Bureau of Animal Industry, of the chemistry of dairy products, including adulterated products and their adulterants, processed or treated butters, and other chemical studies relating to dairy products (76:39). Frequent mention is made of these coöperative studies in their annual reports during the next few years (61—1902–05).

For some three years, beginning about 1904, the Dairy Division of the Bureau of Animal Industry worked with the Storrs Agricultural Experiment Station in Connecticut under a formal agreement. The station furnished laboratories and equipment for making the Camembert type of soft cheeses and the Division furnished a cheese-maker, a chemist, and a mycologist. The first resulting publication appeared under joint authorship in 1905 (60—71), and others, less definitely chemical, followed in 1906 and 1907 (60—82 and 98). As late as 1917 the Dairy Division and the Bureau of Chemistry collaborated in the preparation of a guide for formulating a municipal milk ordinance, which appeared as a joint contribution from the two Bureaus, with other prominent display of the coöperative relations (55—585).

Fish and Meat Composition

Beginning in 1878 and continuing for some ten years, the U. S. Commission of Fish and Fisheries collaborated with the Smithsonian Institution in financing an extensive study of the chemical composition and nutritive value of food fishes and aquatic invertebrates, compared with those of the ordinary meats of commerce. In the three resulting papers (7; 8; 9), totaling some 400 pages, the data are presented in full. Acknowledgments of the coöperation are contained in all the papers, including assistance from the State fish commissioner of New York, who furnished material, information, and $100 toward the cost of the analyses. Private firms and individuals also contributed in these ways. The third paper contains the comparisons with meats, which the Smithsonian Institution helped to finance (9:680), in order that the study might be more complete.

In 1898 the Iowa Agricultural Experiment Station had grown representative lots of eight standard breeds of hogs from birth to maturity under controlled conditions. When about to have the slaughter test made by a Chicago packing house, the Station proposed to the U. S. Department of Agriculture that it coöperate in making complete chemical studies of one representative carcass from each breed. The proposal was accepted, the carcasses shipped, and the analyses made and published by the Bureau of Chemistry (64—53).

Animal Nutrition

In 1898, the Bureau of Animal Industry began formal collaboration with the Pennsylvania State College in a critical study of the nutrition of cattle. This research was continued for more than twenty-five years and resulted in a long series of coöperative publications. From 1903 to 1912 no less than nine of these appeared in the bulletin series of the Bureau (60—51, 74, 94, 101, 108, 124, 128, 139, and 143), mostly under the sole or senior authorship of Dr. Henry Prentiss Armsby, director of the Institute of Animal Nutrition at the College, which was organized about 1908. Two others appeared in the series of bulletins of the Pennsylvania Agricultural Experiment Station (2; 3) in 1907 and 1910. After the establishment of the Federal-State scientific journal, the *Journal of Agricultural Research,* in 1913, eight additional papers in the series (4; 33) appeared in it during the years from 1915 to 1921, and a final paper in 1925 under the senior authorship of Dr. Forbes, who succeeded to the directorship after Dr. Armsby's death (20). The coöperative research was primarily in cattle feeding, but it was done from the standpoint of nutrition and therefore was indirectly a chemical study. In two of the earlier bulletins the author gives credit to the Division of Chemistry for making the analyses. The research will be presented more fully in the chapter on Animal Industries but deserves mention here from the standpoint of coöperation in chemistry and warrants especial emphasis because of consistent prominence given to the statement of coöperation throughout the quarter of a century (See pp. 390–392, below).

In the nine Bureau bulletins, the coöperation is shown plainly and prominently on the cover page and the title page. In six cases it is in prominent capital letters in the center of the page. In the other three the author, Dr. Armsby, carries both Bureau and Station titles in italics, below his name. In all of the nine bulletins the coöperation is mentioned in the Bureau Letter of Transmittal, and in the six bulletins previously noted it appears also in the Pennsylvania Station Letter of Submittal. On the two State bulletins the coöperation is plainly declared on the covers. In the series of papers in the *Journal of Agricultural Research* (from 1915 to 1921) the words, "Coöperative Investigations Between the Bureau of Animal Industry, United States Department of Agriculture, and the Institute of Animal Nutrition of the Pennsylvania State College," are printed in capital letters just below the scientific titles of the authors. In the later papers the order of the two institutions was reversed. In the final paper the relation is shown only by a footnote on the first page.

Leather Quality

The U.S. Bureau of Chemistry has retained jurisdiction of research on leather and paper in spite of the development of many related lines of activity by the Bureaus of Animal Industry, Dairy Industry, Plant Industry, and Forest Service. Most of the leather research has not been coöperative with other official agencies. There have been official relations, however, in two extensive tests of the wearing qualities of shoe leathers subjected to different chemical processes in tanning.

In 1917 a test of the wearing qualities of shoes was planned in coöperation with the United States Army, and the experiment was carried out in 1919. The coöperation covered the selection and inspection of the material used, the manufacture of the shoes in shoe factories supplying army shoes under contract, and subsequent supervision of wearing tests by soldiers. The results were published by the Bureau in 1923 (55—1168). In 1930 the Bureau published the results of a second test of shoes, which included the wearing qualities and other properties of vegetable-tanned and chrome-tanned sole leathers. (56—169). In this case the wearing tests were conducted in coöperation with the Post Office Department and the City Post Office of Washington, D. C., and included both officials and letter carriers, as indicated by footnote and text statement (*op. cit.*, p. 11).

During the War the Bureau collaborated with the Ordnance Office of the War Department in tests of leathers for the heavy duty required in the recoil mechanisms of guns and with the Quartermaster Corps in providing substitutes for neat's-foot oil as harness dressings (39:93).

The publications listed in the 'Literature Cited at the end of this chapter which are cited in this subsection on Animal Chemistry are Nos. 2, 3, 4, 7, 8, 9, 20, 33, 39, 55, 56, 60, 61, 64, and 76.

FEEDING STUFFS

Most feeding stuffs being plant products, studies of their composition might have been discussed under Plant Chemistry. As they are derived from many different groups of plants, however, discussion of them would have been divided under cereals and forages, fruits, vegetables, and miscellaneous crops. But some feeds are of animal origin also, including dried blood and tankage from slaughter houses, and fish meal and scrap from the fisheries industry, so that studies of these might have appeared under Animal Chemistry. It seems preferable, therefore, to treat them all under the one heading: Feeding Stuffs.

Enormous numbers of analyses of these materials have been made by State agencies charged with the enforcement of legislation for the control of the composition of commercial feeding stuffs. In most of this work there has been no coöperation. From time to time, nevertheless, Federal agencies have compiled such analyses and published them for the convenient use of all such agencies. The Office of Experiment Stations of the U. S. Department of Agriculture, which acts in a supervisory and advisory capacity for the State Agricultural Experiment Stations, long has acted also as a clearinghouse for station information. From this standpoint it has published numerous compilations of important but scattered station data.

The first compilation on feeding stuffs dealt with composition, comprised 155 pages, was prepared by officers of the Connecticut Station (29), and was issued in 1892. The second dealt with digestibility, comprised 100 pages, and appeared in 1900 under the authorship of officials of the New York State (Geneva) Agricultural Experiment Station (31).

The Federal Bureau of Chemistry has long been interested in the composition of feeding materials as well as in finding feeding uses for various agricultural and manufacturing wastes. In 1904 the Miscellaneous Laboratory of that Bureau began an intensive study of commercial feeding stuffs, including especially the proprietary stock foods. Arrangements were made with the Massachusetts and New York Agricultural Experiment Stations whereby their representatives collected and forwarded to the Bureau several hundred samples of such feeds and foods (*op. cit. infra, p.* 7). These were studied in collaboration with the Microchemical Laboratory, and the results published jointly in 1908 (64—108).

For fish wastes the Bureau of Chemistry has sought profitable uses as fertilizers and as stock and poultry feeds. In 1916 a full discussion of the value of fish meal for the feeding of livestock and poultry was given (55—378). It included the results of feeding tests carried on coöperatively by the Bureau of Animal Industry on cows, pigs, and poultry, for which credit was given (*op. cit.,* pp. 10–12). Later feeding tests with fish meal were published in 1917 (55—610). In 1924 the Dairy Division of the Bureau of Animal Industry published results of feeding tests with various feeds, including fish meal, prepared by the Bureau of Chemistry (55—1272).

About 1916 the Bureau of Plant Industry and the Bureau of Chemistry built and operated coöperatively a drying plant at the Arlington Experiment Farm near Washington, D. C., in an endeavor to utilize surplus potato crops. The Bureau of Animal Industry coöperated by feeding five tons of the dried potatoes to hogs and published the results in 1917 (55—596), including the chemical analyses of the feed by the Bureau of Chemistry (p. 3). In 1923 the Bureau of Chemistry published the results of studies of apple by-products as stock feeds (55—1166). It had the coöperation of the Dairy Division of the Bureau of Animal Industry in feeding tests, which are presented (pp. 27–32), and the coöperation is acknowledged in footnotes (pp. 1, 27, 29).

The desire to utilize farm and forest wastes and surpluses gave impetus to increasing experiments in feeding such materials to livestock. In 1924 the Dairy Division, Bureau of Animal Industry, published an extensive bulletin (55—1272) on the values of various new feeds for dairy cows. Most of the feeds were prepared by the Bureau of Chemistry, and included fish meal, peanut feed, potato meal, sweet-potato meal, potato silage, and apple-pectin pulp. In addition, the Bureau of Plant Industry furnished velvet-bean meal, and the Forest Service supplied hydrolyzed sawdust. The different collaborations are acknowledged in the text at various points.

FOODS, DRUGS, AND HUMAN NUTRITION

The chemical composition of foods for humans, of feed stuffs for domestic animals, and of drugs for both groups of organisms is very closely connected with the subject of human and animal nutrition. Both are intimately tied up with public health.

Foods and Drugs

Foods and drugs are agricultural products, for the most part, and their chemistry is quite largely agricultural chemistry in fact as well as in origin. The analysis of commercial fertilizers was the first phase of agricultural chemistry to attract widespread official attention. Out of meetings of official chemists engaged in fertilizer control, beginning in 1880, grew the Association of Official Agricultural Chemists, which has had such a large part in shaping the later program of food and drug control.

Much of the great prominence given to the subject in the last fifty years has been largely from the standpoint of adulteration, with the major emphasis on its ill effects on the health of the consumer. There is an economic side, however, quite distinct from the humanitarian, and this must not be overlooked. The Food and Drugs Act of 1906, which culminated a quarter century of research and publicity on adulteration, was an economic measure as well as one designed to protect the public health. From this standpoint it protects the manufacturer from unfair and dishonest competition, and insures to the consumer an honest product (77:14). It was achieved and administered chiefly by agricultural agencies. However, the public-health features are the more prominent and therefore the full presentation of the relations in the chemistry of foods and drugs is left to that volume in this series which deals wholly with Public Health. The agricultural contributions in this field are available to the reader in compact assembly (61; 64; 65; 77). However, there is a large volume of research in the home-economics aspects of dietaries and nutrition which had no relation to adulterations, and should receive mention here.

Dietary and Nutrition Studies

Three different bureaus in the U. S. Department of Agriculture have been concerned with studies on foods and nutrition. These are the Office of Experiment Stations, from its creation in 1888 until 1923; the Division and Bureau of Chemistry throughout their entire period of existence; and the Bureau of Home Economics since its establishment in 1923. Curiously enough, the most extensive research in dietaries and nutrition was conducted by the Office of Experiment Stations. Its first director, Dr. W. O. Atwater, was a nutrition chemist. He served from 1888 to 1900, resigning to become professor of chemistry at Wesleyan University at Middletown, Connecticut, and also director of the Storrs Agricultural Experiment Station at Storrs, Connecticut. He remained director of the Storrs Station through 1902, and thereafter had the title of supervisor of nutrition investigations until 1905, residing at Middletown the while. He remained under appointment also as special agent of the Department of Agriculture for several years. Ten years before 1888 he had studied the composition of fish and other sea foods for the U. S. Fish Commission, with comparative studies of meats under the auspices of the Smithsonian Institution, as has been noted under Animal Chemistry. From these backgrounds he went to his dual position in Connecticut, where he gave large attention to nutritional and dietary studies on foods in the succeeding annual reports of the station from 1901 to 1905.

Dr. Atwater's interest in the subject, with that of his successors in the Office of Experiment Stations, brought the matter to the attention of Congress so successfully that the appropriation bill for the Department in the fiscal year 1895 contained provision of funds "to enable the Secretary of Agriculture to investigate and report upon the nutritive value of the various articles and commodities used for human food." The funds were allotted to the Office of Experiment Stations and that unit in turn arranged with Professor Atwater to supervise a broad program of research in the designated field, with headquarters at Wesleyan University (16).

The Secretary of Agriculture not only was authorized by Congress to coöperate with the various State agricultural experiment stations in these studies but also was given power to require the stations to report to him the results of any such studies, whether conducted coöperatively or independently. This was a rather unusual provision in agricultural legislation, and undoubtedly it had much to do with the plan of coöperation which was followed. It was decided to spend a large part of the fund in assisting already equipped institutions to carry on increased research in their own geographic sections of the country. It was not until some years later that a nutrition or "home economics" laboratory was equipped in the Office of Experiment Stations itself.

The results of this wise policy may be seen in the volume of publication which resulted. In the fifteen years from 1895 to 1910 more than sixty bulletins of the Office of Experiment Stations, or more than one fourth of its bulletin output in that period, contained the results of this coöperative investigation (68). Most of them were large treatises, many exceeding a hundred pages and a few containing more than two hundred. In addition, many contributions containing coöperative results were published through other channels. Assurance of prompt publication of such expensive matter by the Department of Agriculture probably contributed to inducing many institutions to coöperate, although receiving relatively little other financial assistance.

It was the intent of the legislation that the studies should cover not only the dietaries common or peculiar to the different sections of the United States, but also those induced or compelled by the economic levels of different groups in the population. The series of publication therefore provides a fair cross section from both points of view. For example, the four publications from California were concerned rather extensively with fruits and vegetables and with the dietaries of the Oriental elements in the population.

The first of these bulletin publications, issued as the work got under way in 1895, was a very comprehensive discussion (222 pages) of the methods and results of investigations on the chemistry and economy of food (68—21). This was followed in 1896 by a compilation of the chemical composition of American food materials (68—28), in the Letter of Transmittal for which Dr. True reviews the history of dietary and nutrition studies with which Dr. Atwater had been associated (p. 4). In 1897 was published an enormous digest (434 pages) of metabolism experiments (68—45), which was slightly revised and reprinted in the next year. The institutions with which coöperation was effected included municipal, State, Federal, and foreign official agencies, as well as many private schools and homes. The official agencies, with the bulletins of the Office of Experiment Stations for which they were wholly or partly responsible, are listed below.

Alabama Agricultural College (Polytechnic Institute) and Tuskegee Normal and Industrial Institute (68—38) ; California Agricultural Experiment Station (68—68, 84, 107, and 132) ; Connecticut Storrs Agricultural Experiment Station (through Wesleyan University) (68—44, 109, and 136); Georgia University (68—221 in part); Indiana, Purdue University (68—32 and 34); Illinois University (68—96, 102, 141, 162, and 193); Maine Agricultural Experiment Station (68—37, 85, 143, and 149); Minnesota University (68—43, 67, 101, 126, and 156); Missouri University (68—31 and 202); New Jersey Agricultural Experiment Station (68—35 and 67); New Mexico Agricultural College (68—40 and 54); New York, Cornell University (68—98); North Dakota Agricultural College (68—91); Pennsylvania College for Women (68—52); Tennessee University (68—29, 53, 89, 117, 187, and 221); Vermont Agricultural Experiment Station (68—22); and, Virginia, Hampton Normal and Industrial Institute (68—71).

Municipal official agencies collaborating included relief institutions in Baltimore (68—223). Federal studies were made at the Government Hospital for the Insane at Washington, D. C. (68—150). In Japan, the Director of the Hokkaido Agricultural Experiment Station at Sapporo took part (68—159).

Besides these public agencies, many private universities and other institutions in cities coöperated in the studies. Among the universities were Columbia (68—121, 185, and 227); Harvard (68—75 and 152); Virginia (68—66); Wesleyan (68—21, 28, 45, 69, 116, 175, and 208); and Yale (68—75). Furthermore, numerous schools and other private agencies in various cities took part, including some in Baltimore (68—223), Boston (68—129), Chicago (68—55 and 129), New York (68—46 and 116), Philadelphia (68—129), and Springfield, Massachusetts (68—129). As Dr. Atwater remained director of the nutrition investigations for the Storrs Station until 1905, it is probable that many or all of the publications cited under Wesleyan University were in fact the results of coöperation with the Storrs Station also, just as were the three cited under Connecticut.

The coöperation under which the published results were obtained is shown in various ways in the publications. In some of them the title of the paper includes the name of the institution. This was especially true of the earlier papers. The scientific titles of the authors, appearing on the cover under their names, also showed the institution to which they belonged. In the Letter of

Transmittal by the director of the Office of Experiment Stations, the coöperation was fully given in almost every instance. Where results obtained by more than one institution were included in the same bulletin, the institutional responsibility and sometimes the coöperation are mentioned again in the text at the proper points. Except for a direct and prominent statement of coöperation on the cover, such as appeared in the publications containing results of coöperation between the Bureau of Animal Industry and the Pennsylvania State College, for instance (p. 308 *supra;* p. 390 *infra*), these statements are as fully satisfactory as most of those of that period.

Vitamin Research

The Bureau of Home Economics, devoted to studies of foods, textiles, and other home problems, was created in the U. S. Department of Agriculture in 1923. The Purnell Act, largely expanding Federal funds appropriated for the State agricultural experiment stations, became effective in 1925. One of the especial purposes of these funds was to increase studies in home economics. Shortly thereafter, in 1925, the Association of Land-Grant Colleges and Universities, which includes the experiment stations and also the U. S. Department of Agriculture, appointed a Committee on Vitamin Content of Food in Relation to Human Nutrition. This coöperative committee has helped to formulate a nation-wide research program on vitamins as affected by methods of production and handling of the containing materials, and to allocate portions of it to those institutions prepared to undertake the necessary studies. The committee reports annually to the Association (5).

Most of the research in this program is conducted independently, but there is considerable coöperation also. The Bureau of Home Economics furnishes standard white rats to the other institutions for the experiments (69). It coöperated with the Horticultural Department of the Maryland Agricultural Experiment Station in studies of the vitamin content of fresh and canned spinach, and with the Bureau of Chemistry and Soils in tests of the vitamins in cod-liver-oil preparations (69—1928 :3). In coöperation with the Office of Experiment Stations of the Department, the Bureau compiled and published in 1929 a comprehensive summary of the literature on vitamins in foods (48).

In the various States there has been coöperation between the home-economics agencies and other divisions of the experiment station in vitamin studies. For instance, in California, where many of the studies are concerned with fruits and the effects of fruit processing, the Laboratory of Household Science and the Fruit Products Laboratory in the College of Agriculture have collaborated extensively in the research (40).

By the end of 1928, twenty State stations were participating, and fifty-two projects were under way. The committee of the Association had suggested that those stations having to do primarily with production tests or studies in controlled handling make the resulting material available to laboratories in other institutions for determination of the vitamin content of material so produced. Several instances of such coöperation were developed through the efforts of the committee. The Rhode Island Station furnished vegetables grown under definite fertilizer conditions. The Federal Bureau of Home Economics assisted stations undertaking vitamin research by allowing the new workers the facilities of the Federal laboratory for conference and observation.

The publications listed in the Literature Cited at the end of this chapter which are drawn upon in this subsection on Foods and Nutrition are Nos. 5, 16, 40, 48, 61, 64, 65, 68, 69, and 77.

BIOCIDES, REPELLENTS, AND ATTRACTANTS

The word biocides (life destroyers) is used here as a convenient and inclusive term for all those substances employed as avicides, disinfectants, fumigants, fungicides, germicides, herbicides, insecticides, insect powders, mammalicides, poisons, poison gases, rat(t)icides, rodent killers, vermicides, weed killers, etc. It thus covers all of those chemicals used for destroying noxious animal and plant life. The word repellents is used for those substances designed to keep animals away rather than to destroy them. A third group of substances consists of attractants or substances causing positive chemotropic response in insects and other animals. While some of these are primarily concerned with plant and animal chemistry, it seems better to combine their discussion with that of biocides.

The exact chemical composition of biocides is especially important. They must be potent enough to destroy the pest against which they are applied, and yet not strong enough to injure other plant and animal organisms which may absorb or have contact with them. Therefore not only the ingredients but also the strength of the compound must be under complete control. These facts serve to explain the large volume of continuing research and increasing coöperation. Actively concerned in its problems are chemists, on the one hand, and agronomists, biologists, botanists, entomologists, horticulturists, householders, ornithologists, physiologists, phyto-pathologists, and zoölogists, on the other. The interrelations of these different groups of workers give rise to numerous and often complex collaborations.

Insecticides and Fungicides

With the rapid expansion of official agencies and activities occu-pied in finding ways of protecting plants and animals from insect and fungus pests, at about the beginning of this century, knowl-edge of the nature and quality of insecticides and fungicides be-came increasingly important. Investigation, also, of the wide-spread adulterations of foods and drugs was a dominant line of research, and the substances used against insects and fungi were of the drug class. From these two objectives developed an extensive and increasing volume of coöperative studies (61—1900–1905), beginning in 1900, a year before the collaborating Divisions be-came Bureaus. In the early years the chemical or quality (purity) side of the work was dominant, and most of the contributions were published by the Bureau of Chemistry, rather than by Entomology or Plant Industry.

In 1900, the Bureau of Chemistry asked the Bureau of Ento-mology to assemble, from the entire United States, samples of commercial insecticides and fungicides as they were found on the open market. These samples were obtained by Entomology through the assistance of the State agricultural experiment stations (*op. cit. infra,* p. 7), by whom some 300 samples were purchased. Of these, 156 were analyzed and the results (64—68) published in 1902. The words "In coöperation with the Bureau of Entomology" appear prominently in capital letters on the cover pages of the bulletin and the collaboration is acknowledged in the Letter of

Transmittal. In making the analyses mentioned, some samples of pyrethrum powders were found to contain dangerous quantities of lead chromate. The Bureau of Chemistry thereupon asked the aid of the chemists of all State agricultural experiment stations in obtaining additional commercial samples (*op. cit.*, p. 13). The resulting analyses were published in 1903 as Part I of another bulletin (64—76). Part II of the same bulletin contained a compilation of all available analyses of insecticides and fungicides made by State stations, and Part III comprised a compilation of State laws governing the composition and sale of insecticides.

In 1904 the Bureau of Chemistry published the results of co-operative spraying experiments with Paris green (64—82). The cover page states plainly that the work was done in collaboration with the Federal Bureau of Entomology and the State Agricultural Experiment Stations of Maryland, New York, New Hampshire, Rhode Island, South Carolina, and Oregon. The work was done at these Stations and their reports of results are included under large-type center heads and occupy most of the bulletin text. The next study, published in 1907, covered the lime-sulphur-salt wash, undertaken at the request of Entomology (*op. cit. infra*, p. 7). On the cover page stands, in large capitals, "In Collaboration with the Bureau of Entomology," while the Letter of Transmittal also acknowledges the coöperation (64—101). In 1910 appeared the results of a study of lead arsenate in which the Bureau of Entomology coöperated in obtaining samples and in conducting the spraying (*op. cit. infra* p. 6). Both cover page and Letter of Transmittal state the coöperation. Composition and spraying each occupy one half of the bulletin (64—131).

Much of the early work with insecticides and fungicides was done from the standpoint of suspicion of adulteration or misbranding. Studies by the Bureau of Chemistry in this field resulted in the enactment of the insecticide and fungicide law in 1910, and the creation of the Insecticide and Fungicide Board in the same year. This Board, charged with the enforcement of the law, was abolished in 1927, and its functions transferred to the newly-created Food, Drug, and Insecticide Administration. Throughout the entire period, however, the Insecticide (and Fungicide) Division of the Bureau of Chemistry has been the chief research agency.

Naturally the closest contacts have been maintained between the Insecticide Division of the Bureau of Chemistry and the Insecticide and Fungicide Board which enforced the insecticide law. As represented by recent publications in the series of *Departmental Bulletins* (55) from 1913 to 1927 and the succeeding series of *Technical Bulletins* (56) from 1927 to date, the subjects of collaboration are given below. In 1918 the methods of preparing a commercial grade of calcium arsenate were published by the Bureau and the Board, and recorded on the cover as a joint contribution (55—750). In 1920 they issued an extensive contribution on insect powders, with bibliography (pp. 83—100), the cover page again proclaiming joint contribution (55—824). In 1921 the two agencies published jointly the results of coöperative tests of pine oil and pine distillates as disinfectants (55—989).

Relations between the Bureau of Chemistry and the Bureau of Entomology, through one or another of its various divisions, have been numerous and effective, as indicated by the publications in the two series of bulletins named above. Injury to cotton plants from spraying resulted in studies, and a publication by the two agencies which appeared in 1922, on the chemical changes in calcium arsenate during storage (55—1115). In 1923 they published a general treatise on the chemical, physical, and insecticidal properties of arsenicals, under joint authorship with a statement of the collaboration in the text also (55—1147). In 1923 also appeared the results of coöperative studies on contact insecticides for fruit insects, the data being largely chemical (55—1160). In 1926 the two Bureaus published on the effectiveness of dry substitutes for liquid lime-sulphur (55—1371) and on the toxicity of certain organic compounds as contact insecticides (44). In 1928 the Bureau of Entomology and the Food, Drug, and Insecticide Administration published jointly on the ineffectiveness of internal medication for the control of external parasites of poultry (56—60), the Board having furnished the materials and made the analyses. In 1928 also the Bureau of Chemistry published the chemical portion (34) of a joint study of the preparation and insecticidal action of some pyridine derivatives and related substances, of which the entomological portion was published in 1930 (43).

During the World War, the Bureau of Chemistry tested many

insecticides for war purposes. It recommended the control of the arsenic industry in order to insure supplies for both insecticides and chemical warfare. When War Department control of acetic acid threatened a scarcity of Paris green, the Bureau developed the use of distilled vinegar for use in its manufacture (39 :84). At the request of the Chemical Warfare Service of the War Department, the Bureau of Entomology detailed a man to make a study of the insecticidal value of substances developed by the Chemical Warfare Service during and since the World War. The work was done coöperatively at the Edgewood arsenal in 1924 and published by the Bureau of Entomology in 1926 (11).

The Bureau of Plant Industry was intimately interested in spraying materials, especially the Divisions of Fruit-Disease Investigations and Cotton, Truck, and Forage-Crop Disease Investigations. In field testings of copper-spray coatings for fruits, published in 1919, the collaboration of the Bureau of Chemistry was asked (55—785, footnote). From 1916 to 1918, because of the high cost of copper, Plant Industry and Chemistry conducted experiments with the low-copper Pickering sprays. Chemistry prepared sprays of known strengths and analyzed the waters used, while the two coöperated with the Maine Station in spraying tests of potatoes at the Aroostook potato farm and treated grapes, apples, and cranberries independently of State coöperation elsewhere (55—866). This work was continued through 1921 with special reference to the effect of the copper sprays on the yield and composition of potato tubers, apparently in coöperation with several State experiment stations, although this is not declared (55—1146). From 1916 to 1919 the two Bureaus collaborated in tests of mixing emulsified mineral lubricating oils with deep-well waters and lime-sulphur solutions, the results appearing under joint authorship in 1924 (55—1217). In 1922, the three Bureaus, Chemistry, Entomology, and Plant Industry, published under joint authorship the results of experiments apparently conducted in 1915 and 1916 on poisonous metals in spraying fruits and vegetables (55—1027), the analyses of seven different kinds of fruits and three kinds of vegetables being contributed by Chemistry.

Collaboration of the Bureaus of Entomology and Plant Industry was not uncommon in experiments requiring chemical determinations. In 1915 they began studies on the physiological effect of insecticides. In 1917 they published jointly on quassia extract as a contact insecticide (37). A comprehensive study of plants reported to possess insecticidal properties was published (55—1201) jointly in 1924. Plant Industry was represented by the Office of Drug, Poisonous, and Oil Plant Investigations.

Coöperation of other Bureaus occurred occasionally. In 1929 appeared a contribution (56—134) by the Bureaus of Chemistry, Biological Survey, and Plant Industry on red squill powders as rat(t)icides, the coöperation being indicated by a footnote. Drug, Poisonous, and Oil Plants in Plant Industry prepared the entire series of powders (*op. cit.*, p. 5).

The Bureau of Plant Industry has collaborated with certain State agricultural experiment stations and other State agencies in studies of chemical eradication of shrubby vegetation, principally barberries, buckthorns, and currants and gooseberries, which propagate one stage of the rusts affecting grains and pines. The Office of Cereal Investigations, beginning in 1918, conducted barberry eradication in coöperation with thirteen north central States. The chemical studies of barberry eradication were carried on principally with the Departments of Chemistry and Plant Pathology of the Wisconsin Agricultural Experiment Station and the Wisconsin State Department of Agriculture. The experiments continued from 1921 to 1925, and several publications resulted (55—1316 and 1451; 58—268 and 332), the last being a comprehensive summary of the results. The coöperation with the State agencies was shown prominently in a box at the top of the cover pages. Somewhat similar but less extensive studies on chemical eradication of buckthorns (57—133) were conducted in coöperation with the Iowa Agricultural Experiment Station and published in 1930.

In like manner the Office of Blister-Rust Control has been charged with control of the currants and gooseberries which harbor the destructive blister rust of pines. This Office has carried on extensive investigation of chemical killers and their application. Preliminary tests of many substances were made in coöperation with the College of Agriculture of the University of California, through the Divisions of Forestry and Plant Nutrition, as shown by a footnote in the publication. These paved the way for extensive field tests made in Idaho in 1925 and 1926, but not published (56—240) until 1931.

Fumigants

Work with fumigants, or insecticides, fungicides, and germicides, employed in closed spaces, as containers, bins, rooms, cars, or tents, developed at about the same time as that with contact insecticides. Curiously enough, the first separate publication by the Bureau of Entomology on this subject, issued in 1899, was written by two members of the staff of the Division of Vegetable Physiology and Pathology, in what soon was to become the Bureau of Plant Industry (67—37). Thereafter the Bureau of Entomology carried on many independent investigations of fumigants. In 1907, however, it began an extensive investigation of orchard-tree fumigation in California in coöperation with the Federal Bureau of Chemistry, which was continued for three seasons. The assistance of the California Commissioner of Horticulture and of various county horticultural commissioners is acknowledged. The first publication (66—79), appearing in 1909, bears on the cover page the words, "Chemical Work Performed by the Miscellaneous Division, Bureau of Chemistry." The second, entitled *Hydrocyanic-Acid Gas Fumigation in California,* was issued in 1912. Part I covers the work done by Entomology, and Part II, comprising pages 91 to 105, under the heading, "Chemistry of Fumigation with Hydrocyanic-acid Gas," was contributed by the Bureau of Chemistry (66—90).

In 1915 the Bureau of Entomology published on paradichlorobenzene as an insect fumigant (55—167), the bulletin containing a section (pp. 6–7) by the Bureau of Chemistry on the chemical and physical studies made. In 1920, the two Bureaus coöperated in tests of the effects of seven gases on insects, fungi, and seeds (55—893). In recent years also the Division of Stored-Product Insect Investigations has collaborated with the Bureau of Chemistry in studies of fumigants. In 1923 the series of papers was started with a publication, under joint authorship, on the absorption and retention of hydrocyanic acid by fumigated food products (55—1149). In this case there was assistance also from the Federal Horticultural Board. The results of further joint research were published in 1924 (55—1307). In 1925 the two Bureaus published together on fumigating against grain weevils with various organic compounds (55—1313). In 1929 another contribution with joint authorship was published on tests of various aliphatic compounds (bromides, iodides, and related organic substances) as fumigants (56—162).

Attractants and Repellents

A recently developing line of specialized chemical research is the study of the chemotropic responses of certain injurious insects. The practical application lies in the developing of attractants by which the adult insect may be lured to destruction. The Federal Bureaus of Chemistry, Entomology, and Plant Industry have co-operated in studies to determine the precise chemical ingredient responsible for insect preference for a given crop plant or animal.

In connection with boll-weevil control, a study of cotton was made by Chemistry and Entomology, and the first resulting publication appeared in 1918 (74). The coöperative relation appears only in a footnote (p. 345). In 1927 the Bureaus of Entomology and Chemistry published under joint authorship the results of chemotropic tests of the screwworm fly (55—1472). In 1928 they published jointly their studies on blowfly baits and repellents, made in Texas in 1926 (56—80). In 1931 the Division of Insects Affecting Man and Animals, Bureau of Entomology, and the Insecticide Division, Bureau of Chemistry and Soils, published jointly on the chemotropic responses of the housefly, the green-bottle flies, and the black blowfly (56—270). In 1932 the Division of Forest Insects received the coöperation of the Harvard Medical School in the chemical portion of studies on attractants for flying gypsy moths (56—336). In the same year the Division of Japanese and Asiatic Beetle Research, Bureau of Entomology, published on the repellent effect, on Japanese beetles, of extracts made from plants immune from their attack (56—299). This seems to be an extreme illustration of the concentration of widely different functions in one unit. No coöperation of any kind is mentioned and apparently the entomologists not only made the tests of the substances but also prepared the plant extracts and identified and classified the hundred of plants listed (*op. cit.*, pp. 12–21).

The publications listed in the Literature Cited at the end of this chapter which are cited in this subsection on Biocides, Repellents, and Attractants are Nos. 11, 34, 37, 39, 43, 44, 55, 56, 57, 58, 61, 64, 66, 67, and 74.

MISCELLANEOUS SUBSTANCES

Chemical studies involving some degree of official relationship have been made from time to time on substances which do not fall properly into any of the six preceding classes or groups of materials. None of them seems important enough, from the standpoint of the coöperative investigation of it, to deserve being given a group by itself. Those lumped together as miscellaneous substances include alcohol, explosive dusts, honey, hops, waters, and water-proofing and fireproofing materials.

Alcohol

Following the passage of the Denatured Alcohol Act in 1906, the U. S. Bureau of Chemistry undertook to demonstrate the manufacture of industrial alcohol. An appropriation in 1908 enabled the building and equipping of a small experimental distillery at Washington, D. C. The State agricultural experiment stations were invited to send representatives to obtain practical instruction and experience in its manufacture. A course of forty-two lectures was given in the period from October 5 to November 10, 1908, to some one hundred students, representing the U. S. Department of Agriculture, the Internal Revenue Service of the Treasury Department, and eight State Stations, including those of Kentucky, Maryland, Minnesota, New Jersey, New Mexico, North Dakota, Ohio, and Oregon (*op. cit. infra,* pp. 85–86). The experiments and lectures are presented in a comprehensive bulletin of 166 pages (64—130).

Explosive Dusts

Most dusts of plant origin are inflammable or explosive under favorable conditions. The Bureau of Chemistry began to give special attention to this subject after major disasters in mill and field in 1913 and 1914. Its investigations have covered cereal-food plants, flour mills, starch factories, grain elevators, threshing machines, cotton gins, and electric light bulbs, dusty and otherwise. Much of its work has been done independently, or with only commercial coöperation. Some has had the official collaboration of Federal and State agencies. The work has been concerned more with the conditions of explosibility and their removal than with the actual composition of the dusts, although the latter has not been neglected.

A terrific mill and elevator explosion occurring in Buffalo in 1913, which cost many lives, wounded scores of persons, and caused a huge property loss, started a new line of investigation in the Federal Department of Agriculture. The Millers' Association of Buffalo asked assistance, and the Bureau of Mines in the Department of the Interior, long accustomed to deal with coal-dust explosions, made a study of the problem and a preliminary report in collaboration with the Bureau of Chemistry (41). A series of disastrous grain-separator explosions in the Pacific Northwest in 1914 resulted in great property losses. This, with the breaking out of the World War, gave further impetus to conservation of grain. With the entry of the United States into the war, and the creating of the United States Grain Corporation, that agency and the Bureau of Chemistry engaged in a nation-wide campaign to control dust explosions. The explosion and fire in the Dow Storage Elevator in Brooklyn in 1918 gave emphasis to the need. The Grain Corporation furnished some funds for the investigations and demonstrations. The study finally was extended to cover cotton gins in the Southwest, where many destructive fires had occurred (39: 88–89; 57—76; 58—28 and 271).

As a part of the program, coöperation of the Bureau of Chemistry and Pennsylvania State College was inaugurated for study of such explosions under controlled conditions. An experimental attrition mill was built at the latter institution and operated by the two agencies jointly. The results obtained were published by both agencies (18). The U. S. Grain Corporation in 1920 published the results of its coöperation with the Bureau of Chemistry (73). A final comprehensive paper on the control of dust explosions in grain elevators (55—1373), published in 1926, was based, apparently, on commercial coöperation only. A discussion of fires caused by electric light bulbs and dusts was published in 1921 (58—171).

The first major publication (55—379) was concerned with the dust explosions and fires in grain separators in the Pacific Northwest. The study was begun on some dusts collected from the area of destruction of 1914, and was carried into the field in 1915 as a joint study by the Bureaus of Chemistry and Public Roads and Rural Engineering, the results appearing in 1916 under joint authorship. Valuable suggestions from the Washington Agricultural Experiment Station, based on its experience in 1914, are acknowledged. Special acknowledgment is made (*op. cit.*, p. 22) of the coöperation of the Grain Standardization Laboratory (then of the Bureau of Plant Industry) at Portland, the Bureau of Plant Industry (at the Arlington Experimental Farm), and the Bureau of Mines for the use of its laboratory and explosion tunnel at Pittsburgh (see also 56—74:2). In 1920 there was published a joint contribution of the Bureaus of Chemistry and Markets on the coöperative installation of dust-collecting fans on threshing machines for the double purpose of fire prevention and grain cleaning (58—98).

Honey

The Bureau of Chemistry has made several studies of honey, mostly independent of other agencies and mostly from the standpoint of purity. In one such study, however, the results of which were published in 1908, the Division of Apiculture, Bureau of Entomology, collaborated in obtaining samples (64—110), as did also the Hawaii Agricultural Experiment Station (p. 14).

Hops

The Bureau of Plant Industry, through its Office of Drug, Poisonous, and Oil Plant Investigations, enlisted the coöperation of the Bureau of Chemistry in a study of the arsenic content of commercial hops. This was occasioned by complaints from European buyers of the American product. The field investigations of hop treatment and the collecting of hop samples were done by Plant Industry, and the analyses were made by Chemistry. The publication, issued in 1917, was a joint contribution of the two Bureaus (55—588), with joint authorship, and with the coöperation mentioned also in the text (p. 2).

Waters

The Federal Bureau of Chemistry has collaborated with many other Federal agencies in making analyses of water samples. Several of these were cases of routine service rendered, and already have been mentioned under that section of this chapter which deals with Interunit Chemical Services. Others were in the nature of true coöperations. One of the earliest examples of joint investigation was a study made with the Office of Experiment Stations, between 1902 and 1904, on the quality of irrigation waters in Louisiana and Texas. Drought had caused low water in the bayous and permitted a backing up of salt water from the Gulf, to the subsequent injury of the rice fields (61—1902–4).

In 1911 the Bureau of Chemistry published a study of the composition of American mineral waters derived from the New England States (64—139). The Hydrographic Branch of the U. S. Geological Survey coöperated in collecting the samples (p. 141), a fact shown both in the Letter of Transmittal and in the text.

Waterproofing and Fireproofing Substances

During the progress of the World War, the Bureau of Chemistry coöperated with various units of the War Department in studies of methods of waterproofing and mildewproofing fabrics, baling papers, and tool wrappings for overseas shipments, and also in fireproofing various camouflage materials (39 :95).

The publications listed in the Literature Cited at the end of this chapter which are cited in this subsection on Miscellaneous Substances are Nos. 18, 39, 41, 55, 57, 58, 61, 64, and 73.

5. Summary of Coöperation

Coöperation has developed steadily in the field of agricultural chemistry. Proportionately to the great increase in chemical research, however, official relations have not been so numerous nor so long-continued as those in some other fields of agricultural science. Apparently this situation is the natural result of the rapid multiplication of chemical laboratories attached to agencies concerned primarily with plants and animals, and so making coöperation with established chemical agencies less necessary. Thus it happens that lines of collaboration which were active from twenty to forty years ago do not exist today. Some that have developed more recently probably will disappear as the growth of research agencies causes them to establish their own chemical units. The same tendency is discernible in State governments. The relationships in the field of fertilizers and other soil amendments were discussed in the preceding chapter on Soils.

ASSOCIATION OF OFFICIAL AGRICULTURAL CHEMISTS

The Association of Official Agricultural Chemists was organized in 1884 by chemists of Federal and State official agencies. Through the Association organization, these agencies have collaborated extensively for fifty years in devising and standardizing methods of analyses for all classes of chemical substances and compounds. It has been designated by Congress to be the official advisor to the government on chemical questions and its findings are recognized as final in courts of law. For twenty-eight years its proceedings were published by the U. S. Department of Agriculture. Through its many committees, or referees, the Association provides a standing agency for prompt and widespread official coöperation on new or continuing problems which probably never has been equalled in other fields. It is an outstanding example of a national organization devoted to coöperative research.

FEDERAL AND STATE INTERUNIT SERVICES

In the beginnings of the great expansion of science and governments, some forty or more years ago, the few established official chemical agencies rendered a large volume of service to the other units of government at their levels. Much of this was concerned with the examination of materials to be purchased as expendible supplies in construction and administration. Some had to do with articles handled officially in the course of carrying the mails or in collecting customs revenue. Collaboration in this type of service decreased as chemical laboratories increased in number. In the early years also the Federal government had neither field stations nor many branch agencies of headquarters in the field. If materials for chemical analyses were desired by Federal chemical units, the services of some or many State agricultural experiment stations were requested in the collecting of samples or the growing of the crops. This type of relation decreased with the increase of Federal units.

Collaboration of agencies in chemical research is increasing. It has covered studies of the composition of plants and animals, of their products, of their foodstuffs, of the mediums, air, soil, and water, in which they live, and of the chemical substances which are employed to protect useful plant and animal organisms by repelling or destroying their pests. Critical studies of the nutritional functioning of plants and animals are one of the more recent developments in agricultural chemistry.

Many of the collaborative studies recorded in this chapter lie in the borderland between informal assistance rendered by one party to the other, and definite coöperation in researches. This is true in the extensive domain of plant chemistry, and in the smaller fields of soils and fertilizers, feeding stuffs, and miscellaneous substances. On the other hand, in the fields of animal chemistry, foods and nutrition, and biocides and attractants, there have been some unique and important coöperations, some of which have been formal, intensive, and long-continued. The public recognition of the coöperative relations also has varied greatly, from mere footnote acknowledgment or casual text references, on the one hand, through obvious joint authorship to prominent and consistent proclamation of the coöperative conduct of the research and the joint status of the publication, on the other.

An outstanding instance of this last happy condition is found in the section on Animal Chemistry. A coöperative study of animal nutrition by the U. S. Bureau of Animal Industry and the Institute of Animal Nutrition of the Pennsylvania State College was continued for more than twenty-five years. It resulted in some twenty published papers, prominently and consistently displaying the coöperative nature of the work. This is a remarkable and gratifying record. Another noteworthy instance occurs under human nutrition. In 1895, Congress made funds available to the Department of Agriculture for studies in foods and dietaries. The Department was authorized to coöperate with the States and also to require them to report the results of any independent studies. Co-operative arrangements were made to expend the funds on research by qualified State and private institutions. The coöperative results appeared in some sixty Federal bulletins (68), as well as in private journals. The official relations usually were indicated on the cover page and in the Letter of Transmittal and the text.

On insecticides and fungicides there has been long-continued coöperation between the Bureau of Chemistry and the Bureaus of Entomology and Plant Industry. In resulting publication, the collaboration has been shown by cover-page statements of "joint contribution," by joint authorship, and by textual acknowledgment.

6. LITERATURE CITED

1. Agnew, Mary A. Workers in subjects pertaining to agriculture in State agricultural colleges and experiment stations. U. S. Dept. Agric., Misc. Publ. 154:1–133, 1933.

2. Armsby, Henry Prentiss. Feed as a source of energy. Pa. Agric. Exp. Stat., Bul. 84:1–16, 1907.

3. Armsby, Henry Prentiss, and J. August Fries. Influence of type and age upon utilization of feed by cattle. Pa. Agric. Exp. Stat., Bul. 105:1–22, figs. 6, unnumbered. 1910.

4. Armsby, Henry Prentiss, and J. August Fries (or Max Kriss). (Seven separate titles, for which see volume indexes.) Jour. Agric. Research, Vols. 3, 7, 10, 11, 13, 15 and 21. 1915–21.

5. Association of Land-Grant Colleges and Universities. Proceedings of the ——th Annual Convention of the ———, held at ———. 1926–.

6. Association of Official Agricultural Chemists. Proceedings of the ——th Annual Convention of the ———.

These *Proceedings* of the Second to the Twenty-ninth Annual Conventions were published in U. S. Dept. Agric., (Division and) Bur. Chemistry, Bulletins Nos. 7, 12, 16, 19, 24, 28, 31, 35, 38, 43, 47, 49, 51, 56, 57, 62, 67, 73, 81, 90, 99, 105, 116, 122, 132, 137, 152, and 162. 1885–1912. (The first four of these had different titles, and the next two had subtitles of the same sort.)

7. Atwater, W. O. Report on progress of an investigation of the chemical composition and economic values of fish and invertebrates used for food. Undertaken for the United States Fish Commission. U. S. Commission of Fish and Fisheries, Rept. Commr. 1880:231–85, 1883.

8. Atwater, W. O. Contributions to the knowledge of the chemical composition and nutritive values of American food-fishes and invertebrates. U. S. Commission of Fish and Fisheries, Rept. Commr. 1883:433–99, 2 unnumbered colored plates (charts), 1885.

9. Atwater, W. O. The chemical composition and nutritive values of food-fishes and aquatic invertebrates. U. S. Commission of Fish and Fisheries, Ann. Rept. Commr. 1888:679–868, pl. 89, 1892.

10. Breazeale, J. F. Vitamin-like substances in plant nutrition. Arizona Agric. Exp. Stat., Tech. Bul. 16:401–17, figs. 1–2, 1927.

11. Brinley, F. J. Insecticidal value of certain war chemicals as tested on the tent caterpillar. Jour. Agr. Research 33:177–82, 1926.

12. Brown, Ryland T. The wastes of cities and towns. Pp. 145–54, *in* Report of the Chemist, in U. S. Dept. Agric., Rept. Commr. Agric. 1872:145–54, 1874.

13A. Caffey, Francis G. A brief statutory history of the United States Department of Agriculture. 26 p. Oct. 23, 1916. (Reprinted from *Case and Comment* 22(9–10):723–33, 850–56, February and March, 1916.)

13B. California State Board of Forestry. Report to the legislature on Senate Concurrent Resolution No. 27 (Legislature of 1921) by the California State Board of Forestry. 165 p., 44 figs., 3 maps. (Sacramento: State Printing Office, 1923)

14. Carleton, Mark Alfred. Macaroni wheats. U. S. Dept. Agric., Bur. Plant Indus., Bul. 3:1–62, figs. 1–2, pls. 1–11, 1901.

15. Carleton, Mark Alfred, and Joseph S. Chamberlain. The commercial status of durum wheat. U. S. Dept. Agric., Bur. Plant Indus., Bul. 70:1–70, fig. 1, pls. 1–5, 1904.

16. Conover, Milton. The Office of Experiment Stations: its history, activities, and organization. Institute for Government Research. Service Monograph 32:[i]–xii, 1–178. (Baltimore: Johns Hopkins Press, 1924)

17. Cook, F. C. Absorption of copper from the soil by potato plants. Jour. Agr. Research 22:281–87, 1921.

18. Dedrick, B. W., and R. B. Fehr, in collaboration with David J. Price. Grain-dust explosions: investigation in the experimental attrition mill at the Pennsylvania State College. U. S. Dept. Agric., Dept. Bul. 681:1–64, figs. 1–5, pls. 1–4, 1918. (Bibliography, pp. 53–54)
 Printed also as Bulletin No. 26 of the Engineering Experiment Station of Pennsylvania State College.

19. Eisenhower, M. S., and A. P. Chew. The United States Department of Agriculture: its growth, structure, and functions. U. S. Dept. Agric., Misc. Publ. 88:i–iv, 1–147, 21 charts (unnumbered). September 1, 1930.
 This publication was prepared "with the assistance of officials in all the Bureaus and Offices of the Department."

20. Forbes, E. B., J. August Fries, and W. W. Braman. Net-energy values of alfalfa hay and alfalfa meal. Jour. Agr. Research 31:987–95, 1925.

21. Formad, Robert J. The effect of smelter fumes upon the livestock industry in the Northwest. U. S. Dept. Agric., Bur. Animal Indus., Ann. Rept. 25(1908):237–68, figs. 30–35, pl. 4, 1910. (Bibliography, pp. 265–68)
 See also four papers by Harkin and Swain and by Swain and Harkin in Jour. Amer. Chem. Soc. 29:970–98; 998–1009, 1907, and 30:915–28; 928–46, 1908.

22. Garner, W. W., J. E. McMurtrey, Jr., C. W. Bacon, and E. G. Moss. Sand drown, a chlorosis of tobacco due to magnesium deficiency, and the relation of sulphates and chlorids of potassium to the disease. Jour. Agr. Research 23:27–40, pls. 1–7, 1923.

23A. Garner, W. W., J. E. McMurtrey, Jr., J. D. Bowling, Jr., and E. G. Moss. Magnesium and calcium requirements of the tobacco crop. Jour. Agr. Research 40:145–68, figs. 1–6, 1930.

23B. Garner, W. W., J. E. McMurtrey, Jr., J. D. Bowling, Jr., and E. G. Moss. Rôle of chlorine in nutrition and growth of the tobacco plant and its effect on the quality of the cured leaf. Jour. Agr. Research 40:627–48, figs. 1–2, 1930.

24. Gates, Otis H. Laws applicable to the United States Department of Agriculture, 1923. iv, 897 p. (Washington: Government Printing Office, 1924)

25. Greathouse, Charles H. [compiler]. Historical sketch of the U. S. Department of Agriculture: its objects and present organization. U. S. Dept. Agric., Div. of Publ., Bul. 3:1–74, front. and 2 pls., 9 half-tones, 1898; rev. ed., same paging, 1898; sec. rev. :1–97, front. and 2 pls., 9 half-tones, 1907.

26. Handy, R. B., and Minna A. Cannon. List by titles of publications of the United States Department of Agriculture from 1840 to June, 1901, inclusive. U. S. Dept. Agric., Div. Publ., Bul. 6:1–216, 1902.

27. Hunt, Mabel G. List of publications of the United States Department of Agriculture from January, 1901, to December, 1925, inclusive (compiled by comparison with the originals.) U. S. Dept Dept. Agric., Misc. Publ. 9:i–vi, 1–182, 1927.

"Supplementary to Bulletin No. 6, Division of Publications, issued in 1902, but duplicating that list for months of January-June, 1901."

28. Hunt, Mabel G. List of publications of the United States Department of Agriculture from January, 1926, to December, 1930, inclusive, compiled by comparison with the originals. U. S. Dept. Agric., Misc. Publ. 153:1–46, 1932.

29. Jenkins, E. H., and A. L. Winton. A compilation of analyses of American feeding stuffs. U. S. Dept. Agric., Off. Exp. Stat., Bul. 11:1–155, 1892.

30. Jodidi, S. L. (*et al.*), See journals listed in discussion of the chemistry of cereal kernels in the subsection on Cereals and Forages (pp. 288—*supra*).

31. Jordan, Whitman H., and Frank H. Hall. The digestibility of American feeding stuffs. U. S. Dept. Agric., Off. Exp. Stat., Bul. 77:1–100, 1900.

32. Kearney, T. H., L. J. Briggs, H. L. Shantz, J. W. McLane, and R. J. Piemeisel. Indicator significance of vegetation in the Tooele Valley, Utah. Jour. Agr. Research 1:365–418, figs. 1–13, pls. 42 (col.)–48, 1914.

33. Kriss, Max. Observations on the body temperature of dry cows. Jour. Agr. Research 21:1–28, figs. 1–46, 1921.

34. La Forge, F. B. (Three separate but consecutive papers on the chemistry of pyridine and related compounds, published as noted.) Jour. Chem. Soc. Amer. 50:2471–77; 2477–83; 2484–87, 1928.

35. LeClerc, J. A., with the collaboration of Sherman Leavitt. Tri-local experiments on the influence of environment on the composition of wheat. U. S. Dept. Agric., Bur. of Chem., Bul. 128:1–18, 1910.

36. LeClerc, J. A., and Yoder, P. A. Environmental influences on the physical and chemical characteristics of wheat. Jour. Agr. Research 1:275–91, January 10, 1914.

37. McIndoo, N. E., and A. F. Sievers. Quassia extract as a contact insecticide. Jour. Agr. Research 10:497–531, figs. 1–3, 1917.

38. Merritt, Dixon. The United States Department of Agriculture; what it is and how it serves. U. S. Dept. Agric., 47 p., mim., 8½″ × 11″ [about 1920].

39. Merritt, Dixon. Department of Agriculture in the War. U. S. Dept. Agric., Press Service, 208 p., mim., 8½″ × 11″ [about 1920].

40. Morgan, Agnes Fay, Anna Field, and P. F. Nichols. Effect of drying and sulphuring on vitamin C content of prunes and apricots. Jour. Agr. Research 42:35–45, 1931.

41. Price, D. J., and H. H. Brown. Preliminary report on the explosibility of grain dusts. Millers' Committee of Buffalo, N. Y. July, 1914.

42. Ramsey, G. B., and L. F. Butler. Injury to onions and fruits caused by exposure to ammonia. Jour. Agr. Research 37:339–48, pl. 1, 1928.

43. Richardson, C[harles] H., and H. H. Shepard. The insecticidal action of some derivatives of pyridine and pyrrolidine and of some aliphatic amines. Jour. Agr. Research 40:1007–15, 1930.

44. Richardson, Charles H., and C. R. Smith. Toxicity of dipyridyls and certain other organic compounds as contact insecticides. Jour. Agr. Research 33:597–609, 1926.

45. Shaw, G. W. Report of progress in cereal investigations. Calif. Agric. Exp. Stat., Bul. 185:261–312, figs. 1–4, 1907.

46. Shaw, G. W., and Walters, E. H. A progress report upon soil and climatic factors influencing the composition of wheat. Calif. Agric. Exp. Stat., Bul. 216:549–74, 1911.

47. Shepard, Jas. H. Macaroni wheat: its milling and chemical characteristics. So. Dak. Agric. Exp. Stat., Bul. 82:1–45, pls. 1–6, 1903.

48. Smith, Sybil L. Vitamins in food materials. U. S. Dept. Agric., Cir. 84:1–54, pls. 1–3, 1929.

49. Swank, James M. The Department of Agriculture: its history and objects. U. S. Dept. Agric., Rept. 7. 64 p. (Washington: Government Printing Office, 1872)

50. U. S. Department of Agriculture. Report of the (Commissioner) Secretary of Agriculture for the year ———. 1862–.

51. U. S. Department of Agriculture. Report of the Secretary: Chemistry. U. S. Dept. Agric., Yearbook 1912:197–207, 1913.

52. U. S. Department of Agriculture. The Bureau of Chemistry of the United States Department of Agriculture. Organization, enforcement of Food and Drugs Act, enforcement of Tea Act, research work. U. S. Dept. Agric., Dept. Circ. 137:1–23, figs. 1–4, Dec., 1920; rev. ed., Feb., 1924. (7.5″ × 3.75″)

53. U. S. Department of Agriculture. Chemistry in the United States Department of Agriculture. 36 p. U. S. Dept. Agric., unnumbered publ., 1927.

54. U. S. Department of Agriculture. List of technical workers in the Department of Agriculture and outline of Department functions, 1931. U. S. Dept. Agric., Misc. Publ. 123:1–165, 1931.

55. U. S. Department of Agriculture. Department Bulletins 1–1500, 1913–29.

56. U. S. Department of Agriculture. Technical Bulletins 1–, 1927–.

57. U. S. Department of Agriculture. Circulars 1–, 1927–.

Circulars in this series should not be confused with those in the series designated as Department Circulars (see following entry), or with those in the series designated as Miscellaneous Circulars 1–, 1923–.

58. U. S. Department of Agriculture. Department Circulars 1–425, 1919–27.

59. U. S. Department of Agriculture. Reports 1–117, 1862–1917.

60. U. S. Department of Agriculture, Bureau of Animal Industry. Bulletins 1–167, 1893–1913.

61. U. S. Department of Agriculture, Bureau of Chemistry. Report of the Chief of the Bureau of Chemistry. 1862–.

62. U. S. Department of Agriculture, Bureau of Chemistry. Organization of the Bureau of Chemistry. U. S. Dept. Agric., Bur. Chem., Circ. 14:1–15, 1904. Rev. to July 1, 1907, 23 p.

63. U. S. Department of Agriculture, Bureau of Chemistry. Publications of the Bureau of Chemistry, 1901. U. S. Dept. Agric., Bur. Chem., unnumbered publ., 1901; rev. ed. 1902, 1903.

64. U. S. Department of Agriculture, Bureau of Chemistry. Bulletins 1–166, 1883–1913.

65. U. S. Department of Agriculture, Bureau of Chemistry. Circulars 1–115, 1894–1913.

66. U. S. Department of Agriculture, Bureau of Entomology. Bulletins (New Series) 1–127, 1895–1913.

It should be noted that there was an earlier series of bulletins of the Division of Entomology, comprising Nos. 1–33, issued 1883–95, since designated as *Old Series*. There also was a series bearing the name *Bulletins, Technical Series*, of which Nos. 1–27 were issued between 1895 and 1914.

67. U. S. Department of Agriculture, Bureau of Entomology. Circulars (Second Series) 1–173, 1891–1913.

68. U. S. Department of Agriculture, Office of Experiment Stations. Bulletins 1–256, 1889–1913.

69. U. S. Department of Agriculture, Bureau of Home Economics. Report of the Chief of the Bureau of Home Economics. 1924–.

70. U. S. Department of Agriculture, Bureau of Plant Industry. Report of the Chief of the Bureau of Plant Industry for ———. 1916–27.

71. U. S. Department of Agriculture, Bureau of Soils. Report of the Chief of the Bureau of Soils for ———. 1894–1932.

72. (U. S.) Government Printing Office, Superintendent of Documents. List of publications of the Agriculture Department, 1862–1902. 623 p. (Washington: Government Printing Office, 1904)

73. U. S. Grain Corporation. Grain dust explosion prevention. U. S. Grain Corporation with the Bureau of Chemistry, U. S. Department of Agriculture. New York, no publr. 28 p., 1920.

74. Viehoever, Arno, Lewis H. Chernoff, and Carl O. Johns. Chemistry of the cotton plant, with special reference to upland cotton. Jour. Agr. Research 13:345–52, 1918.

75. Walling, William English, and Harry W. Laidler. State Socialism: pro and con. Official documents and other authoritative selections—showing the world-wide replacement of private by governmental industry before and during the war. (649 p.; chemistry, pp. 181–85) New York: Henry Holt & Co., 1917)

76. Weber, Gustavus A. The Bureau of Chemistry and Soils: its history, activities, and organization. Institute for Government Research, Service Monograph 52:i–xi, 1–218. (Baltimore: Johns Hopkins Press, 1928)

77. Weber, Gustavus A. The Food, Drug, and Insecticide Administration: its history, activities, and organization. Institute for Government Research, Service Monograph 50:[i]–xii, 1–134. (Bibliography, pp. 113–29) (Baltimore: Johns Hopkins Press, 1928)

78. Wiest, Edward. Agricultural organization in the United States. xxiii, 618 p. University of Kentucky, Lexington, 1923. (The University of Kentucky: Studies in Economics and Sociology, Vol. 2) (Bureau of Chemistry, pp. 129–41).

79. Wiley, H. W. Division of Chemistry. U. S. Dept. Agric., Yearbook 1897 (Sep. 99):76–84, 1898.

80. Wiley, H. W. Historical sketch of the Association of Official Agricultural Chemists (in Proceedings of the Sixteenth Annual Convention of the Association of Official Agricultural Chemists) *in* U. S. Dept. Agric., Bur. Chem., Bul. 57:16–49, 1899.

81. Wiley, H. W. The relation of chemistry to the progress of agriculture. U. S. Dept. Agric., Yearbook 1899 (Sep. 180):201–58, pls. 4–5, 1900.

82. Wiley, H. W. Influence of environment on the chemical composition of plants. U. S. Dept. Agric., Yearbook 1901:299–318, figs. 27–29, 1902.

Chapter V: ANIMAL INDUSTRIES

[Because each chapter covers a different subject and therefore will be used chiefly by a different constituency, it seems desirable to make each one complete and self-contained. For this reason, among others, a complete table of chapter contents is placed at the beginning of each chapter, rather than at the front of the volume. A list of all literature cited in the chapter will be found at the end of the chapter and the numbers in parentheses in the text refer the reader to the corresponding entries in this list. All entry numbers occurring in each major section of a chapter are also listed in numerical sequence at the end of that section, thus forming what is in effect a section list of literature cited. These several features all should prove of great convenience to readers.]

CHAPTER CONTENTS

Chapter V

ANIMAL INDUSTRIES

1. Introduction

THIS INTRODUCTORY PORTION is a discussion of scope and definition, historical development, official agencies involved, and official literature of Animal Industry.

SCOPE AND DEFINITION

Domestic animals of concern to agriculture include, as shown above, livestock, poultry, and honeybees. The principal livestock groups are the equine, or horses, mules, and asses; the bovine, or cattle, both beef and dairy; the ovine or sheep; the caprine, or goats; the porcine, or swine; and, finally, the leporine, or hares and rabbits. Poultry in turn includes fowls (both egg and meat breeds), turkeys, ducks, geese, guinea fowls, and pigeons. Honeybees, while not always classed as farm animals, are properly so placed because they are animals kept under complete domestication for the production of an agricultural commodity. They thus differ fundamentally from the different classes of wild or semidomesticated animals which comprise the natural resource designated as game. For convenience, reindeer, now long domesticated, are discussed with cattle.

The two major functions of the agencies concerned with the various animal industries are production and improvement, on the one hand, and protection from all unfavorable factors in the environment, on the other. Protection of domesticated animals necessarily brings in some consideration of predatory or destructive wild animals and of poisonous plants, as will be true also in plant industries. One of the large activities in animal protection is the weather-forecasting service, which already has been discussed in the chapter on Climate and Weather.

The raising of domestic animals is one of the oldest occupations of man. At first these animals were used only to furnish food and clothing. Later they were employed also as means of transporta-

tion and sources of power. Animals furnishing food or food and
clothing include those classed collectively as livestock, as well as
those known collectively as poultry. Animals of other groups have
been domesticated by modern civilized man. Some of these are of
importance in agricultural operations. Dogs, for instance, assist in
handling as well as protecting livestock, and in some countries
furnish power and means of transportation also. Cats have been
employed for many centuries to protect granaries and similar
storage places from rodents and other vermin. Hares and rabbits
are grown for meat and fur. The Federal government has established the reindeer industry on a large scale in Alaska. The honeybee has been domesticated from time immemorial and produces an
important article of food. It is difficult to draw a hard and fast line
between livestock, poultry, and honeybees, on the one hand, and
game animals, birds, and fish (including crustaceans and mol-
lusks), on the other. For the purposes of this investigation those in
the first group will be taken as constituting the basis of animal industries and therefore as pertaining to agriculture, and those in the
latter group as representing natural resources.

HISTORICAL DEVELOPMENT

It is an interesting historical fact that official agencies were concerned with the protection of animal industries long before they
became charged with animal production and improvement. In general, this was true also in the field of plant industry (23 ; 37).* The
reasons are obvious. Animals and plants have been a major concern
of most of the population of the world for untold centuries. The
individuals were large, visible, and manageable. Most of the simple facts necessary to their production were generally known. No
action by official agencies was necessary until there arose the modern economic problems of special use, market quality, market competition, and production costs, including losses from disease.

In the matter of protection the case was just the reverse. There
was no fund of simple knowledge of diseases which had been accumulated and was generally available. The causes of diseases were
unknown. The organisms were not large, visible, and manageable,

---

* Numbers in parentheses refer to the Literature Cited, at the end of the
chapter.

but were microscopic, invisible, and uncontrollable. In the face of sudden, mysterious, and destructive epidemics of animal disease the individual grower, ancient or modern, was quite helpless. As livestock production moved from the farmyard to the range, whether in swamp, desert, plain, forest, or mountain, the grower likewise could not protect his property from the visible factors in the new environment. He could not forecast the coming of cruelly destructive storms, could not determine and destroy stock-poisoning plants, nor alone control the predatory animals that often killed enough stock to make the difference between profit and loss.

Even local official agencies could not cope with these several problems. They might investigate losses, determine causes, and work out methods for control. But they could not prevent invasion of their limited territory, or eradicate disease infection already established unless effective action to the same end was being taken by surrounding communities at the same time. Hence a centralized program of protection was found to be absolutely essential to safety. This brief statement of the fact is written in minutes, but it took a full century of local failure and financial loss to drive home conviction to the point of concerted action.

OFFICIAL AGENCIES INVOLVED

Official agencies concerned with livestock or livestock products are found at all four levels of government in the United States, namely, Federal, State, county, and municipal. Among them they cover all of the three major phases of activity, that is, research, extension, and regulation or law enforcement. Some agencies have to do with the production and improvement of the animals themselves and some with the manufacture, handling, and quality of their various products. Still others are charged with the protection of the animals or their products from diseases and other unfavorable factors in the environment. Of these protective agencies some are agricultural in emphasis, while others safeguard the public health. In both groups, some are concerned with biological entities and others with economies, such as statistics, production costs, or import duties and other revenues.

Federal Agencies

Federal units having responsibility for activities affecting animal industries are found in the Departments of Agriculture, Interior, Treasury, and War, with minor and occasional outreach into yet others.

U. S. Department of Agriculture.—The Department of Agriculture, naturally, has by far the major part of the responsibility and resultant activities. Among its bureaus, Animal Industry, Dairy Industry, Biological Survey, Entomology, Extension Service, Forest Service, Chemistry, Agricultural Economics, Home Economics, Agricultural Engineering, and Weather all have a part. The first two, Animal Industry and Dairy Industry, are the primary Federal agencies concerned wholly with animal industries.

Bureau of Animal Industry: This Bureau, created directly by the Congress in 1884, was charged from the first with the protection of domestic animals from diseases, and inferentially with all matters belonging to their production and management (23; 37). Its functions extended also to the production and protection of most of the products of such animals, including meat, milk (and butter and cheese), eggs, and wool, but excluding leathers. The organization of the Bureau into definite Divisions took place in 1891 and a reorganization, chiefly to separate research and regulatory activities, took place in 1917. The major technical Divisions which exist now, or have been in existence in recent years, are named below, with the date of their establishment, and a summary of the scope of their work. Some of the early units were designated as Laboratories or Offices in the years mentioned and became known as Divisions later. They are arranged in the order of their establishment, which aids in the gaining of a picture of the development of the work. Of course, several of the activities covered by some of these present Divisions were carried either by the Bureau as a whole or by some other Division before the present Division was organized.

Biochemical: 1890; research on dips, disinfectants, serums, toxins, and viruses; inspection of plants manufacturing the latter three (and of the products themselves).

Field Inspection: 1891; control of animal diseases in the field; the inspection of animals and products before import or export, and control of quarantines (after 1922, when the Quarantine Division was abolished), and, more recently, the inspection of public stockyards and the enforcement of the twenty-eight–hour or humane-transportation law.

Meat Inspection: 1891; ante-mortem and post-mortem inspection of slaughter animals and inspection of prepared products.

Pathological: 1891; research on animal diseases.

Quarantine: 1891; inspection of animals and products before export or import and the control of quarantines (the Division was abolished in 1922 and its functions transferred to the Field Inspection Division).

Zoölogical: 1891; studies of the internal and external parasites of domestic animals, including life histories and identification.

Dairy: 1895; dairy-cattle production and dairy-products manufacture, promotion, and protection.

Animal Husbandry: 1907 (about); animal breeding, feeding, and production.

Hog-Cholera Control: 1916; campaign for control of hog cholera.

Tick Eradication: 1917; campaign for eradication of cattle ticks, which transmit Texas fever. (Segregated from Field Inspection Division.)

Tuberculosis Eradication: 1917; campaign for control and eradication of tuberculosis in cattle and hogs.

Virus-Serum-Toxin Control: 1917; inspection of plants manufacturing these biological products and of the products themselves. (Segregated from Biochemical Division.)

Bureau of Dairy Industry: Since July 1, 1924, the former Dairy Division of the Bureau of Animal Industry has been a separate bureau with several divisions of its own (13) as follows:

Division of Dairy Research Laboratories investigates the chemistry, bacteriology, manufacture, and quality of dairy products.

Division of Market-Milk Investigations conducts research, partly coöperative, on the factors of the quality and the cost of market milk, and on the sanitation of the product and its environment, and aids official agencies in formulating ordinances to govern the sanitary handling of milk supplies.

Division of Dairy Manufacturing and Introduction is a research and service agency with regard to the factories making dairy products, and also conducts inspection of renovated-butter factories under Federal law.

Division of Dairy Cattle Feeding, Breeding, and Management conducts field investigations, often coöperative, on these subjects in several States.

Division of Dairy Herd Improvement works in close coöperation with the private dairy-herd improvement associations and bull associations to increase the individual and average producing power of the animals through culling poor animals and using better breeding stock.

Bureau of Biological Survey, through its Division of Predatory Animal and Rodent Control, conducts campaigns in coöperation with State and local agencies, to control or eradicate wild animals which prey on livestock. Through its Division of Biological Investigations it conducts research on reindeer in Alaska, in coöperation with other agencies.

Bureau of Chemistry and Soils has shared in minor ways, by chemical analyses, many lines of production and protection research. Through its Industrial Farm Products Division it conducts some coöperative research on leathers.

Bureau of Entomology, through its Division of Insects Affecting Man and Animals, has taken part in some studies of insects injuring animals either directly or through introducing disease organisms, or both. Its Division of Bee Culture is charged with the work on production and protection of the honeybee, with some coöperative relationships.

Extension Service, in complete coöperation with the States and many counties, conducts a nation-wide program of agricultural demonstration in animal-industry subjects, including the 4-H Boys' and Girls' Calf, Pig, Sheep, and Chicken Clubs.

Bureau of Home Economics has a coöperative part in the Federal-State research program in vitamin and meat-quality research.

Weather Bureau maintains a protective warning service against storms and cold waves, intense heat, water scarcity, and impending floods. Relatively little of this is directly coöperative, as noted in the chapter on Climate and Weather.

Bureau of Agricultural Economics, through its Division of Farm Management and Costs, conducts many coöperative studies in costs of production and methods of handling livestock. Its Division of Crop and Livestock Estimates makes annual estimates of numbers of livestock. Its Division of Livestock, Meats, and Wool conducts a market-news service on these commodities in coöperation with States, conducts research in standards of quality for livestock, meats, and wool, and maintains a market-inspection service for certain of these products.

Bureau of Agricultural Engineering, through its Division of Mechanical Equipment, has made coöperative studies involving the use of horses for power, and through its Division of Structures has collaborated in improvement of barns and dairy structures.

U. S. Department of the Interior.—Bureau of the Census coöperates with the Bureaus of Animal and Dairy Industry in the preparation of the livestock and product schedules used at the recurrent decennial censuses.

General Land Office has coöperated with agencies of the Department of Agriculture in accomplishing the selection and withdrawal or transfer of parts of the public domain for crop and livestock stations and ranges.

Office of Indian Affairs coöperates in campaigns for the control of various livestock diseases on Indian Reservations, and with the Bureau of Biological Survey in the control of predatory animals.

Office of Reclamation provides land and water-supply for the various field stations maintained by the Bureau of Plant Industry on Reclamation Projects, on several of which livestock experiments now are being conducted by the Bureau of Animal Industry.

National Park Service has had minor relations with livestock activities in the campaigns to control predatory animals and in the eradication, in 1924, of foot-and-mouth disease among deer in California.

U. S. Departments of the Treasury, War, and Navy.—Bureau of Customs, Treasury Department, collaborates with the Field Inspection Division of the Bureau of Animal Industry with reference to inspection and quarantine of imported animals and livestock products to prevent the entrance of diseases.

There has been collaboration with the Bureau of Animal Industry in the breeding of horses for military purposes and in the control of outbreaks of disease among cavalry and artillery horses.

The Naval Academy has had coöperation from the Dairy Division of the Bureau of Animal Industry in safeguarding the commercial milk supplied to the cadets and, later, in establishing their own herd and milk-handling plant.

State Agencies

The principal State agencies concerned with animal industries are the State College of Agriculture and the State Department of Agriculture. Other State agencies having a minor interest are those under names equivalent to departments of forestry, highways, natural resources, public works, and so forth.

State College of Agriculture.—The State college of agriculture is a college of the State university in many States and an independent institution in more than twenty States, though in a few of these, as for example in Connecticut, Massachusetts, and Rhode Island, there is no State university. The college of agriculture, in recent years, usually comprises three major functions or divisions, namely, resident teaching, experiment station, and agricultural extension. In a few States, e.g. Georgia and Ohio, the experiment station is not located with the college of agriculture, but in these cases there is developing an increasing amount of coöperation between the two institutions and some degree of unified control. Occasionally, as in North Carolina, the State Department of Agriculture shares in the maintenance of the experiment station.

The division of resident teaching contains a department of animal husbandry and a department of dairying as well, for purposes of student instruction. The agricultural experiment station, which in each State is subsidized to the extent of $90,000 annually by the Federal Government, contains a division of animal husbandry, and often a division of dairy husbandry also, for the purposes of experiment, investigation, and research. Other divisions which affect the animal industries are those that conduct investigations in chemistry, economics, entomology, forestry, etc. The extension division, which comprises the Federal-State coöperative agricultural extension service, maintains in coöperation with the counties the system of county agricultural agents, home demonstration agents, and leaders of boys' and girls' 4-H Clubs, which carry the results of investigation to farm and home.

State Department of Agriculture.— The State department of agriculture is primarily a regulatory agency, under the relatively recent setup. Such State departments date from long before the Civil War. In their early years they developed in a general way the three functions of teaching, experimentation, and extension. With the rapid rise of the State experiment stations after the Federal subsidy beginning in 1887 (Hatch Act), the activities of these two agencies more and more overlapped. The development of the agricultural extension services, both before and after the passage of the Smith-Lever Act in 1914, inaugurated another series of duplications of effort. The increasing coöperation of Federal agencies with one or another of these State agencies led to a series of conferences which resulted in an understanding that the Federal government would work with the State college of agriculture in activities in the fields of research and extension and with the State departments of agriculture in regulatory matters. The State department usually coöperates extensively with the county and municipal agencies and in many States, as in California, has considerable authority over county agricultural officials and activities. Departments of agriculture vary more widely than the State experiment stations in the number and naming of their subordinate units, usually called bureaus or divisions, or both, as in California. Usually there is one such unit concerned wholly with animal industries, and there may be additional separate units for dairying and for quarantine administration. Others may cover entomology (including honeybees and insect pests of animals) and markets. Then there is likely to be the Federal-State Crop and Livestock Reporting Service, and the likewise coöperative Market News Service, both of which include livestock and their products, with other commodities.

Local Agencies

In most of the States there are agencies in both counties and municipalities which are concerned at times with animal industries. In counties there usually is some official who has power, under the Board of County Supervisors or under State law, to protect livestock and honeybees against pests and diseases and the people against transportation and sale of diseased animals or products. In California, for example, each county must have a County Agricultural Commissioner, and his duties, powers, and salary are fixed under State law. He must be selected by the county supervisors from a list of eligibles supplied by the State Department of Agriculture. With him the State Department coöperates in the control of epidemics of animal diseases, and in campaigns for the eradication of pests and diseases.

In the municipalities there are relatively few relations with county or State or Federal agencies in livestock matters except as they affect the public health, in which case the contacts are with the city health officers. Most of these contacts belong to the volume in this series which will deal with the entire subject of Public Health.

OFFICIAL LITERATURE OF ANIMAL INDUSTRY

The official literature of the agencies concerned with animal industries falls into seven general classes. These are, respectively, (*a*) annual administrative reports, including proceedings of annual meetings of official organizations; (*b*) technical or service publications, usually in numbered series, as bulletins, circulars, etc., or in journal or serial form; (*c*) histories of organizations and activities; (*d*) annual or less frequent lists of personnel, with official titles and organization assignment; (*e*) lists of officials, organizations, and/or institutions concerned with given activities; (*f*) compilations of laws, regulations, etc., of foreign countries, of the United States, and/or of the different states, concerned with a given subject or field of activity; and (*g*) lists of publications of a given agency. The last five kinds of publications, (*c*) to (*g*), inclusive, may be issued in one or more of the numbered series or as issues of a journal, or they may be independent special publications, or they may be found in both classes. In the list of literature cited, at the end of the chapter, each series of publications of a given agency, such as annual reports, bulletins, circulars, etc., has been assigned one single entry number. The issue numbers of bulletins, the year numbers of annual reports, and the volume numbers of journals follow the entry number, from which they are separated by a dash. When it is necessary to cite page numbers these follow the issue, year, or volume number, with a colon between. Thus if the entry number for the whole consecutive series of annual reports of the Chief of the Bureau of Animal Industry,

U. S. Department of Agriculture, is (*56*), then the report for 1925 would be cited thus: (*56—1925*). If it is desired to indicate a certain page the entry would be (*56—1925:67*) or (*56—1931:67-74*).

Publications of or about Federal Agencies

An early publication of the Federal Bureau of Animal Industry, issued in 1898, was the *Proceedings of the Second Annual Meeting of the Association of Experiment Station Veterinarians* (58—22). The Letter of Transmittal refers to the publication, by the Department of Agriculture, of the proceedings of the annual meetings of other official or semiofficial organizations, such as the Association of Agricultural Colleges and Experiment Stations, the Association of Official Agricultural Chemists, and the Association of Economic Entomologists. However, in spite of these other examples, some of which were continued for a quarter century or more, no further proceedings of the veterinarians appear to have been published by the Department.

The Federal Bureau of Animal Industry is somewhat peculiar in having had two entirely different series of annual reports for the twenty-two years from 1884 to 1905. The first was the annual administrative report of the chief of the Bureau from 1884 to date (56). The second series was the annual report of the Bureau itself, each consisting of a collection of technical papers. The first to the twenty-second were issued for the years 1884 to 1905, inclusive (57). The Bureau of Dairy Industry was created in 1924 and has issued annual administrative reports from 1925 to date (65). Similarly, the other Federal bureaus listed in the previous section issued their annual administrative reports, which will be cited later as occasion requires.

Federal Bureaus and independent Divisions in the U. S. Department of Agriculture issued their own series of bulletins, circulars, etc., up to June 30, 1913. After that date only Department series were published. These various series are cited freely in the text. The Dairy Division compiled at intervals and published in the various series issued by the Bureau of Animal Industry all Federal and State dairy laws (57—14; 58—26; 59—25, 49, 74, and 218). It also compiled annual or biennial lists of the officials, associations, and educational institutions connected with the dairy industry of this country (59—10, 18, 22, 26, 29, 33, 36, 40, 44, 80, 99, 135, 162, and 204).

Another series of compilations of general interest comprises the Federal laws, and the regulations of the Department itself under those laws, covering the control of animal diseases (58—9 and 28) or of both Federal and State laws (58—43 and 54). Still others contained lists of State officials charged with the control of livestock diseases (59—164).

Publications presenting the history and activities of official agencies are important sources of information regarding the interrelations of these agencies and others at different levels of government. The United States Department of Agriculture has published several historical summaries of its organization and activities (16; 19; 29; 30), since activities in animal industry were begun. It has published also a brief statutory history (3), and compilations of the laws relating to the Department (17). Still another type of publication consists of lists of the Federal agricultural personnel with their scientific titles, arranged by the administrative units and therefore constituting successive organization charts as well (52—123; 55), or discussions of personnel as to number, training, and activities (54—1931:190–92). Finally, there may be mentioned the various lists of publications of the entire Department, for different periods of years. These are arranged by series for the Department and for the component units previous to June 30, 1913 (21; 24; 25; 74). To these may be added indexes to the annual reports (70—1; 72), 1837–93, and of the year-books (20; 70—7, 9, and 10) from 1894 to 1910. A comprehensive compilation, also, of all literature relating to animal industry in the publications of the Department from 1837 to 1898 has been published (45; 70—5). Likewise, there are several private publications which discuss the history, organization, and activities of all or some of the units of the Department of Agriculture (75; 77).

Certain publications discuss the history and organization of the Bureau of Animal Industry itself (23; 37) or of the Bureau of Dairy Industry (13). Others list animal industry publications (70—5), or activities and personnel (61).

Publications of or about State Agencies

Official documents relating to the administration, including organization, personnel, activities, budgets, publications, etc., of State agencies, arise from two major sources, the Federal government and the State institutions themselves. The U. S. Department of Agriculture, for instance publishes annually a comprehensive list of the personnel of the workers in subjects pertaining to agriculture in State agricultural colleges and experiment stations, which includes also the extension staffs. As they are arranged by institutions and by subject-matter groups, the list serves somewhat as an outline of organization also (1 ; 52).

The U. S. Department of Agriculture also publishes consecutive lists of the bulletins of the State agricultural experiment stations, covering longer or shorter periods of time. The first such list covered the period from the establishment of the stations (mostly 1887 or thereafter) to the end of 1920 (47—1199). Biennial lists have been issued thereafter (47—1199 Suppl. 1, 2, and 3 ; 52—65, 128, 181, and 232).

The State agricultural experiment stations, the State agricultural extension services, and the State departments of agriculture all issue annual reports. In some States these are published as numbers in a regular bulletin series, whereas in others they are not included in such series. In some States the department of agriculture publishes a journal or serial, and the final number in each year usually comprises the annual report. This is true in California (10). The State experiment stations also publish various series of informational issues, such as bulletins, circulars, technical bulletins, etc., which occasionally contain administrative documents. Some stations publish serials or journals also (22). Likewise some State departments publish bulletins.

The publications listed in the Literature Cited at the end of this chapter which have been cited in the Introduction are Nos. 1, 3, 10, 13, 16, 17, 19, 20, 21, 22, 23, 24, 25, 29, 30, 37, 45, 47, 52, 54, 55, 56, 57, 58, 59, 61, 65, 70, 72, 74, 75, and 77.

2. LIVESTOCK

AS CERTAIN ACTIVITIES and relationships have to do with livestock in general rather than with any single class of livestock, as horses, or cattle, they are considered under this general heading before proceeding to the separate classes.

PRODUCTION AND IMPROVEMENT

The Federal Bureau of Animal Industry was established by Congress, effective July 1, 1884. As has been shown in the preceding section on Historical Development, it was created primarily as an agency for the control of destructive livestock diseases, which not only were causing severe farm losses but were hampering our export trade in animals and their products. Under these circumstances it was only natural, as pointed out in the Introduction, that little attention was paid then to the problems of production. During the eighties and early nineties the production of dairy products increased enormously in this country and a large export business in butter and cheese was built up. The poor quality of much of the butter, however, and the commercial adulteration of the cheese, caused a heavy decrease in exports and awakened America to the need of action.

General Development

To meet the pressing problems of the times a Dairy Division was organized in the Bureau of Animal Industry on July 1, 1895. It gave prompt and effective attention to the manufacture and quality of dairy products. Six years later, following a suggestion by Secretary of Agriculture Wilson, an expert in animal husbandry was employed. In 1905 the Bureau chief described the breeding and feeding investigations conducted by the Bureau (54—1904: 527–38). In 1905, also, the expert was given the title of Animal Husbandman, about 1907 his organization became known as the Animal Husbandry Office, and on January 1, 1910, the present Division of Animal Husbandry was established. In the meantime, however, Director Armsby of the Pennsylvania Agricultural Experiment Station had suggested to Secretary Wilson that the Department undertake work in animal nutrition similar to that done on human nutrition through coöperation of the Office of Experiment Stations with Dr. W. O. Atwater of Wesleyan University and the Connecticut (Storrs) Agricultural Experiment Station as discussed in the preceding chapter on Agricultural Chemistry. This coöperative work on animal nutrition began officially on July 1, 1898 (23 :218). As the work was confined to cattle it is discussed later, under cattle production. Work directed toward animal production began, therefore, in 1898, fourteen years after the Bureau was created, but was closely limited in scope and extent for several years.

In 1904, just before the investigational program was started, the Bureau published a discussion of score cards used in judging livestock at the various State agricultural colleges (58—61). The discussion is arranged by States and the author acknowledges the assistance of professors of animal husbandry in the various institutions, and especially that of Professor Boss of Minnesota in loaning charts.

In 1918, the Bureau compiled a list of national and State livestock associations and allied organizations (54—1917 :595–603). In 1921, livestock associations again were listed and published (54— 1920 :510–33).

The real beginning of experiments in livestock production dates from July 1, 1904, when an appropriation of $25,000 became available for breeding experiments in coöperation with the State agricultural experiment stations (33 U. S. Stat. L, 276, 281). This was just twenty years after the creation of the Bureau in 1884. A project on egg production was immediately arranged in coöperation with the Maine Station, the nutrition studies in Pennsylvania were expanded, a test of sugar-beet pulp in steer feeding in Colorado was given financial assistance, and a project of horse breeding in Colorado was proposed (56—1904 :66). By 1905, the Colorado horse-breeding program was under way, steer feeding had been begun in Alabama, coöperative turkey breeding for disease resistance had started in Rhode Island, and a project for breeding goats for milk production was arranged in Connecticut at the Storrs Station (56—1905 :54). This last was never started, however, because the imported milk goats were found to be affected with Malta fever and were destroyed at the New York quarantine station. These and many other specific projects will be presented under the classes of livestock concerned. Only those enterprises covering livestock in general will be discussed at this point.

The annual appropriation act for 1907 provided for promotion of the dairy industry in the southern States. The similar act for 1910 authorized the use of $25,000 for the purchase of a livestock experimental farm which was located near Washington at Beltsville, Maryland. In 1912, extension activities in the organization of boys' and girls' pig and poultry clubs were undertaken in coöperation with the Bureau of Plant Industry. In 1915 the Iberia (Jeannerette) Livestock Experiment Substation in Louisiana was established by the Bureaus of Animal Industry and Plant Industry in coöperation with the Louisiana State Agricultural Experiment Station (68—1915 :141), for the purpose of developing a livestock industry in connection with cropping systems. In the fiscal year 1917 (37 :20; 39 U. S. Stat. L, 446, 491) the Bureau was authorized to coöperate in experiments in livestock production and dairying in the semiarid and irrigated portions of the West.

Most of the work in the first twelve or fifteen years was carried on in coöperation with a few of the State agricultural experiment stations. In recent years a few especially selected Federal livestock experiment stations have been established, either independently or in coöperation with the States. Animals under domestication are less influenced by environment than are plants, and therefore it is not necessary to have breeding and feeding stations so widely distributed as in the case of plant industries. It is chiefly in the fields of feeding investigations that the work must be done more locally, because of the regional variations in feeding and pasture crops and in the relative duration of the winter feeding period and the summer grazing period. For these reasons coöperative relations in animal industry have not occurred at so many points as in the case of plant industries. Since 1925, when a considerable expansion of both State and Federal research funds was started, the coöperation has included a larger number of States.

The summer grazing of privately owned livestock in the National Forests is a large scale industry, very important to the adjacent agricultural areas. It develops very few direct coöperative relations, but indirectly is important from this standpoint also. The Federal forest revenues derived from grazing fees, and other sources, are partly returned to the counties of origin. State and county official agencies likewise coöperate extensively in fire protection of these forests.

The Great Plains

From about 1903 onward there was rapid expansion of Federal investigations of crop production under the semiarid conditions prevailing in the Great Plains Area. Numerous dry-land field stations were established by the Bureau of Plant Industry, either independently or in coöperation with the States. A series of stations was developed on the irrigated lands of the U. S. Reclamation Projects of the Bureau of Reclamation, Department of the Interior, by the Office of Western Irrigation Agriculture. By 1913 the desirability of including livestock on some of these farms, if they were to serve the agricultural néeds of their respective localities, had become apparent. Conferences were held between representatives of the two Bureaus, and in September a joint committee was appointed, consisting of the Chiefs of the Animal Husbandry and Dairy Divisions in Animal Industry and of the Offices of Dry-Land Agriculture and Western Irrigation Agriculture in the Bureau of Plant Industry. The committee made plans for the work, and in 1916 Congress appropriated $40,000 for starting livestock investigations.

The work was begun on the dry-land station at Ardmore, South Dakota, and the three irrigated stations on the reclamation projects at Newell, South Dakota, Huntley, Montana, and Mitchell, Nebraska. Beef-cattle studies were begun at the first and swine-production studies at the other three (23 :249). Investigations with dairy cattle were started in Montana and South Dakota in 1919, and at Woodward, Oklahoma, in 1921. In 1918 and 1919 droughts in parts of the dry-land area made necessary the movement of large numbers of livestock to other areas. Through prompt and extensive coöperation of Federal, State, county, and private agencies, effective results were accomplished (54—1919 :391–405).

Special Feeding Stuffs

In 1892, the Federal Office of Experiment Stations published (66—11), a comprehensive compilation of analyses of American feeding stuffs, prepared by officials of the Connecticut Agricultural Experiment Station. In 1900 the Office published (66—77) an extensive assemblage of results of digestibility tests of feeding stuffs, prepared by officers of the New York State Station. Another compilation of data on utilization and efficiency of American feeding stuffs was made by the Department itself in 1916 and published (53—112) as Part 4 of a coöperative economic survey of the meat situation (53—109 to 113).

From time to time the Bureau of Animal Industry has collaborated with the Bureau of Chemistry or the Bureau of Plant Industry in tests of new types of feed stuffs. For instance, in 1916 appeared a joint contribution of Chemistry and Animal Industry concerned with the use of fish meal as a feed for both stock and poultry. Chemistry furnished the material, and the Dairy and Animal Husbandry Divisions conducted the feeding tests at the Beltsville Experimental Farm (47—378), their data being included (pp. 10–15). In 1917 another joint contribution (47—610) covered similar feeding experiments with swine. In 1917 also the Bureau published the results of feeding dried pressed potatoes to swine (47—596), the material being furnished from coöperative experiments of the Bureaus of Plant Industry and Chemistry in utilizing surplus potatoes. In 1931, four separate experiments to determine the influence of fish meal on the flavor and aroma of pork were made in coöperation with the New Jersey Agricultural Experiment Station (56—1931 :10). In 1930, the California Station published studies on the effect of animal metabolism on the reproductive functions (22—5 :101–18). The later phases of the study were in coöperation with the U. S. Department of Agriculture.

In 1934, the Bureaus of Plant Industry and Animal Industry published under joint authorship a discussion of the utilization of sugar-beet byproducts, primarily as feed for different classes of animals (1718 *Farmers' Bulletin*). They acknowledged assistance received from the Bureau of Dairy Industry and from the Colorado and Utah Agricultural Experiment Stations, as well as from several commercial sugar companies.

A special study on animal metabolism, conducted jointly by the Department of Animal Husbandry of the California Station and the Federal Bureau of Animal Industry, covered some effects of varying calcium and phosphorus intake on the oestrus cycle and reproduction of the rat. The study was made in 1929 and published in *Hilgardia* (vol. 5, No. 5) in 1930.

Economics of Livestock Production

In 1916 the Federal Department of Agriculture published, in five parts, a very comprehensive survey of the meat situation (53—109, 110, 111, 112, and 113). The Bureaus of Agricultural Economics and Animal Industry and the Forest Service collaborated.

With the rapid expansion of agricultural economics after the World War, and the critical condition of the agricultural industry in this country, it was only natural that some investigations should be made in animal husbandry. Many of them resulted from co-operation between the Federal Bureaus of Animal Industry and Agricultural Economics. These studies will be fully discussed in the chapter on Agricultural Economics, and are mentioned here merely to round out the picture of livestock investigations. The Division of Animal Husbandry and the Division of Farm Management and Costs were the participating units of the two Bureaus. Among the studies made were the costs and methods of fattening beef cattle in the corn belt, conducted from 1919 to 1923 in co-operation with several State stations. In 1928 the two Bureaus published jointly the results of a study of ranch organization and methods in the northern Great Plains area, made in coöperation with the experiment stations of four States. In 1926 the Bureau of Agricultural Economics made an economic study of the possibilities of livestock production in the coastal plain of the southeastern United States, in coöperation with various official agencies in several States. In 1927 and 1928 the North Carolina State Station published the results of coöperative studies of systems of livestock farming in the coastal plains and mountainous areas, respectively, of North Carolina (35—252 and 260). Recently, studies of farm power, including horse power, have been made in coöperation with the Bureaus of Agricultural Economics and Agricultural Engineering.

The publications listed in the Literature Cited at the end of this chapter which have been cited in the subsection on Production and Improvement in this section on Livestock are Nos. 22, 23, 35, 37, 47, 53, 54, 56, 58, 66, and 68.

PROTECTION FROM ENVIRONMENT

Livestock require protection from several different environmental influences. Among these are diseases, insect pests, predatory animals, poisonous plants, and certain physical factors, such as weather and poisons. Most of the diseases are specific to a single class of animals, as bovine or equine, and therefore will be discussed under the protection of that class. Others, however, affect two or more distinct classes and therefore must be discussed under the general protection of livestock. Among these are anthrax, which affects cattle, sheep, and swine, and also man; and foot-and-mouth disease, which attacks cattle, sheep and goats, deer, and swine. In the same way, some insects, such as the cattle tick, are specific to one class of animals, while others, like many kinds of flies and mosquitoes, are general livestock pests. The same is true of most predatory mammals, of the poisonous plants, and of physical conditions in the environment.

From Diseases

The Bureau of Animal Industry of the U. S. Department of Agriculture, and some of the veterinary units and livestock agencies in the States, were created primarily for protective rather than for productive activities. The creation of the Federal Bureau by the Congress in 1884 was a direct response to an increasing demand for the protection of our national animal industries from the steadily mounting losses caused by contagious diseases. These not only destroyed or made unprofitable the flocks and herds of the farmer but their presence caused growing restriction on the sale of animals and their products abroad. From time to time the Department had employed experts to investigate one or another of these diseases, or the quality of export products. In 1883 a qualified expert was obtained and on the creation of the Bureau he became its first chief. The investigation of specific diseases was immediately begun. Most of the results published in the earlier years were not coöperative with any other official agencies (56; 57; 58; 59; 60).

One of the earliest and most important activities has been rigid supervision of the importation of animals in order to prevent diseases from gaining entrance. In coöperation with State and other agencies, the Bureau of Animal Industry also has conducted many successful campaigns, during the fifty years of its history, for the control or eradication of domestic or introduced animal diseases. In 1904, the chief of the Bureau outlined the relations of the Federal government to the control of diseases of animals (54—1903 : 491–506). The first eradication campaign was against contagious pleuropneumonia of cattle, begun in 1884 and completed in 1892. Other notable achievements have been the reduction and control of dourine of horses, mange of cattle, and scab of sheep, and the eradication of several successive outbreaks of the Old World foot-and-mouth disease affecting cattle, sheep, and swine. In addition, action for the eradication of Texas fever, or tick fever, of cattle is well advanced, and campaigns for the control and gradual elimination of hog cholera and bovine tuberculosis are making rapid headway. Effective action has been taken also against less important or less widely distributed diseases. In most cases progress in control has had to wait on the results of critical research on the causation and method of distribution of the disease. In these studies the Bureau and the State agricultural experiment stations have played leading rôles. In 1920 the chief of the Bureau reported in graphic form the progress made in eradicating contagious diseases (54— 1919 :69–78). Only those diseases which affect more than one class of animals will be discussed at this point.

Port and border inspection.—One important phase of the protection of American livestock from disease is prevention of the importation of diseased animals and animal products from other countries. This requires inspection and quarantine detention at entry points by land and sea. Reciprocally, also, in order to maintain amicable and profitable trade relations, and to comply with import regulations abroad, animals and animal products presented for export to other countries are inspected before shipment. In 1930, live poultry were included in the animals requiring inspection. Numerous coöperative relations grow out of these various activities.

The first national legislation to prevent the entry of diseased animals was passed in 1865 after rinderpest had been discovered in cattle in England. A few months later hides also were barred. This and succeeding legislation was administered by the Treasury

Department, which then as now was concerned both with import duties and with public health. By 1879 the Treasury Department was under severe criticism because of its erratic enforcement regulations, caused by lack of veterinary knowledge. This fact, augmented by restrictive action taken by Great Britain against American animals, led to the appointment of a Treasury Cattle Commission, consisting of three eminent official and private veterinarians. In 1883 they developed animal quarantine stations near Portland (Maine), Boston, New York, and Baltimore. Previously, in quarantining animals arriving from abroad, the Treasury Department had coöperated with certain State and municipal officials who had the necessary legislative authority.

In 1884 the Bureau of Animal Industry was created and all later collaboration involved that Bureau (54—1918 :239–46, 1927 : 101–5). An act of August 30, 1890, included sheep, other ruminants, and swine, with cattle under the import regulations. In the same way the activities in the inspection of American livestock for export have steadily increased. Live poultry was included in 1930.

Numerous coöperative relations have developed through the years as the activities in protecting animals from present or threatened diseases have increased. Some of these are between Federal departments, some between the United States and other nations, and some between Federal and State official agencies.

Federal interdepartmental coöperation: Relations between the U. S. Department of Agriculture and other Federal Departments occur from time to time in the conduct of port and border inspections.

After the Bureau was established the regulations governing the importations of animals were made by the Department of Agriculture. The approval of the Secretary of the Treasury still was required, as he was charged both with the collection of import duties and with the protection of the public health. In 1897 the Congress vested in the President the authority to permit the importation of cattle and hides from foreign areas certified by the Department of Agriculture as free from dangerous diseases. In 1909 this power was transferred to the Secretary of the Treasury, where it remained at least until the end of 1916, although the Department of Agriculture administered the regulations. The danger from hides lay in their carrying diseases which were communicated to tannery workers, a matter of concern to the Public Health Service of the Treasury Department. In 1917 the emergency legislation for "stimulating agriculture" provided for handling these matters, and especially for handling the importation of cattle from tick-infested countries for purposes of immediate slaughter, through "Joint Orders" of the Department of Agriculture and Treasury.

The State Department coöperates heartily in the making of arrangements for Bureau inspectors to examine and test American livestock arriving in foreign countries, and in the making of treaties governing shipments of livestock between the United States and other countries. In January, 1930, for example, a treaty convention between this country and Mexico was ratified, the regulations thereunder becoming effective in 1931.

During the World War the animal-quarantine station near Baltimore was turned over to the War Department as a munitions depot. That Department constructed two large buildings for munitions storage, built concrete roads, and dredged a deep channel to the station dock. After the close of the war the station with its improvements was returned to the Department of Agriculture (23:134).

For some years after the purchase of the Virgin Islands from Denmark, they were under the control of the Navy Department. During 1917 and 1918, both before and after the passage of the act for stimulating agriculture, the two Departments coöperated in regard to shipments of cattle into the Islands. (23:135). The Navy also collaborates with the Department of Agriculture in preventing the introduction of foot-and-mouth disease by animals or animal products on naval vessels returning from abroad.

Relations with foreign governments: Before the creation of the Bureau of Animal Industry in 1884, and for some time thereafter, many foreign governments placed various restrictions on the import of American livestock. Through the active coöperation of the State Department, the Department of Agriculture obtained from the British Government in 1890 the privilege of stationing veterinary inspectors in Great Britain, and the practice has been continued to the present time. They inspect all imports of American livestock and are present at post-mortem examinations of animals killed at the import wharves because of suspected disease. For several years after 1890, animals inspected in this country before export were tagged in a way that permitted those showing disease on or after arrival abroad to be traced to their point of origin in the United States. A representative of the Bureau of Animal Industry inspects all livestock and poultry offered for shipment abroad in order that compliance with foreign import requirements may be assured. Recently the United States and Mexico have concluded a treaty governing livestock movements between the two countries.

In 1900, the tuberculin testing of all imported cattle was required. At first this was done wholly at American quarantine stations. A few months later an arrangement was made with the government of Great Britain whereby an authorized American inspector was permitted to apply the test in England, in order to save the heavy expense of returning rejected animals. In 1923 the regulation was modified to permit acceptance of certificates of test by an official veterinarian of the shipping country, with a subsequent test during the American quarantine period.

From 1919 to 1923, the Bureau of Animal Industry aided largely in testing the great numbers of dairy and breeding animals purchased in the United States for shipment to the war-devastated areas in Western Europe.

Frequently, when applications are received from foreign countries for permits to ship livestock to the United States, there exists some doubt as to the freedom of the country from dangerous animal diseases. In such cases arrangements are made with the foreign government to permit an investigation of livestock conditions there by an inspector of the Bureau of Animal Industry. Thus a veterinary inspector and a livestock specialist traveled widely in Honduras in 1910. In 1915 a similar party was sent to Guatemala, and in 1923 a reported outbreak of foot-and-mouth disease was investigated in that country. In 1913 a malady suspected by the American consul to be foot-and-mouth disease broke out near Tampico, Mexico. Arrangements were made promptly with the Mexican Government to allow an official of the Bureau of Animal Industry to make a thorough investigation, which resulted in the diagnosis of the disease as vesicular stomatitis instead of the dreaded plague.

In 1915, animal diseases prevailing in Colombia were studied by American official veterinarians. During the period from 1916 to 1918, a Bureau inspector made an extensive study of livestock diseases in Argentina, Brazil, Paraguay, and Uruguay. In all these official relations our livestock interests were safeguarded, our livestock authorities greatly extended their knowledge of animal diseases abroad, and the countries visited were benefited and were pleased with the results.

Federal-State relations: When the U. S. Department of Agriculture, in 1900, purchased a tract of land at Athenia, New Jersey, for a permanent animal quarantine station at the port of New York, the State ceded jurisdiction to the Federal Government (23:133). In 1914 a new regulation provided that all dairy and breeding animals presented for export must pass a tuberculin test made by an inspector of the Bureau of Animal Industry. In 1919 this was modified to permit testing also by an authorized representative of the importing country. Later in the same year it was modified again to permit tests to be made by veterinarians authorized by the States. In 1921 those accredited veterinarians who were taking part in the Federal-State accredited-herd tuberculosis-eradication campaign also were included.

In California, port inspection is maintained at San Francisco, Los Angeles, and San Diego, office space being provided in the Customhouse Building, the Post Office Building, and the Federal Building, respectively. Informal coöperation is maintained with the Bureau of Customs and the Public Health Service of the Treasury Department in the matter of import inspection. Mexican border inspection is maintained only at Calexico in the Imperial Valley, where there is informal coöperation with the U. S. Bureau of Customs. There is no State or county coöperation or expenditure except in emergencies, such as occurred in the outbreak of foot-and-mouth disease in 1924–25. The total annual Federal budget for this work upon the ocean and Mexican borders probably does not exceed $15,000 per year.

These duties devolve upon the Field Inspection Division of the U. S. Bureau of Animal Industry, and under two California acts (of 1921) similar action is required by the Division of Animal Industry of the State Department of Agriculture (10—18:448–52).

Under California statute also, the chief of that Division, who is State Veterinarian, is charged with the supervision of county livestock inspectors who, in turn, are charged with the enforcement of State and county laws and regulations regarding livestock. All three agencies, therefore, are concerned in port and border inspection activities. In practice, however, the actual inspection is performed almost exclusively by Federal agents, because the Federal statutes are broader and more inclusive in their requirements than California statutes, and by mutual consent the Federal agency takes charge, as in the case of similar Plant Industry inspections on the Mexican border. Close contacts between the agencies are maintained, however, and in any emergency, such as occurred in the outbreak of foot-and-mouth disease in 1924–25, State and county inspectors take active part in the work.

Inspection for interstate movement.—Inspections are made prior to interstate movements of livestock in connection with the Federal and State quarantines maintained as part of the campaigns for the control or eradication of various livestock diseases. In 1924 the Bureau of Animal Industry compiled State sanitary requirements governing admission of livestock (50—14) and published a revised edition in 1928. Inspection for interstate movement will be noted under the discussion of the protection of each class of animals, where the diseases are specific to a class. There is inspection also with relation to humane treatment of livestock, which will be presented under Protection from Physical Environment. For discussion here, there remains inspection of all livestock handled through public stockyards to insure that diseased animals are not in transit to other sections of the country and to learn where centers of infection exist. Such inspection covers also the disinfection of contaminated stockyards, cars, etc.

The work is done by regular inspectors of the Bureau of Animal Industry stationed at both public stockyards and the railroad stockyards where livestock are unloaded for feeding and rest. In some cases their duties include dipping or other treatment of animals in order to comply with requirements of the particular destination State. Usually, this work is done in coöperation with the State livestock sanitary commission or equivalent official body. In many localities, headquarters are provided in Federal buildings.

In California, Federal inspectors are stationed in South San Francisco and Los Angeles. Coöperation is with the livestock sanitary officer representing the Division of Animal Industry in the State Department of Agriculture and with county livestock inspectors. Office space is provided in the Customhouse in San Francisco and in the Post Office building in Los Angeles. The work in San Francisco, established in 1930, requires only part of the time of the inspector, whereas in Los Angeles three men are required (with a budget of some $6,000 to $7,000 annually).

Intrastate inspection and quarantine.—Within the various States, the duly authorized State and county livestock sanitary officials, and the municipal boards of health coöperate in the enforcement of State laws regarding livestock inspection and quarantine and animal-disease control and eradication. Their relations with Federal agencies and with each other already have been presented in the discussion of port and border inspection and of inspection for interstate shipment. They are discussed hereafter as they occur in the campaigns for the control and eradication of specific animal diseases. For California they are published in the annual reports of the State Division of Animal Industry (9). Such regulatory activities in the State were reviewed (10—20:491–514) in 1931, with a brief history and plan of organization (pp. 491–94).

Anthrax.—Anthrax, a virulent bacterial disease which affects horses (and mules), cattle, sheep, and swine, has received widespread attention by veterinary authorities. As early as 1901 the Bureau of Animal Industry reported unusually destructive outbreaks of the disease and no Federal funds or laboratory facilities for supplying the protective vaccine, although often the commercial product was poor in quality (56—1901:15). In recent years attention has been focused on the production of satisfactory vaccines for immunizing animals against anthrax attacks. In 1911, the Federal Bureau of Animal Industry published (58—137) the results of studies on anthrax, with special reference to the production of immunity, which had been made by the Delaware Station in coöperation with the Pathological Division of the Bureau, as noted in the Letter of Transmittal. Some other phases of the anthrax problem are discussed under serums, vaccines, etc.

Earlier studies had to do with the possibility of transmission of the disease by means of insect parasites. In 1907 the Louisiana Station published a comprehensive and fully illustrated bulletin (28—29) on the horseflies of the State. The study was made by an expert from Ohio State University, employed by the Louisiana Crop Pest Commission. In 1919 the Veterinary Division of the Louisiana Station published on anthrax transmission by nonbiting flies (28—168). They acknowledged the aid of the Federal Bureau of Entomology in identifying the insects studied and in permitting a locally stationed entomologist to assist in breeding and feeding the flies used (*op. cit.,* p. 12). An earlier study of biting flies was conducted by the State without coöperative relations.

Foot-and-mouth disease.—Foot-and-mouth disease is a livestock disease widely occurring in the Old World, and affecting cattle, sheep, goats, swine, and deer.

Outbreak of 1902–3: An outbreak covering parts of all the New England States, except Maine, became known in November, 1902. In February, 1903, the Congress extended the powers of the Bureau and the disease was eradicated early in that year through full coöperation of State officials in quarantine and eradication activities (56—1903:47–57). The cost of the Federal campaign was about $300,000. The Federal government paid seventy per cent of the cost of eradication, including the value of animals, and the States paid thirty per cent. The total appraised value of 4461 head of cattle, sheep, goats, and hogs slaughtered was $128,903 (23: 282–84).

Outbreak of 1908–9: Another outbreak covering parts of Pennsylvania and New York and smaller portions of Maryland and Michigan was discovered in November, 1908, and was completely eradicated by the end of April, 1909. Coöperation of State officials was given at once in control and eradication, the Federal government paying two thirds and the States one third of the total cost, including compensation for animals slaughtered. The infection was traced to Detroit, and full investigation by the Bureau of Animal Industry and Public Health and Marine Hospital Service showed that the point of origin was some calves used by a Detroit laboratory to produce smallpox vaccine. Further research showed that their standard vaccine was contaminated with the foot-and-mouth disease organism, that it had been obtained from a Philadelphia firm, that the cultures of this firm also were contaminated, that the contamination probably came from virus imported from Japan in 1902, and that it also might have caused the 1902–3 outbreak starting in Massachusetts (56—1909:55; 23:284–86). All suspected virus and vaccine was destroyed and the importing licenses of both firms were revoked. Again the cost of the Federal campaign was approximately $300,000. Cattle, sheep, hogs and goats, totaling 3636 animals, appraised at $90,033, were destroyed.

Outbreak of 1914–16: In October, 1914, the disease again was discovered, this time in Michigan and Indiana, where apparently it had been smoldering for some months. The Chicago stockyards became infected and the outbreak rapidly spread to twenty more States and the District of Columbia. The area affected extended from New Hampshire west to Washington, and south to Virginia, Kentucky, and Kansas. Apparently completely eradicated by June, 1915, new outbreaks occurred in three States, traced later to infected serum for treating hog cholera. Final eradication was accomplished in May, 1916. Cattle, sheep, goats, deer, and swine, numbering 172,222 and appraised at $5,865,720, were slaughtered. Total expenses were $9,000,000, shared equally by the Federal and State governments, among which the fullest coöperation was accomplished (23:286–91; 49—325).

Preparation for future outbreaks: Early in 1917, the Bureau of Animal Industry began active preparation of a program to be followed in case of future outbreaks. The program was submitted to the proper authorities of each State and was approved by all. It provided for complete coöperation, immediate telegraphic action, uniform procedure, joint direction of eradication activities within the States, and equal sharing of all expenses. The provisions covered activities of transportation companies and stockyards.

California outbreak of 1924–25: Foot-and-mouth disease broke out in California on February 17, 1924, and quarantines were laid on February 23. Starting at West Berkeley in Alameda County, it spread first to several counties in the coast range and interior valleys, and eventually to some counties in the Sierra Nevada, and to Los Angeles. In all, a total of sixteen counties became infested. The epidemic differed from preceding ones in reaching summer

grazing areas in public lands of the Sierra Nevada, in the involve-
ment of several Federal units besides the Bureau of Animal Industry, in affecting large numbers of wild deer, and in the restrictions laid by States and counties on the movements of large
numbers of tourists, including disinfection of person and property.
Moreover, the situation was complicated, as compared to that in
other epidemics, by the fact that there is a seasonal spring migra-
tion of livestock in California from the valleys to the mountain
grazing areas, and a return to the valleys in the fall; by the fact
that operations in these mountain regions are hampered by the
rugged and timbered topography, and the consequent difficulty of
locating stray stock; and by the further fact that wild deer in the
Sierra became infected.

Prompt Federal and State action was taken, as in other outbreaks, to quarantine all infested areas, to slaughter all infected
and exposed animals of susceptible kinds, to destroy the carcasses
promptly and safely, to disinfect all infested premises, and to
maintain inspection for a sufficient time thereafter. The coöperation included not only the field force of the Federal and the State
Departments of Agriculture, through their Bureaus or Divisions
of Animal Industry, but also the Federal Forest Service, National
Park Service, Bureau of Biological Survey, and Federal Horticultural Board, the California Division of Fish and Game, the county
supervisors, agricultural commissioners, and veterinary officers,
and, in some cases, the city police officials, as well as many agricultural and livestock organizations. Because of various stringent
embargoes and quarantines laid down by other States and sometimes by individual counties in California, the movement even of
plant products was greatly restricted, and Federal, State, and
county inspectors of such products were placed under heavy additional burdens of work and responsibility (10—13:157).

On April 24, 1924, the U. S. Bureau of Animal Industry was
asked to take complete charge of the eradication campaign. The
request was made to the Secretary of Agriculture by a committee
of influential California citizens who were impelled by the effects
of the very drastic and conflicting quarantines and embargoes laid
by other States and by some California counties, it being hoped
that complete Federal control might help to allay the hysteria ex-

isting in a large part of the country. Owing to the successive spread of the disease from the lowlands to the Sierra Nevada mountains, to the Los Angeles area, and finally to deer in the Sierra, there were four somewhat successive stages to the campaign of eradication. In spite of the difficulties involved, however, the outbreak was brought substantially under control before the end of 1925.

On July 12, a new and difficult phase of the situation was developed by discovery of an infection among deer in the Stanislaus National Forest. Immediate action was taken to prevent the spread of infected deer to other parts of the Sierra Nevada, or to the lowlands. Coöperation of the Federal Forest Service, National Park Service, and the Bureau of Biological Survey, and the California Division of Fish and Game was enlisted, and the situation was well under control by the end of the year. The last active infection of deer was found in June, 1925. More than 22,000 deer were killed before the disease was exterminated. Of this number slightly more than ten per cent were or had been visibly infected.

Summaries show that sixteen California counties became infested, and that nearly 110,000 head of domestic livestock were destroyed, together with large amounts of contaminated property. The livestock included about 59,000 cattle and more than 21,000 hogs, 28,000 sheep, and 1000 goats. The appraised value of this livestock was $4,286,000, and that of the property destroyed $25,500. The cattle losses included one of the finest and also about the largest herd of registered Holstein-Friesian cattle in America. The expense of operation and of remunerating owners for livestock and property destroyed was shared equally by the Federal and State governments. Burial expenses of destroyed animals, totaling much more than $100,000, were borne by the owners. The State estimate of total operating expenses was $1,890,000. The State estimated that the various counties infested expended approximately $800,000. This would make a grand total exceeding $7,000,000. The State discussed the outbreak in the annual report of its Division of Animal Industry for 1925 (10—14:135–45) and again in 1926 in a 54-page special bulletin (27) of the Department of Agriculture. The latter contained a full and appreciative statement of the coöperation involved (p. 7).

In order to guard the State in case of future outbreaks of this or similar diseases, the California State Department of Agriculture obtained additional legislation. This included authorization for immediate slaughter of animals which had been exposed to such disease, authorization for appraisal of animals before slaughter, and for legal payment when expense is shared equally by the Federal government; strengthened quarantine powers; and a new law preventing one political subdivision of the State from placing quarantines against another without the sanction of the State Department of Agriculture (10—14:143). The Federal Bureau also formulated anew its plans for future coöperative procedure by Federal and State authorities in case of other outbreaks (54— 1926:378–81). This plan had been submitted to State livestock sanitary officials and approved by them.

In 1926, the Federal Bureau of Animal Industry published a full discussion of the recent outbreaks in California and Texas (49—400). The number and diversity of the agencies involved are so well set forth in a footnote on the first page of this publication that it seems desirable to quote it in full (49—400:1) :

> The writer desires to express his appreciation of the splendid spirit of coöperation that was shown in the States where the outbreaks occurred, and to thank the governors of the States and State departments of agriculture, the livestock sanitary authorities, the Forest Service, the Bureau of Biological Survey, the Federal and State horticultural boards, the State fish and game commissions, Federal, State, county, and municipal officials, veterinary practitioners, livestock, dairy, and civic organizations, railroads, stock-yards, and other business organizations, the press service, and the owners of livestock, especially those whose herds were sacrificed, for the valuable assistance which all rendered and which made it possible to eradicate the troublesome outbreaks of 1924 and 1925.

California outbreak of 1929: The disease was diagnosed by animal inoculations on January 18 in a herd of 3271 garbage-fed swine near Whittier. The garbage was obtained from ships at San Pedro, and had contained meat-scraps from supplies which the vessel had obtained at Buenos Aires, Argentina, where the disease was prevalent. On January 23, regulations were adopted requiring that ship garbage either should be dumped beyond the three-mile limit or unloaded in tight containers for incineration. Provision was made also for sealing containers of meats of foreign origin found in ship stores when the vessel entered port. Infection was found later successively in four herds of cows, totaling 227 head. All infected and exposed animals were immediately slaughtered. Complete quarantine of the closed area was maintained and daily inspection made of all herds therein. Splendid coöperation was obtained from the owners of livestock as well as from all official and private agencies concerned. Orange County, the city of Los Angeles, and several nearby cities furnished traffic officers, and the State furnished sixteen motor vehicle inspectors. With these men the entire area was patrolled, and the closed area was guarded by a strict 24-hour patrol.

As in previous outbreaks, the expenses were shared equally by the Federal and the State Departments of Agriculture. For convenience during the campaign, the Federal agencies paid indemnities for livestock and property destroyed, and the State paid all running expenses. The livestock indemnity totalled $170,540, the property indemnity $2420, and the running expenses $88,980, making the total cost of the eradication campaign $261,940. A summary account of the outbreak of foot-and-mouth disease in 1929 was published by the State (10—18 :240–41) and also by the Federal Bureau (52—68).

This outbreak raised anew the question of disposition of ship garbage and the handling of foreign meat at ports. During the outbreak, veterinary inspectors had to be called from their regular duties to cope with the outbreak itself, but when it was checked more effective measures were taken to prevent the recurrence of infection. Ships may not enter U. S. ports if carrying food supplies or living animals obtained in countries where either foot-and-mouth disease or rinderpest exists. Special orders prohibit the landing or feeding of garbage from ships carrying meat supplies obtained in such countries. In the enforcement of these regulations the Bureau has the coöperation of the representatives of the Bureau of Customs and the Public Health Service of the Treasury Department, the former obtaining the declarations of the masters of thousands of ships (56—1931 :36–37).

California outbreak of 1932: In April, 1932, another outbreak occurred in California. Starting in northern Orange County, it spread to an immediately adjacent portion of Los Angeles County, and eventually to one farm in San Bernardino County. Federal quarantines and supplemental State quarantines were laid immediately. The value of the previously formulated program of operation was completely demonstrated. The fullest coöperation obtained between the Federal Bureau of Animal Industry, the Division of Animal Industry of the State Department of Agriculture, the Division of Veterinary Science of the University of California College of Agriculture, the board of supervisors, agricultural commissioners, and other officials of the three counties involved, interested commercial agencies, and the farmers whose premises were inspected or threatened. All these agencies contributed quotas of men, and the Forestry Department of Los Angeles County furnished power sprayers for disinfection and trained men to operate them. Eradication was completed in ten days. Indemnity expenses for hogs and cattle destroyed were shared equally by Federal and State Departments of Agriculture. A description of the outbreak was published by the Federal Bureau (52—163) in 1933.

United States Research Commission: After the outbreak in California had been suppressed in 1925, the Federal Bureau of Animal Industry recommended to Congress the appointment of a national commission to investigate the disease in Europe. Congress granted the necessary authority and funds to the Federal Department of Agriculture and the United States Foot-and-Mouth Disease Commission was created. It consisted of one representative of the Rockefeller Institute for Medical Research, one representative of the Department of Veterinary Science of the University of California, and one representative of the Bureau of Animal Industry. In 1928 it published a comprehensive report of 172 pages (48—76), based on the results of a year of study abroad (p. 2).

Virus-serum-toxin inspection.—Early in its history the Federal Bureau of Animal Industry began the manufacture of tuberculin and mallein. These diagnostic agents were distributed free to Federal, State, county, and municipal officials who agreed to furnish results of tests and of autopsies. A summary of results published in 1907 showed 500,000 doses of tuberculin so distributed (54—1906 :347–54).

The appropriation act of 1909 for the Bureau of Animal Industry provided for investigation of tetanus antitoxin. In its report (58—121) the Bureau emphasized the need of control measures. The

Federal Virus-Serum-Toxin Act was passed by the Congress, effective July 1, 1913, as a result of the rapid development of the manufacture of viruses, vaccines, serums, and toxins designed for the protection of livestock against disease. The quality of these biological products was not always good nor the advertising truthful, owing to ignorance, carelessness, or dishonesty. The law forbade the manufacture, sale, or interstate shipment of any such biological product, intended for the treatment of animals, if worthless, contaminated, dangerous, or harmful, or if not made in an establishment licensed and inspected by the U. S. Department of Agriculture. The importation of such products was permitted only to persons holding licenses from the Department. At first the work was divided between the Biochemic and Pathological Divisions of the Bureau of Animal Industry, but early in 1917 an Office of Virus-Serum Control was formed and in 1920 this became a Division. The Pathological Division still collaborates in the technical testing of new or suspected products.

One of the first acts under the law was to supervise the remodeling of domestic plants which did not meet the specifications necessary to insure safety in manufacture and to systematize the methods of production and of plant operation. Many of the States had official agencies which engaged in the manufacture and distribution of these products, and the State plants are licensed and supervised exactly as the more numerous commercial plants. In 1913, eight States were manufacturing anti-hog-cholera serum alone, but the number has gradually diminished. The manufacturing plants now number, in all, more than four score, and the Bureau maintains inspection headquarters in many of the States, while the number of separate products is now nearly one hundred (23:342–48). The total quantity produced is enormous. In 1931 more than 890,000,000 cubic centimeters of anti-hog-cholera serum and nearly 240,000,000 cc. of virus alone were made, with 40,000,-000 doses of other products (56—1931:67). More than 13,000,000 cc. were rejected on inspection. The Biochemic Division manufactures anti-hog-cholera serum and virus, as well as mallein and tuberculin for its own use and for official use by some coöperating State officers. In its inspection of imported biological materials the Division receives coöperation from the Customs Bureau and the

Public Health Service of the Treasury Department, from officials of the Post Office Department, and from the Food and Drug Administration of the Department of Agriculture (56—1931:68).

In California, the Division of Virus-Serum Control maintains a supervising headquarters in the Federal Building at Stockton, from whence supervision is exercised over all factories in the States producing veterinary biologics for interstate shipment. The headquarters, originally established at Berkeley in 1916, were removed to Stockton in 1926. During the outbreak of foot-and-mouth disease in 1924, when the possibility was always present that the serums produced from cattle and hogs might be contaminated with the causative organism of this disease, the coöperative Federal-State eradication campaign exercised rigid supervision over the animals used by these plants.

At the present time there are four such factories in California, of which two, at the University of California, Berkeley, and under the State Division of Animal Industry at Sacramento, are conducted by State agencies. The State Department of Agriculture manufactures approximately 30,000 cc. of tuberculin annually for the use of its veterinarians in the coöperative tuberculosis eradication campaign. The inspection is not coöperative with any State agency, because State law provides that no tuberculin may be sold in California that has not been produced under Federal license. The total annual Federal budget for this work in California amounts to approximately $3600. The total expenditures for this purpose from the beginning of the work in the State in 1916 have been estimated at $70,000.

From Insect Pests

Insect pests may be harmful to livestock through the annoyance, pain, and blood loss caused by biting, as by many flies and mosquitoes; through invasion of the body tissues by the larvas of the insect, as of screwworms, cattle warbles, etc.; or through the introduction of a disease-producing microparasite into the blood, as by the tick causing Texas fever. It seems best to discuss the relations in work done on the first two groups under the protection of general livestock, although some of the insects are pests of only one class of animals. The examples are so few and the relations so rare that space is saved and clarity increased by combining the discussion. The examples of the third group will be discussed under the class of animals they injure, because in all cases the disease caused by the parasite is specific to one class, although the insect may not be thus specialized.

Experiments in the chemical control of housefly larvas in stable manure were conducted from 1913 to 1915 by the Bureaus of Entomology and Chemistry of the U. S. Department of Agriculture. The Bureau of Plant Industry also took part in order to determine the possible harmful effect of the boron used on plants grown on land fertilized with the treated manure. Several publications resulted (47—118, 245, and 408). A part of the experiments were conducted in winter at the Audubon Park Sugar Station of the Louisiana Agricultural Experiment Station. These relations are presented in the chapter on Soils and Soil Management under discussion of toxicity of boron in potash fertilizers (p. 201 *ante*). In 1915 the Bureau of Entomology published on maggot traps as an experiment in housefly control (47—220), part of the work being done in coöperation with the Maryland Station (p. 1).

In 1924, the Division of Insects Affecting the Health of Animals, Bureau of Entomology, published an extensive discussion of the horseflies in relation to western agriculture (47—1218). The studies were conducted in coöperation with the Nevada Agricultural Experiment Station from 1916 on (33—102), and the species were determined through coöperation with Ohio State University, as shown by footnote and textual statements. Description of a new species by the collaborator was included (*op. cit.*, pp. 29–31).

Chemotropic responses of insects have been studied with a view to finding attractants (baits) on the one hand and repellents on the other. Much of the work done in this field by the Bureau of Entomology naturally has been coöperative with the Bureau of Chemistry. In this chapter we are concerned only with experiments having to do with the protection of livestock. The Division of Insects Affecting the Health of Animals (later designated as Insects Affecting Man and Animals) has done some work in this field in coöperation with the Insecticide and Fungicide Division of the Bureau of Chemistry, and the Food, Drug, and Insecticide Administration. Mention also has been made of these coöperations in the chapter on Agricultural Chemistry.

In 1927 the two Federal agencies published jointly the results of a coöperative study of chemotropic substances with the screwworm fly (47—1472), the larva of which infests sheep. In 1926 the Bureaus of Entomology and Chemistry coöperated in a study of baits and repellents for blowflies, and published in 1928 under joint authorship (48—80). The studies were continued on the chemotropic responses of the housefly, the green-bottle flies, and the black blowfly, and the results published under joint authorship (48—270) in 1931.

From Poisonous Plants

Poisonous plants growing in the grazing areas cause an enormous annual loss to the growers of horses, cattle, and sheep, especially on the western ranges. Investigations have been made by the Federal government and by many of the States concerned. Some coöperative relations have developed.

The Federal study began actively in 1894 when the then Division of Botany, from 1901 a unit of the Bureau of Plant Industry, employed a plant chemist for the purpose. Laboratory facilities were furnished to him by the Biochemic Division of the Bureau of Animal Industry and by the Bureau of Chemistry at different times during the next ten years. In 1904, poisonous plant investigations were assigned to the Office of Drug Plant, Poisonous Plant, and Tea Investigations in the Bureau of Plant Industry. In 1905, Dr. C. Dwight Marsh was employed to devote full time to the work, beginning with a study of locoweed poisoning.

Under formal coöperation with the Colorado Agricultural Experiment Station and with the collaboration of citizens of Hugo, Colorado, a small temporary experiment farm was equipped at that point. The work was carried on there for four years, from 1905 to 1908, inclusive. The State Station furnished the first lot of animals for testing with poisonous plants. At about the same time a temporary station was established at Imperial, Nebraska, with the coöperation of the Agricultural Experiment Station of that State (23 :80). The work in coöperation with the Colorado Station was concerned chiefly with larkspurs and with the various leguminous plants causing the loco disease. It resulted in a comprehensive publication by the State (14—113) in 1906, with full statements of the coöperation (pp. 4, 16), and in several papers published in the bulletin series of the Federal Bureau of Plant Industry (69). The first one discussed larkspur poisoning (69—111), the field tests having been made in Colorado in 1905 and dried material sent to the Laboratory in Washington for chemical analyses and toxicity tests. The second (69—121) does not mention the coöperation with Colorado, but like the third (69—129) and the fourth (69—246), on locoweeds, it covers field tests at Hugo, Colorado, from 1905 to 1908, and laboratory experiments in Washington with material shipped from Colorado. Some of the results on loco were published also by the Bureau of Animal Industry (58—112). The field station in Colorado was closed at the end of 1908.

From 1909 to 1914 the Bureaus of Plant Industry and Animal Industry coöperated with the U. S. Forest Service in these investigations. In 1909 a temporary field station was established near Mt. Carbon in the Gunnison National Forest in western Colorado. The Forest Service equipped the station with the necessary buildings and fenced pastures and paid the expenses of a Plant Industry botanist connected with the work. The Bureau of Plant Industry contributed its chief field expert, who had been at the Hugo Station, and a specialist and laboratories in Washington for the chemical and pharmacological studies. After completing the needed studies in Colorado, a similar temporary station was opened in the national forest near Graycliff in the Yellowstone Valley of Montana, in 1912, where it continued for three seasons under the same coöperative relations. The Bureau of Animal Industry coöperated directly by assigning a veterinary inspector to assist with the feeding tests on livestock.

Some of the results of the investigations during these six years were published in the series of *Department Bulletins* and others appeared in the *Journal of Agricultural Research*. The four *Department Bulletins* covered studies on *Cicuta* or water hemlock (47—69), *Zygadenus* or death camas (47—125), larkspurs (47—365), and lupines (47—405). All were under the joint authorship of the physiologists of the Bureau of Plant Industry and a veterinary inspector of the Bureau of Animal Industry and were issued as "Joint Contributions" of the two Bureaus. Number 365 (pp. 28–29) shows the contributions made by the Forest Service at the two stations.

In 1915, the project and personnel on stock-poisoning plants was transferred from Plant Industry to Animal Industry. In coöperation with the Forest Service a more permanent field station for the experiments was established in the Fishlake National Forest at Salina, Utah. The Forest Service supplied houses, barns, corrals, and extensive fenced pastures (23 :81; 47—575). The Bureau of Plant Industry continued to coöperate by assigning a botanist to make field studies on the identity, abundance, and distribution of the plants known or suspected to be poisonous. From time to time the Bureau of Chemistry rendered assistance in the analysis of plants or preparation of toxic material. As at the previous locations, extensive coöperation was received also from the stockmen in the area affected.

A continuous flow of publication has resulted from the investigations. Many papers have appeared in the series of *Department Bulletins* (47—575, 710, 767, 800, 942, 947, 969, and 1012), *Department Circulars* (49—81, 82, 101, 180, 272, 279, and 283), and *Technical Bulletins* (48—29, 93, 113, 114, 202, and 219), of the U. S. Department of Agriculture. Many others occur in the *Journal of Agricultural Research,* managed by a Federal-State committee and printed by the Department. Most of them have been wholly under Animal Industry authorship. In some, credit is given in text or footnote to the botanists of the Bureau of Plant Industry for supplying the identifications and descriptions of the plants involved (47—942, 947, and 969; 48—29, 113, and 114). Occasionally the botanical phases of the research were extensive and important enough to warrant joint authorship with Plant Industry, as in the study of the whorled milkweed (47—800).

Smelter smoke and fumes settling on vegetation, and smelter waste entering streams, have caused destructive poisoning to livestock (57—25 [1908] :237–68). This condition occasioned considerable coöperation between the Bureaus of Animal Industry and Chemistry, the Department of Justice, and various State agencies, as set forth in the chapter on Agricultural Chemistry.

From Predatory Animals

Animals predatory upon livestock include both mammals and birds. The mammals include chiefly dogs, coyotes, wolves, bobcats (lynxes), mountain lions, and an occasional bear. Bird predators in the United States are confined to magpies, which sometimes injure or kill sheep and other livestock (48—24). A few years ago it was estimated that these predatory animals caused an annual loss of some $20,000,000, this figure including the value of both livestock and game destroyed by them.

Attention to the problem began in early colonial days and hundreds of laws, chiefly bounty laws, have been passed. Control of predators on Federal lands had become a live topic by 1905, the year in which the Bureau of Biological Survey was created from the previous Division of the same name. Intensive studies of the losses caused to livestock and game were made and published from 1905 to 1907 by the Bureau (62—20; 63—63) and the Forest Service (67—72) including fencing of lambing grounds (67—97). The first-mentioned Forest Service Bulletin was authored by a Biological Survey naturalist. In 1907 these two Federal agencies cooperated in an intensive drive against coyotes and wolves in the National Forests. Some 28,000 of the former and 1800 of the latter were killed. The hunters were chiefly forest rangers or other experts employed by the Forest Service. For several years thereafter action by the Bureau was confined to advising other Federal and State agencies on the problem when requested, especially in the matter of bounty frauds.

In 1914, western livestock interests, the chief sufferers from predatory animals, obtained a small Federal appropriation for the Biological Survey, to be used in demonstrations of predator control. In 1915, the fund was increased to $125,000, made immediately available in March, and the Bureau of Biological Survey was directed to undertake the destruction of predatory animals on the public domain, including the National Forests. This definitely transferred predator control from the Forest Service to the Bureau, where it has remained ever since. Late in 1915 an outbreak of rabies occurred among coyotes in southwestern Idaho and soon spread to the adjacent portions of Oregon, Nevada, and California. By the infected coyotes it was communicated to dogs and livestock and through them to human beings. An emergency appropriation of $75,000 was made available to the Biological Survey in March, 1916, and an intensive campaign of control and eradication begun immediately in coöperation with State livestock and health officers (6—320; 12:47; 54—1920:289–300). The rabies outbreak was under control by 1919, although others have occurred since.

The coöperative campaign for the control of animals predatory on livestock has continued on an increasing scale to the present time. In 1920 the restriction of the operations of the Biological Survey to the public lands was removed. Coöperation between the Federal and the State agencies is based on formal signed agreements. Not only the eleven western mountainous States are taking part, but also several of the Central States having timbered or broken territory. In 1927 the coöperation was extended to Alaska. The collaborating agencies include such Federal units as the Forest Service and the Bureaus of Animal Industry, Chemistry, and Plant Industry in the U. S. Department of Agriculture and the National Park Service and Office of Indian Affairs in the Department of the Interior. Within the States, the State legislatures, departments of agriculture, livestock sanitary commissions, game commissions, agricultural extension services, and agricultural experiment stations have taken part. Associations of cattle and sheep growers, and some individuals also, have contributed to the campaigns.

The Federal appropriations have continued to increase as the coöperation has grown. The coöperative funds from State and private agencies have grown faster, however. In the fiscal year 1925, when the Biological Survey had $291,000 available for predatory-animal control, the States, counties, and private agencies contributed $389,000. In the fourteen years from 1915 to 1928, the coöperative funds contributed for this purpose from all sources other than Federal amounted to $3,090,000 (12:315). In that same period more than 419,000 predators were destroyed, including 367,000 coyotes, 42,000 bobcats and lynxes, 6,000 wolves, and 2,000 mountain lions. In general, the Federal funds are applied to control on Federal lands and the State and private funds to control on State and private holdings. The campaign within any State, however, is conducted as a unit. The State leader usually is either the Federal man or one employed jointly by Federal and State agencies, and he has charge of all the work done in the State without regard to land ownership or the source of the funds used to employ men and purchase materials. Not all of these moneys are devoted only to the protection of livestock, of course, for game birds and animals are protected by the same measures and at some times and places may be the primary object of the work.

Coöperation in California.—The coöperative agreement and the procedure thereunder in California are typical of the work in all States. The Federal Bureau began work in California in 1915 and a Federal headquarters was established in Berkeley in October, 1920, at about the time the restriction of Federal activities to the public lands was withdrawn. Earlier in that year the State Agricultural Experiment Station had published on coyote control in California (6—320), and suggested Federal-State coöperation (p. 379). On January 1, 1922, coöperation was begun with the California State Department of Agriculture and the headquarters were moved to Sacramento. The agreement provides for joint operations in the control of predatory animals destructive to livestock, poultry, and game, with funds from both parties (the Federal not to exceed $30,000 per year), the agreement to be in effect as long as it is satisfactory. The Federal agency supplies a State Leader of Pest Control, the State Department of Agriculture furnishes office quarters and designates the chief of its Bureau of Pest Control or other representative.

The work is planned jointly, and the Federal leader acts as joint executive officer for both agencies. Work in coöperation with counties is conducted on the same plan. Men may be appointed on Federal, State, county, or private funds, expenses for travel and equipment for any or all of these may be paid from Federal funds so authorized, the employing and dismissal of State-paid employees is by joint agreement, all employees operate under supervision of the Federal-State leader, and State funds are expended under his supervision, with full report of monthly payrolls and expenses. Skins and scalps obtained by hunters on Federal payroll belong to the Federal government, those obtained by hunters on State payroll belong to the State, and those by hunters on county or private payroll are disposed of as agreed between the Federal agency and those agencies.

Special and regular reports, monthly, quarterly, and annual, with the coöperation indicated, are to be furnished by the State leader to the State agency. Data therein are available to both for

use in correspondence and publicity, and important publications
are approved by both agencies and the coöperation shown on the
title page. Summaries of the annual and other reports are published in the monthly bulletin of the State Department of Agriculture (10), often under joint authorship (10—13 :165–67 ; 10—14 :
188–89), and in 1931 a ten-year summary was published (10—20 :
467–69). The Bureau has published a full discussion of the principles, legislation, and procedures involved (38; 52—115).

The Federal and State agencies concerned coöperate directly,
also, with individual counties of the State, under a signed memorandum of coöperation. Under this agreement, in which the Federal and State agencies act as a unit, the county agrees to make
available a stipulated sum of money for a given year, to be used
in paying salaries of hunters and trappers employed within the
county limits. The State-Federal agency allocates other funds, not
necessarily equivalent, to be used for expenses of supervision, supplies, equipment, and salaries. The county moneys are disbursed
wholly and only on the approval and order of either the Federal
or State supervising officer. The Federal-State agency employs and
discharges the hunters and trappers used. The county usually
covenants to pay no bounties on predatory animals, except mountain lions, during the period of the contract. At least thirty days'
notice must be given in order to terminate the agreement.

Twenty-seven counties were coöperating in 1931. One county,
Placer, carries on similar work independently, the one agent employed receiving some salary, all skins taken, and any bounty re-
ceivable. The Federal-State campaign receives some commercial
and individual coöperation in furnishing materials and occasionally in the supplying of small sums of money.

In the ten years from 1922 to 1931, inclusive, the work has increased greatly. The number of employees varies between thirty
and seventy in different years and seasons and the funds range
from $50,000 to $90,000 annually. The total annual Federal budget
is now about $25,000 and $166,000 has been expended in the last
seven years. In 1931 the total State contribution was about $23,000
and the total county contributions about $53,000. The gross total
therefore is about $100,000 per year. Federal funds are carried in
the annual appropriation bills. State funds were provided by spe-

cial legislation in the first two bienniums, and since then by items
in the appropriations for the State Department of Agriculture.

It is estimated that large savings in livestock, poultry, and game
have been made, that human life has been safeguarded through prevention of the spread of such diseases as rabies, that successful
stockraising has been made possible in areas where it could not be
conducted previously, and that game has increased materially in
many localities.

From Physical Environment

There are a few other activities, looking toward the protection of
livestock, in which some collaboration of official agencies is involved. None of these is large enough in itself, or in the relations
involved, to deserve a separate heading. Chiefly, these cover protection in transportation and handling.

Protection on highways.—Livestock must travel upon or cross
highways at times. The advent of the fast-moving automobile having made this a matter of consequence on major highways, special
safeguards are required. It is recognized, of course, that these pre-
cautions are taken primarily in the interest of human safety, but
they serve equally to protect stock. Where farm animals, such as
work horses and milk cows, are obliged to cross a main road daily
in passing to and from pasture or field, it is customary to erect a
warning sign, "Livestock Crossing," at the side of the road, just as
other warning and directional signs are displayed. Other activities
safeguard the livestock which must be transported on foot. Under
California law, for instance, wherever the State Highway Commission considers it necessary, the Division of Highways of the State
Department of Public Works acquires, constructs, and maintains
stock trails paralleling and adjoining or near any State highway.

In all the mountainous States of the West there is a spring transfer of livestock from valley feeding to mountain forest grazing,
with a reverse movement in the autumn. Within the mountain areas
livestock must cross main highways at selected points in order to
utilize forage areas and to obtain water. At such crossings it is
customary for the highway officials or the Forest Service to erect
"Cattle Crossing" warning signs.

Protection from weather effects.—In the chapter on Climate it
has been pointed out that forecasts of coming weather are of great

importance to the livestock industry. Severe cold waves and blizzards are very harmful to livestock on the range or in course of shipment. The coöperation which exists in the gathering of weather observations and in the dissemination of the forecasts also has been presented in the discussion of climate. The Weather Bureau has pointed out how farmers may utilize its special warnings (54—1909 : 387–98).

Still more important at times are the activities to protect livestock from destruction by protracted droughts. Usually these entail the removal of large numbers of animals to more favorable districts. No individual farmer can accomplish much by himself. Such removals require the coöperation of many official and commercial agencies in both the affected and the proposed relief areas. Usually, in the hope that the drought will be broken and drastic action rendered unnecessary, removal measures are not undertaken until the need is urgent. Speedy action then is imperative, or the already weakened stock will be unable to travel on foot to the railroad or to withstand the effects of the trip.

Two outstanding examples of such action are recorded in the history of the Federal Bureau of Animal Industry (23 : 251–52). In 1916 a drought began in the near Southwest, centering on Texas, and continued until the autumn of 1918. In 1917, an organized movement to save the cattle was sponsored by the Animal Husbandry Division of the Federal Bureau, aided by the Railroad Administration and the Agricultural Extension Service. As a result, some 150,000 head of cattle were moved to the southeastern States. In 1918 a drought began in Montana and lasted through 1919. In July of the latter year a conference was called at St. Paul, Minnesota, and as a result of widespread official and commercial coöperation, headed by the Federal Division of Animal Husbandry, some 300,000 cattle and more than 500,000 sheep were moved to pastures in Texas and adjacent States (54—1919 :391–405). Similar action has been taken in other sections, on a smaller scale.

Protection from transportation cruelties.—The Livestock Transportation Act or so-called twenty-eight-hour law, which governs feeding, watering, and rest of livestock during rail shipment, is administered by the Federal Bureau of Animal Industry. The work is done by a few special inspectors of the Bureau, together with the regular force of field and stockyards inspectors engaged in control of animal diseases. There is little or no coöperation, except with the Solicitor of the Department of Agriculture and with the Department of Justice over legal cases arising from violations of the law, which total a few hundreds each year. The law and its enforcement have been fully described and the history of its development from 1873 discussed (47—589). There is large coöperation with commercial agencies in bettering conditions without resorting to legal action. The proper fitting of ships, also, for the transportation of cattle, is under the supervision of the Field Inspection Division. All of this legislation grew out of proof of horrible cruelties practiced on livestock through overcrowding and through long confinement without food, water, or rest. These facts outraged public opinion, both from the standpoint of the cruelties involved and of the heavy losses to livestock owners and shippers which resulted. The enforcement of the Packers and Stockyards Act (54—1926:563–65), also, is under the Bureau of Animal Industry, through a Packers and Stockyards Division. As it is concerned with fair dealing, charges for services, etc., it will be discussed in the chapter on Agricultural Economics.

The publications listed in the Literature Cited at the end of this chapter which have been cited in the subsection on Protection from Environment in this section on Livestock are Nos. 6, 9, 10, 12, 14, 23, 27, 28, 33, 38, 47, 48, 49, 50, 52, 54, 56, 57, 58, 59, 60, 62, 63, 67, and 69.

3. HORSES, MULES, AND ASSES

WHILE THE TITLE of this section is inclusive of all equine animals, most of the investigations involving official relations have had to do with horses only. The campaigns to control such diseases as dourine and glanders have served to protect mules and asses also. Only very minor attention has been given to zebras.

HORSE BREEDING AND PRODUCTION

In 1903, just before the Bureau of Animal Industry began its experiments in livestock production, the Office of Experiment Stations compiled a comprehensive digest of recent experiments on horse feeding (66—125). The Letter of Transmittal acknowledges the coöperation of the Maryland and Wisconsin Agricultural Experiment Stations, the Bureau of Animal Industry, and the Department of the Interior. In 1917, the Bureau published data on stallion legislation by States, with lists of State officials, and some statistics (54—1916:289–99). In recent years an investigation of hay requirements of city work horses has been made by the Bureau of Animal Industry in coöperation with the Connecticut (Storrs) Agricultural Experiment Station (56—1931:19).

Breeding Different Types

Utility horses.—In the autumn of 1904 the Bureau of Animal Industry began experiments in the breeding of American utility horses in collaboration with the Colorado Agricultural Experiment Station (23:230; 37:23). This program was maintained in Colorado until June 30, 1919. In 1908 the plan was changed to provide that thereafter the expense should be shared equally by the two agencies (56—1908:259). A description of the project and its purpose was published by the State (14—166) in 1910, under Bureau authorship. A committee consisting of two Bureau men and one from the Iowa Station (*op. cit.*, p. 8) supervised the project and made annual inspection of progress and results. On July 1, 1919, the utility breeding project was transferred to the Wyoming Soldiers' and Sailors' Farm, on the site of the former Ft. McKinney military reservation near Buffalo, in north central Wyoming, where the work was continued for four years in coöperation with the State. In 1921 the Bureau published a discussion of developing an American utility horse (49—153). On July 1, 1923, the project was transferred to the Wyoming Agricultural Experiment Station at Laramie, where again it is conducted coöperatively (23:230).

Carriage horses.—These horses have been an important class at many shows, fairs, and expositions, but the class standards have varied greatly. A committee composed of Federal, State, and registry-association officials being formed, it developed a classification which was published in 1907 (56—1907:236–38; 59:113) and was adopted and used thereafter.

Morgan horses.—An agreement for a coöperative breeding program was signed with the Vermont Agricultural Experiment Station in the autumn of 1905 and horses were purchased in June of 1906. The Vermont Station contributed the services of one member of its staff who remained with the work until his death in 1913. In 1906 a private citizen donated land for the breeding work near the town of Middlebury and the experiments were transferred in 1907 to the new location, known as the United States Morgan Horse Farm, where they continue (23:231; 49—199; 56).

Draft horses.—In the summer of 1907, coöperation was begun with the Iowa Station in an attempt to produce an American breed of draft horse by crossing English Shires and Clydesdales. The foundation material was selected in Great Britain by Professor Kennedy of the Iowa Station and in due course the eight horses were paid for by the Department of Agriculture (56—1908). For several years past, the work of the United States Range Livestock Experiment Station, at Miles City, Montana, conducted in coöperation with the Montana Agricultural Experiment Station, has included the production and management of purebred and grade horses of both draft and light types, and also feeding experiments with the colts of both types (56).

Military horses.—In 1910 the Secretary of War suggested to the Secretary of Agriculture the desirability of encouraging the production of horses suitable for cavalry remounts, which were becoming increasingly difficult to obtain. An appropriation was asked and made available to the War Department as of July 1, 1912. That Department, on the other hand, already had transferred to Agriculture some noted stallions donated to it. In 1913 an appropriation was made available to Agriculture and the work was begun in three districts with headquarters in Vermont, Virginia, and Kentucky, respectively (54—1917:341-56). On July 1, 1920, however, the Congress made $200,000 available to the War Department for this horse breeding and the work was extended throughout the country. The Department of Agriculture transferred much of its material and personnel to the military establishment (23:233). There has been continued contact and coöperation between the two departments in this work (56—1931:19).

HORSE PROTECTION FROM DISEASES

Research on the diseases of horses has been an important work of the Bureau of Animal Industry since its creation. As in the case of the other classes of livestock most of the studies have been independent laboratory investigations entailing little or no coöperative study in the field. In some cases, however, there have been extensive and long continued relations with official agencies.

Dourine

This disease, imported in 1884, was definitely recognized in 1886, and in 1892 an investigation was started by the Pathological Division. By 1903 it was found to be so widespread, and was so little understood, that the chief of the Division was sent to the National Veterinary School in France to study the disease and methods for its control. Through the coöperation of the French officials he was enabled to bring to America a dog infected with the trypanosome or protozoön causing the disease, which permitted research to be continued in this country. Eradication campaigns were begun in the affected areas in coöperation with State officials and good progress was made in testing and slaughter in the farming areas. More difficulty was experienced in the range areas of the West, where quarantines were laid and where by 1905 eradication was thought to be complete. New outbreaks were discovered in 1911, at which time the work was transferred to the Quarantine Division, and later, in 1917, to the Field Inspection Division (23:66, 151, and 279). Many of the infected animals were on Indian Reservations in various parts of the West. Coöperation with the Bureau of Indian Affairs of the Department of the Interior and with State officials was begun and continued for some twelve years before the disease was under control. About 350,000 tests were made in that period and some 10,000 reactors found and destroyed.

Glanders

As early as 1888 the Commissioners of the District of Columbia asked the Bureau of Animal Industry to take charge of the health of horses in the District. Immediate tests for glanders were given. During the current campaign to exterminate pleuropneumonia of cattle, unexpected amounts of glanders were discovered whereupon active efforts were made in coöperation with various States to combat the disease. Great difficulty was met in obtaining destruction of the infected animals. In 1900 the disease broke out among Army horses in Virginia and the Pathological Division of the Bureau confirmed the diagnosis and aided in the eradication (23:60). In 1904 there was coöperation with the U. S. Military Academy at West Point in controlling an outbreak (56—1904:58).

Swamp Fever

In 1907 the Bureau gave help to the Minnesota Station on a study of swamp fever of horses in the Red River Valley (56—1907:212–13), and the coöperation was continued in the next year (56—1908). In 1917 the Zoölogical Division of the Bureau undertook a coöperative investigation with the Health of Animals Branch of the Canadian Department of Agriculture into the relation between a disease of horses caused by an internal parasite and the so-called swamp fever. This was continued in 1918 (23:105) and was published by the bureau in 1918.

The publications listed in the Literature Cited at the end of this chapter which have been cited in this section on Horses, Mules, and Asses are Nos. 14, 23, 37, 49, 54, 56, 59, and 66.

4. CATTLE AND REINDEER

IN OLDEN TIMES the term "cattle" was nearly synonymous with livestock, just as the term "corn" in Great Britain today means small grains in general and not maize. Nowadays, however, the word "cattle" is reserved exclusively for the cud-chewing, cloven-hoofed, and normally horned animals belonging to the mammalian genus *Bos* and including both *Bos Taurus* of Europe, from which our common breeds were developed, and *Bos indicus* of the Orient, represented by the zebu, humped, or Brahman cattle. Many of the latter have been imported into the United States and part of the experiments conducted coöperatively by the U. S. Bureau of Animal Industry and the Louisiana Agricultural Experiment Station at the Iberia Livestock Experiment Farm at Jeanerette are concerned with the Brahman cattle and with hybrids of the two species.

Reindeer are treated as livestock in this chapter, rather than as game in the volume on Natural Resources, because they were imported to Alaska from Lapland as already domesticated animals, have been produced in large numbers as domesticated animals in Alaska, comparable in every way to our cattle, and are now the basis of an impressive meat and leather industry, as well as a source of power for transportation.

In chronological sequence of its work with cattle, the Bureau of Animal Industry first took up the control of cattle diseases, then the improvement of dairy products, then cattle nutrition, next beef-cattle production, and finally dairy-cattle improvement. In the treatment of livestock in general and of the different classes of livestock in particular, in the present study, it has been customary to present production and improvement first and protection last, and that sequence will be followed here, without regard to the actual order of the official development of these activities.

CATTLE-NUTRITION RESEARCH

The first work of the Bureau of Animal Industry relating to cattle production was a critical research in cattle nutrition. This was begun in 1898, three years after the creation of the Dairy Division and antedating by two years the appointment of an animal husbandman and by six years the beginning of feeding and breeding experiments on a comprehensive scale. While much if not most of the work was done with dairy cattle, this fundamental research is applicable to cattle in general and therefore is so presented here.

The Federal Bureau of Animal Industry, in 1898, began formal coöperation with Pennsylvania State College in a critical study of the nutrition of cattle. This research was continued for fully a quarter of a century and resulted in a long series of coöperative publications. The work involved the use of the calorimeter and other expensive and delicate apparatus. The coöperation was with the State Agricultural Experiment Station at first, but about 1908 a special Institute of Animal Nutrition was established at the college as an independent unit and thereafter it appeared on the publications as the official agency for Pennsylvania State College. These researches have been discussed briefly in the chapter on Agricultural Chemistry because of their nutritional aspects and the coöperation of the State College Division of Chemistry in the analyses of the feeds used (See p. 307, above).

The coöperative relations in this research are remarkable, not only for their long duration but also for the consistent and prominent display of the fact of coöperation in all of the more than a score of publications which have resulted. From 1903 to 1912 no less than nine papers appeared in the bulletin series of the Bureau of

Animal Industry (58–51, 74, 94, 101, 108, 124, 128, 139, and 143), mostly under the sole or senior authorship of Dr. Henry Prentiss Armsby, director of the work from the beginning, and Director of the Institute. Two other papers appeared in the series of bulletins of the Pennsylvania Station (36—84 and 105) in 1907 and 1910. After the establishment of the *Journal of Agricultural Research*, conducted coöperatively by the U. S. Department of Agriculture and the State agricultural experiment stations, no less than nine papers of this series appeared in it (26) during the years from 1915 to 1921. Of these, eight were under the senior authorship of Dr. Armsby (26—3 :435; 7 :379; 10 :599; 11 :451; 13 :43; 15 :269; 21 :343) and one by Kriss (26—21 :1). A final paper appeared in 1925 under the senior authorship of Dr. Forbes, who succeeded to the Directorship of the Institute after the death of Dr. Armsby (26—31 :987–95). In the mean time a single paper had appeared, in 1924, in the series of Federal *Department Bulletins* (47—1281), covering experiments begun in 1915 and making a total of twenty-two papers in the four places of publication.

One of the most remarkable facts in the twenty-five years of joint endeavor is that not once did the two coöperating agencies omit the consistent and prominent printed recognition of the relation. In the nine bulletins of the Federal Bureau the coöperation is shown plainly and prominently on the cover and title pages. In six it is in capital letters in the middle of the page, and in the other three the author, Dr. Armsby, carries both bureau and station titles in italics below his name. In all of the nine bulletins the collaboration is stated in the Bureau Letter of Transmittal, while in the six previously mentioned it is shown also in the Letter of Submittal from the Pennsylvania Station. In the two State bulletins, likewise, the coöperation is plainly stated on the covers.

In the long series of nine papers appearing in the *Journal of Agricultural Research* from 1915 to 1921, the words, "Cooperative Investigations between the Bureau of Animal Industry, United States Department of Agriculture, and the Institute of Animal Nutrition of the Pennsylvania State College," are printed prominently in capital letters just below the scientific titles of the authors. In the final paper in this series the relation (which then had been terminated) is shown only by a footnote on the first page.

In the single Department bulletin, however, which appeared at nearly the same time, the words, "United States Department of Agriculture in coöperation with the Pennsylvania State College," appear in a box at the top of the cover page.

The protection of cattle from such diseases as anthrax and foot-and-mouth disease already has been discussed under livestock protection, because these diseases affect other classes of livestock also. For the same reason, the protection of cattle from other environmental factors of ill health, such as insects, poisonous plants, predatory animals, and weather influences, likewise has been presented under livestock protection. There remain for discussion here the official relations in the control of those major disease which are restricted to cattle only or chiefly, such as contagious pleuropneumonia, mange or scab, granular venereal disease, and tuberculosis.

Contagious Pleuropneumonia

The Bureau of Animal Industry was created by Congress, effective July 1, 1884, primarily for the purpose of controlling animal diseases, which not only were causing heavy losses of livestock but also were making increasingly difficult the export of American cattle to Europe. One of the most destructive and dangerous of these diseases was contagious pleuropneumonia, which had been introduced from England to Long Island, New York, in 1843. By 1884 it had been spread to Connecticut, Massachusetts, continental New York, New Jersey, Pennsylvania, Maryland, Virginia, West Virginia, and the District of Columbia. Delaware also became infected in January, 1885, but Massachusetts and Connecticut had freed their territory of the plague by determined and persistent action, although Connecticut was reinfected from time to time from adjacent Long Island.

The wording of the Federal act creating the Bureau made it clear that its first duty was to wage a campaign of eradication against pleuropneumonia, in coöperation with State authorities. A small force of veterinarians was organized and inspection of cattle in the States of known infection was begun. Hardly had the work started when the disease was discovered in Illinois, from where it soon was traced to Kentucky, Ohio, and Missouri. While this new outbreak had the unfortunate effect of nearly doubling the work of the infant Bureau, it had the helpful result of arousing the country to the peril and actually aided in getting effective laws passed by the States and effective coöperation developed.

At first there was much opposition to the work of the Bureau for the eradication of the disease. It was based on several ideas, including resentment of so-called Federal invasion of the States, disbelief in the contagiousness of the disease, differing views as to the necessary control measures, fear that publication of the facts would do more harm than the disease, and lack of adequate State laws for control or to provide for compensating the owners for animals slaughtered. In spite of these handicaps, the disease had been confined to a small area around New York City by 1890 and was completely eradicated by 1892, at a Federal cost of only $1,500,000. The result of the coöperative endeavor was to bring the States generally into harmony with the Federal program of disease-control and to establish the Bureau firmly as an efficient agency for such work (23:38–47).

Cattle Mange or Scab

This disease, like sheep scab, is caused by a mite, and protection results from dipping the affected animals to destroy the parasite. In March, 1904, the Bureau of Animal Industry placed a Federal quarantine on all the United States west of the Mississippi River, in order to prevent the out-shipment of cattle without inspection (and subsequent dipping if infested). In June, 1905, a Federal quarantine was placed on interstate movement within the infected parts of this enormous area and a campaign of eradication through inspection and dipping was begun in coöperation with the livestock sanitary authorities of the States. In the nine years from 1905 to 1913 from 15,000,000 to 18,000,000 or more cattle were inspected each year and on an average 1,000,000 were dipped. Within the next ten years the disease was so completely under control that all Federal quarantines were lifted (23:298–99). During the progress of the campaign the Zoölogical Division of the Federal Bureau began coöperation (in 1908) with the Veterinary Department of the South Dakota Agricultural Experiment Station on treatments of scabby cattle with coal-tar preparations. This followed the discontinuation of similar coöperation on treatments against sheep scab. The Biochemic Division collaborated by preparing creosote and cresol dips of known strength. The results were published by the State (43—131), with acknowledgment of the coöperation in the text (pp. 203 and 208).

Texas Fever and Tick Eradication

This disease was introduced, probably, with Spanish cattle in colonial days. As early as 1795, North Carolina enacted legislation restricting the movement of cattle within the State. By 1814, Virginia law governed the movement of cattle into that State from South Carolina. Restrictions gradually increased as cattle shipments increased and, by the time of the Civil War, Missouri, Kansas, and adjacent States were up in arms to prevent the movement of Texas cattle across those States on the way to market. Laws were passed and the farmers themselves enforced them at gun point. Rail shipment then took the place of the trail drive, and the disease steadily spread from the rail centers.

In 1868 the Department of Agriculture and the Medical Department of the Army coöperated in an extensive investigation which accumulated much information but which both failed to discover the cause and unfortunately discredited the increasingly prevalent tick theory. From 1879 to 1883, Dr. D. E. Salmon, young veterinarian of the U. S. Department of Agriculture, also conducted research in the field. He arrived at the conclusion that it was necessary to determine the line between the infected area and the fever-free areas, and to develop quarantines to prevent movement of cattle from the former to the latter. This required a strong central organization and was one of the reasons for the creation of the Federal Bureau of Animal Industry in 1884 (23:15–21).

In 1883, Dr. Salmon determined the northern limits of Texas fever infection for some two hundred miles from the Atlantic Ocean westward across Virginia. When he became chief of the new Bureau of Animal Industry in 1884, this work went on. The line was extended to the Mississippi River in 1884 and to the Rio Grande in 1885. Ten years later it was taken up again and completed to the Pacific Ocean. Little else was done on Texas fever

while the Bureau and the States were eradicating pleuropneumonia. In July, 1889, however, the area below the line was quarantined and cattle shipped from that area to northern markets
were required to be yarded separately during certain months and
the cars which had carried them were made subject to a cleaning
and disinfection (23 :318). At the same time, studies of the disease
were begun by Dr. Theobald Smith of the Pathological Division.
He discovered a protozoön in the red corpuscles in 1889 and later,
with his associates, proved that ticks carried the disease to cattle.
The five years of research are presented in the first bulletin of
the Bureau (58—1). In 1892, a new quarantine was laid on the
infected area, covering all of what are now eight States and
parts of five others. California was added in 1895. The regulations permitted shipment of cattle for purposes other than immediate slaughter only during three months in winter.

From 1892 to 1906, extensive experiments with different chemicals to destroy ticks on cattle were conducted by Federal and State
agencies, occasionally in coöperation. Even after the beginning
of the eradication campaign in 1906, the testing of dips went on
for another five years, until the arsenical dip was perfected in
1911. In 1906, the Bureau coöperated with the Texas Livestock
Sanitary Commission, and in 1907 with the Alabama Station and
the Alabama Livestock Sanitary Board on improved tick dips (23 :
333 ; 56—1907 :232).

Following years of study by State and Federal experts on methods of destroying ticks by chemicals and by starvation through
pasture rotation and other practices, the idea of wholesale eradication began to develop. In certain States, notably North Carolina,
extensive areas were freed from ticks by State and local endeavor
and were thereupon released from Federal quarantine. At the
Convention of the Southern States Commissioners of Agriculture
in 1905, the veterinarians of North Carolina and Alabama, as well
as the chief of the Pathological Division of the Bureau of Animal
Industry, discussed tick eradication. The Secretary of Agriculture was present and was so much impressed that he called the
Chief of the Bureau of Animal Industry to Richmond for conference, after which he announced to the convention that he would
ask Congress for funds to enable the Bureau to coöperate with the

States in tick eradication. On recommendation by the Secretary of Agriculture, warmly supported by State officials, the Congress appropriated $82,500 for the work in the fiscal year beginning July 1, 1906. Meantime a survey showed that only seven States, including California, out of the thirteen infested, had laws of sufficient scope and requirement to permit the Federal coöperation on an effective basis. Nevertheless, the eradication campaign was begun on July 1 and the coöperation of States, counties, and private citizens was developed as rapidly and effectively as possible.

Publicity, educational programs, and conferences were employed to create support for the movement, which met both indifference and opposition in the early years. In order that all official agencies might have the same information and that all field workers should be well informed and tactful, a conference of State and Federal representatives was held in Tennessee in December, 1906. The published proceedings of the conference (58—97) contain a paper by the State veterinarian of Missouri, strongly advocating Federal-State coöperation. At this conference plans were developed for two short training conferences for field workers. These were held in Virginia and Tennessee early in 1907, the States furnishing the staffs.

The beginning of eradication did not stop research by Federal and State agencies. Some coöperative studies were conducted. In 1907 coöperative studies on the biology of the cattle tick were begun with the Veterinary Department of the Alabama Polytechnic Institute and continued through 1909. The results of the first two years and of the last year were published successively by the Federal Bureau (58—130 and 152). The instructional conferences, the more favorable public attitude, the increasing number of States with satisfactory legislation, and the perfecting and final approval of the arsenical dip in 1911, marked the transition to the second and more effective period in eradication (59—187 and 196).

In 1912, the Field Inspection Division was created to handle the eradication programs. In 1917, with increased appropriations for the work, a Division of Tick Eradication was established and still carries on. In the fifteen years from 1906 to 1921, more than 500,-000 square miles, or about one-sixth of our national area, was cleared of ticks. In the same period, the number of cattle below the original quarantine line increased by 4,000,000, or twenty-six per cent, especially in the older settled areas. To show further the magnitude of the enterprise and of the coöperation, it may be noted that the total cost from 1906 to June 30, 1923, or seventeen years, was more than $22,400,000, of which the Federal government contributed $7,100,000, the States $3,000,000, and the counties $13,-300,000 (23:318–40). A summary of State laws and court decisions relating to cattle-tick eradication was published by the Federal Bureau (49—184) in 1921.

Eradication in California.—California was not included in the tick quarantine area until an investigation in 1894 brought infection to light. Federal coöperation was begun with the State on July 1, 1906, and continued until the complete extermination of cattle ticks in California in 1916. California enacted a tick-eradication law in March, 1907, through the efforts of the State veterinarian, providing for compulsory eradication measures where voluntary action could not be obtained. This law regulated the movement of tick-infested cattle, provided for disinfection at the direction of State officers, and provided that, in case of failure of the owner to disinfect, the work should be done by the State official and the cost thereof become a lien on the stock treated.

The area infested in 1906 included the present fifteen southernmost counties, with a total area of about 75,000 square miles, or nearly one-half of the entire State. Almost five sixths of the infested area, however, had been cleared at the end of the first four years of operation. This was rapid progress, when it is considered that the area contained more than 660,000 head of cattle, of which more than 150,000 were on infested range. The status of the campaign in California was discussed in 1911, under joint Federal-State authorship (57—26; 59—174).

Expenses were shared by Federal, State, and private interests. The Tick-Eradication Division furnished a force of veterinary inspectors and also constructed a fifty-five-mile stock-proof drift fence along accessible portions of the Mexican border. The State Veterinarian furnished additional men for the work, and the livestock owners furnished the necessary dipping apparatus and chemicals.

Two subsequent infestations have occurred in California. One was discovered in Kings County in 1918, and eradication effected within a year. A single ranch in San Diego County became infested in 1925 from Mexican cattle which had broken through the international boundary fence. This infestation also was promptly eradicated. The only Federal expense at the present time is a small one for the maintenance of the fence along the Mexican border.

Tuberculosis Control

Tuberculosis of cattle is a widespread and very destructive disease which, like most of our pests, has been brought to this country from the Old World. The movement for its control started from the discovery that the germ causing the disease may be transmitted to human beings through milk from tuberculous cows. Swine and goats also contract the disease, which is widely distributed and often very destructive among swine in this country. Because, however, these other classes of animals ordinarily become infected through tubercular cattle, and because the gigantic eradication campaign is concerned primarily with cattle, this disease is discussed under cattle protection rather than under the protection of livestock, as was foot-and-mouth disease, for example.

Tuberculosis is a most insidious disease because infected animals, including man, often may show no external symptoms of the disease and yet carry and give off infective material which may spread the disease to others. Tuberculin, a serum for diagnosing the presence of the disease in animals, was introduced to the medical world by Koch in 1890 and opened the way for effective control measures. The Bureau of Animal Industry immediately began tests which proved the value of tuberculin as a diagnostic agent. By 1895 their researches had shown that bovine and human tuberculosis were caused by two different varieties of the same germ species. Research on the transmission of bovine tuberculosis to man also was conducted by the Bureau, as by many other agencies. In spite of Koch's announcement in 1901 that bovine tuberculosis was not dangerous to human beings, world-wide research in this field continued and by the time of the International Tuberculosis Conference held in Washington, D. C., in 1908, it had been shown that nine per cent of the cases of tuberculosis in children were caused by the bovine type of tubercle bacillus (23 :68–70).

The movement for tuberculosis control gained impetus from the increase of city ordinances forbidding the sale of raw milk from tubercular cows. The development of the process of sterilizing milk by pasteurization had made it possible to protect the public health in this way, but the expense of production was increased. From these beginnings of tuberculin invention and municipal restriction there has developed the present nation-wide coöperation of Federal, State, county, municipal, and private agencies in the control and eradication of bovine and porcine tuberculosis. In general, there were three stages in the development of the program. The first stage was a survey to determine the distribution and severity of infection among cattle. The second was careful testing to prevent interstate shipment of tubercular animals. The third stage was the campaign for the eradication of the disease from the dairy herds of the country. No definite period was characterized by any of these stages, for eradication was in progress in some jurisdictions before survey had begun in others.

Survey of distribution and severity.—In 1901 the Wisconsin Station published (78—84) some statistics on the prevalence of tuberculosis among cattle in Wisconsin and other States, showing that from four to fifty per cent were infected. In 1906 the same Station reported tests of seventy Wisconsin herds tested by the State Livestock Sanitary Board and showing fifty per cent of infected animals. Tests of herds owned by official institutions in different States showed infection to range from sixteen to one hundred per cent (23 :349–50). In 1908, the Congress authorized the Department of Agriculture to investigate the prevalence of tuberculosis among dairy cattle in the United States. This work was immediately begun by the Quarantine Division through the application of the tuberculin test to herds in different parts of the country. In the spring of 1909, more intensive local studies were made in coöperation with State and municipal authorities, especially in Iowa and Nebraska. In the same year tests were begun at various government Indian Schools, in coöperation with local and national officials of the Office of Indian Affairs, Department of the Interior. The annual reports of post-mortem inspection of cattle and hogs by the Meat-Inspection Division also served to show the extent of infection throughout the country. Even as late as 1917, these figures showed that more than two per cent of the cattle and nearly ten per cent of the hogs slaughtered were infected.

Tuberculin testing for interstate shipment.—Previous to 1909, several States had established testing of cattle with tuberculin as a prerequisite to their admission to those States. In that fiscal year ten additional States took the same action. As cattle obviously could not be tested at State boundaries, it was necessary to accomplish the inspection at central points. Accordingly the Quarantine Division of the Bureau of Animal Industry entered into coöperation with numerous States to establish the work at eight of the major stockyards throughout the country, under the supervision of the Division (23:148). In 1911 this work was transferred to the Field Inspection Division, and in 1917 to the Tuberculosis Eradication Division except in relation to cattle for import and export.

Tuberculosis eradication campaign.—Eradication activities began in 1900, some seventeen years before the nation-wide campaign was started. In 1900, the Bureau tested the dairy herd at St. Elizabeth's Asylum, an institution of the Federal Government in the District of Columbia, and helped to weed out infected cattle (58—44). In 1906, the Pathological Division of the Bureau of Animal Industry began the application of the tuberculin test to dairy cattle in and around the District of Columbia, in coöperation with the Health Department of the District, with the intent to protect the milk supply. In 1907, the work was transferred to the Quarantine Division. The testing was done under a voluntary agreement by the owners to abide by the Federal and State regulations, to slaughter or segregate reacting animals, to disinfect premises, and to meet many other requirements. In 1909 the District was quarantined by the Commissioners and an active eradication campaign waged in coöperation with the Bureau. In 1910 nearly 19 per cent of the cattle reacted, in 1917 less than 1 per cent, and in 1922 only .17 per cent (23:146–49 and 351). In 1910, following the preliminary survey mentioned above, the Quarantine Division began the eradication of tuberculosis from cattle at thirty-one Indian schools and reservations, in coöperation with the Office of Indian Affairs, and continued it to completion. In 1909 a plan was adopted which still continues. At plants where meat inspectors found tuberculous carcasses of cattle and swine, their origin was traced whenever possible and the former owners and the proper State officials notified. This has enabled the discovery of infection centers and their eradication by local and State action.

The Federal-State nation-wide campaign for the eradication of tuberculosis in cattle dates from July 1, 1917. The present Tuberculosis Eradication Division was organized on May 1 of that year, and has had charge of the work from the beginning. In December of that year, at the annual meeting of the United States Livestock Sanitary Association, the accredited-herd plan of eradication was adopted, later approved by the Federal Government, and then presented to the livestock owners (54—1918:215–20, and 1919:277–88). The experience gained in the coöperative control of the disease in the District of Columbia was not only exceedingly useful in the broader field, but was the basis for the official willingness to undertake such a gigantic task. State headquarters gradually were established in nearly all of the States, usually in the State capital, and always in coöperation with the State officials charged with the control of livestock diseases. In December, 1919, a committee representing State and Federal agencies and the cattle-breeders' organizations drafted methods and rules for the conduct of the work. Effective July 1, 1918, an appropriation of $500,000 became available with the further provision that such portion as was necessary migh be expended as indemnity to owners for reacting-cattle slaughtered, contingent, however, on the sharing of this expense by the State, county, or municipality. A year later the amounts to be available for operating expenses and for indemnity were separated. In 1920, the Bureau of Animal Industry published three circulars (49—142, 143, and 144), listing all herds accredited as free and those in process of being freed. A general description of the work and value of tuberculin testing of livestock was published (49—249) in 1922.

Three different methods of attack have been used. These are, in brief: (*a*) the Accredited-Herd Plan, (*b*) the Tuberculosis-Free Area Plan, and (*c*) the Tuberculosis-Eradication Calf-raising Plan. The first two date from 1917, the third only from 1929. All look toward the gradual elimination of tubercular animals from herds or areas. The set-up in California and the methods of procedure are typical for the country as a whole. Federal coöperation in California was begun in 1918 and headquarters established at Sacramento, where quarters now are provided in the Federal Building.

The primary coöperation is between the U. S. Bureau of Animal Industry, through its Division of Tuberculosis Eradication, and the Division of Animal Industry of the State Department of Agriculture. The Federal agency may collaborate directly, however, with a county or municipality, under the Federal law. Federal-State coöperation is covered by a formal memorandum of agreement signed by the Chief of the Federal Bureau and the chief of the State Division. The Federal Bureau agrees to designate a veterinary inspector, to be known as the inspector-in-charge; to detail additional inspectors to the extent of available means and in proportion to State funds expended, to furnish tuberculin, and to supply certain necessary blank forms. The State Division of Animal Industry agrees to detail one veterinary inspector for every such inspector provided at Federal expense, to coöperate under the leadership of the Federal Inspector-in-Charge, to enforce State laws and regulations covering reactors, and to supply State quarantine blanks and copies of State regulations. The two agencies jointly agree that tuberculosis eradication in California shall be coöperative, that the official leaders of the two agencies shall confer at least bi-monthly and welcome suggestions for improvement, that charts, reports, and other records shall be exchanged, and that the agreement may be terminated by either party on thirty days' notice in writing.

Accredited-herd plan: This plan is designed primarily to free breeding herds from tuberculosis. Federal-State coöperation is provided by State law (Calif. Stats. 1921, chap. 1128, sect. 8, p 2394). Under this plan, the owner signs an agreement to abide by the necessary regulations. The tuberculin test is administered by veterinarians accredited by Federal and State agencies, reactors are isolated and disposed of, and, when the herd is tuberculosis-free, the owner is given an accreditization certificate which enables him to sell his breeding animals as tuberculosis-free, so long as regular retesting fails to discover infected animals. By 1930, some 341 California breeding-herds were accredited or in the process, only 159 reactors remaining among 25,074 animals. For the entire country nearly 26,000,000 cattle had been tested under this plan to the end of fiscal year 1931. In the last three years of the period the number had averaged about 3,000,000 per year. At intervals the Bureau publishes a list of accredited herds (49—54 and 142) and those in process of becoming accredited (49—143 and 144).

Tuberculosis-free areas: In this activity, the area instead of the herd is the basis of eradication, the county being the standard unit of area, though a group of counties may constitute a single area. Originally such areas were surveyed only on request of county supervisors, and eradication was not undertaken if more than ten per cent of the animals were found infected on random sampling. Under recent legislation the movement may be otherwise originated, and the limit of infection has been removed. The program includes quarantine action to prevent the introduction of diseased cattle, discovery of infection centers, removal and slaughter of infected animals, disinfection of premises, and retesting of herds at intervals to detect reinfection. When infection is reduced to 0.5 per cent, or less, the county or area is declared to be a modified tuberculosis-free area, and when eradication is complete it is certified as tuberculosis-free. Under the area plan nearly 63,000,000 cattle had been tested to the end of fiscal year 1931, the number in the last three years of the period having averaged nearly 10,000,000 per year. The counties engaged in the campaign to the end of fiscal year 1931 numbered 1578, or slightly more than half the total number of counties in the United States. Of these, 1223 had been proclaimed modified accredited areas, or modified tuberculosis-free areas. New counties to the number of 164 took up the work in 1931. Approximately 78 per cent of the cattle tested were under the area plan.

Calf-segregation areas: Under the revision of the California Bovine Tuberculosis Law in 1929, a third plan of eradication was set up in that State, the county being the unit area by which tuberculosis is eradicated through the raising of healthy calves. This is especially desirable where infection runs high and much time and money would be required for eradication by the slaughter of reactors. Following a public hearing, county supervisors may request such action by the State Department of Agriculture. In this plan, newborn calves are promptly segregated from other stock and raised under conditions of noncontamination and regular retest (11A—9 :30). Eventually a new herd of tuberculosis-free animals is developed thereby, the old herd of infected animals gradually disappearing through age. No indemnity payment is made for slaughtered reacting calves. California is the first State to undertake such a program, and Del Norte the first county to begin operations under it.

Payment for slaughtered animals: Under the Federal law and the State law in California, these two agencies and the counties concerned join in paying the owner for the animals compelled to be destroyed as reactors. The Federal law permits Federal payment of not to exceed one-third of the difference between the appraised value of the animal destroyed and the value of the slaughter salvage therefrom, provided that no payment exceeds $25 for any grade animal or more than $50 for a purebred animal, and that no Federal payment shall exceed the amount paid from State or other official sources. The California State law now limits State payments to one-third of the difference between the appraised value and the amount received by the owner from slaughter salvage, provided that the maximum does not exceed $35 for a grade animal or $70 for a purebred, and that no payment is made by the State for grade steers or bulls (Calif. Stats. 1921, chap. 1128, sect. 9c, p. 2395; 11A—9 :26–27). This leaves the county responsible for the final one-third of the difference between appraised value and salvage.

General summary: Progress made in national tuberculosis eradication is summarized annually in the reports of the Federal Bureau of Animal Industry (56) and at intervals in other publications (54—1926 :180–83; 1931 :133–36). That for 1931 shows the results after fourteen years of concentrated effort in coöperation with States, counties, and municipalities (56—1931 :60–66). The economic benefits of the campaign were summarized by the Bureau in 1929 and the assistance of many public officials acknowledged (52—66). More than nine hundred veterinarians were engaged in the campaign, of whom nearly two hundred were Federal, more than four hundred were State, and more than three hundred were county employees. The Federal appropriation for that fiscal year was $6,190,000, of which $5,000,000 was for payment of indemnities for animals slaughtered. Combined State and county appropriations were more than $13,500,000. The grand total available in that year, therefore, was approximately $20,000,000. More than 88,000,000 cattle had been tested in the fourteen-year period, of which 2,184,000 or 2.5 per cent had proved to be reactors. The percentage had decreased, however, from more than four per cent in the early years to less than two per cent in the last three years, and 1.5 per cent in fiscal year 1931. More than 160,000 cattle were slaughtered in the year named, at a total cost of $10,424,880, of which the States (including counties) paid $6,197,638 and the Federal government $4,227,243. Forty per cent of the counties in the United States had been designated as modified tuberculosis-free areas, or as containing less than 0.5 per cent of reactors. Four entire States, Indiana, Maine, Michigan, and North Carolina, were modified accredited or tuberbulosis-free areas.

For California, reports of progress are made annually in the reports of the State Division of Animal Industry (9), and in 1930 the progress made was summarized (9—19 :673–76). In 1928, the results of the nation-wide program were summarized by the State (10—17 :347–54). In 1929, the California Station and the State Department united in joint authorship of recommendations on bovine tuberculosis which were published by the Extension Service (8—32).

Other Diseases

Occasional relations have developed between Federal and State agencies in the course of investigations of less prevalent or less destructive diseases of cattle.

Cornstalk disease.—In 1896 the Federal Bureau published on an investigation of the cornstalk disease of cattle (58—10), in which (p. 6) it was stated that the Illinois and Iowa Agricultural Experiment Stations gave the use of their bacteriological laboratories for the work.

Granular venereal disease.—In 1914, the Bureau published (47—106) the results of a comprehensive study made by the Veterinary Department of Cornell University, with coöperation from the Pathological Division of the Bureau and from various meat inspectors of the Meat Inspection Division (p. 1).

Contagious abortion.—A study of methods for the isolation of the causal organism, conducted by the Division of Veterinary Science at the California Station, and supported in part by a grant of funds from the Pathological Division of the Federal Bureau of Animal Industry, was published in *Hilgardia* (Vol. 6, No. 12) by the California station in 1932.

The publications listed in the Literature Cited at the end of this chapter which have been cited in this section on Cattle and Reindeer Protection are Nos. 8, 9, 10, 11A, 23, 26, 43, 47, 49, 52, 54, 56, 57, 58, 59, and 78.

BEEF-CATTLE PRODUCTION

The development of investigations in beef-cattle production by the Division of Animal Husbandry, in the Federal Bureau of Animal Industry, has been somewhat on a regional basis. This has been conditioned in part on the relative periods of development of livestock units in State and Federal institutions. The State agricultural colleges and experiment stations were organized and well established in the last century, whereas the Bureau did not add an animal husbandman to its staff until 1901 and did not establish the Division until 1910. During the period of State-station development the production of beef cattle had become stabilized on the farms of the North and Northeast and the system of extensive ranching had become established in the dry-land West. There was little call for Federal activities in those areas. But unexpected biologic and economic factors soon changed the scene.

The boll weevil gradually overspread and devastated the Cotton Belt, beginning in 1892. The growing demand for agricultural land, plus changing economic conditions, spelled the doom of the immense cattle ranch. Diversified farming in the South and dry-land cropping for livestock in the Near West opened up many new problems in livestock production. The gradual elimination of cattle ticks in the South, beginning in 1906, and of cattle mange and other diseases in the West offered new opportunities in cattle breeding and fattening. So it came about that the first Federal participation in coöperative beef-cattle production experiments took place in the South and the second developed in the dry-land West. For convenience, the work in each of these two sections is discussed separately. Climatologically and agriculturally, Maryland, Virginia, and West Virginia belong to the Northeast rather than to the

South, especially in their mountainous sections, but they are placed
with the other southern States in this discussion.

In the Southern States

Alabama.—Experiments in beef-cattle production were begun by
the Bureau of Animal Industry in coöperation with the Alabama
Agricultural Experiment Station at the Alabama Polytechnic
Institute in 1904, immediately on the availability of the appropriation for livestock breeding and feeding. At first the studies were
confined to calves, but from 1908 onward they included steers also.
The investigations were concerned particularly with production
under southern conditions and with utilizing southern feedstuffs,
including pasturage. A considerable series of coöperative publications resulted (47—73 and 110; 58—103, 131, 147, and 159), beginning in 1908 and continuing until 1914. The first publication
was under Alabama authorship, but thereafter they appeared under joint authorship. The coöperation always was mentioned in the
Letters of Transmittal and often in the introductory portion of
the text. Only once (58—147) did the phrase: "Investigations in
coöperation with the Alabama Agricultural Experiment Station"
appear in capital letters on the bulletin cover, as it always did
in the case of the Pennsylvania Station coöperation in nutrition
studies during the same years (58).

Mississippi.—In 1914, the experiments on both calves and steers
were transferred to Mississippi in order to be in tick-free territory, and thereafter were conducted in coöperation with the Mississippi Agricultural Experiment Station, though mostly on the private farms of stock-raisers. In 1917, the Mississippi Station published on feeding calves for market (31—183). The bulletin included results of both independent and coöperative experiments
(*op. cit.*, 6–7, 22–35), the coöperative being conducted from 1914 to
1916 at West Point, Mississippi, on a private farm. Two Federal
publications in 1918 and 1919 included the more recent results from
both Alabama and Mississippi (47—631 and 777). The coöperation
with the Mississippi Station was continued and in 1925 resulted in
a publication on fattening steers with velvet bean, a southern-
grown legume of increasing importance (47—1333). It was under
Federal authorship, the Bureau of Animal Industry having placed

a man in direct supervision of the experiments (*op. cit.*, pp. 3–4). The work was done on a farm at Collins in 1917 and on the State Substation at McNeill from 1920 to 1922. Some of the analyses of beans were made by the U. S. Bureau of Chemistry. The coöperation was shown only in the text, no boxes appearing on the title page although they had been used as early as 1922. Soon after this work was completed, a long-time study of the effect of the burning of pasture land on subsequent gains of cattle and on survival of young longleaf pines was begun and is still under way at the Coastal Plain Experiment Station, at McNeill (56—1931:12). The U. S. Forest Service also takes part in this study (56—1930:12).

Louisana.—With the appearance of certain economic conditions in the sugar-cane district of Louisana the development of increased livestock production began to receive additional emphasis. In about 1914 the Iberia Livestock Experiment Farm, near Jeanerette, was established as a coöperative enterprise of the U. S. Department of Agriculture and the Louisiana Agricultural Experiment Station. The livestock project entailed much attention to forage and feeding crops, and in this phase of the work the Bureau of Plant Industry coöperated with the Bureau of Animal Industry and the State. The chief of the Plant Industry Bureau was chairman of the Federal-State committee in charge of the Farm. The first animal-husbandry contribution appeared in 1925 and covered steer-feeding experiments (47—1318) conducted from 1915 to 1919. The coöperation between the Federal Department and the State Station was prominently displayed in a box at the top of the cover page, and the participation of the Bureau of Animal Industry is mentioned also in the text.

Missouri.—In 1915 large-scale breeding operations with beef cattle were begun by a private citizen of Missouri. On his death in that year he willed that the work should continue for thirty years. It has been placed under the general direction of a committee of three men appointed one each by the presidents of the Universities of Missouri, Kansas, and Oklahoma. By agreement the results of the first ten years were published by the U. S. Department of Agriculture, under joint authorship of the Bureau of Animal Industry, the supervising committee, and the University of Missouri (50—74). In 1925, the keeping of detailed records of the feeding of steer calves was begun under arrangements made by the Federal agency and the University of Missouri. In 1930 the results of part of the experiments in calf feeding during 1925 to 1927 were published (48—208) under joint authorship of the two official agencies named. The only statement of coöperation is a reference to the previous publication. More recent experiments were published under joint authorship (48—397) in 1933.

North Carolina.—In the autumn of 1913 the Federal Division of Animal Husbandry began experiments on the wintering and fattening of cattle in North Carolina. The work was done on a private farm but in coöperation with the State Agricultural Experiment Station, which in turn is maintained jointly by the North Carolina State College of Agriculture and the State Department of Agriculture. Results of the first three years of work were published under joint authorship by the Department of Agriculture (47—629) and—simultaneously—as Bulletin 240 of the State Department of Agriculture. The experiments of the next three seasons, 1916 to 1919, on wintering and summer fattening of steers, were also published under joint authorship and simultaneously by the Station and the Department (35—243; 47—954).

West Virginia.—In December, 1914, the Federal Division of Animal Husbandry began a series of feeding experiments with cattle in West Virginia. The work, done on a private farm, was shared with the State Agricultural Experiment Station, under a resident expert employed in common by the two agencies. His name has been carried by the station in the list of its staff appearing in the front of all bulletins, with a footnote showing the Federal coöperation. The lists show also that other staff members were employed in coöperation with the State Department of Agriculture. A series of publications resulted, all appearing under joint authorship. The first three, covering experiments in the three feeding seasons from 1915 to 1919, were issued by the Federal government. The first, appearing in 1920, dealt with yearling steers (47—870). The second and third, dealing with cows with calves, and with calves alone (47—1024 and 1042) appeared in 1922. The State Station published the same data in two bulletins (76—186 and 190) in 1924 and 1925. The effects of winter rations on the pasture gains of two-year-old steers, covering experiments conducted from 1919 to 1922, were published by the Federal agency (49—166 ; 47—1251) in 1921 and 1924 and by the State station (76—191) in 1925. The Federal bulletins show the coöperation on the first page in text and footnote. The State bulletins show it in footnote only. The analyses of the feeds used were made by the Division of Chemistry of the West Virginia Station. A briefer account, also, of these last experiments appeared in the *Journal of Agricultural Research* (26—28 : 1215–32) in 1924, the coöperation being stated in the text (p. 1215) with a footnote reference to the Department bulletin. Studies conducted from 1922 to 1925 on the gains of calves marketed as two-year steers were published by the Department (47—1431) in 1926 and by the State (76—218) in 1928. The statement "United States Department of Agriculture in coöperation with the West Virginia Agricultural Experiment Station" appears in a box on the front cover of the Federal publication for the first time in this coöperation, although it had appeared on other Department bulletins as early as 1922. In 1930 a coöperative three-year experiment in the use of grass alone and grass variously supplemented by concentrates for fattening two-year steers was begun by the two agencies (56—1931 :11).

In 1931 there appeared under joint authorship of the Division of Animal Husbandry and the West Virginia Station the results of experiments conducted from 1925 to 1927 on beef production and quality as affected by the grade of the animal and the fattening methods (48—217). The prominent cover statement of the coöperation declares that the Federal Bureaus of Animal Industry, Agricultural Economics, and Home Economics all were coöperating with the State and that the research was part of a national project in which some twenty-seven States were taking part.

Other Southern States.—Arkansas: In 1924 the Bureau began a five-year experiment in coöperation with the Arkansas Station and the State Agricultural and Mechanical College on the college farm at Jonesboro, members of the faculty being appointed part-time employees of the Bureau for the purpose of supervising the experiment. The results were published under joint authorship in 1930, with the coöperation shown plainly on the title page and in the text (48—203).

Georgia: In coöperation with the Georgia Agricultural Experiment Station, feeding experiments in the use of molasses and corn for steers were begun in 1931 by the Federal Division of Animal Husbandry (56—1931:12) at Moultrie.

Virginia: The three-year experiment on grass and concentrates for two-year steers, previously mentioned under West Virginia, is conducted also in coöperation with the Virginia Agricultural Experiment Station at Blacksburg (56—1931:11).

Maryland: At the U. S. Animal Husbandry Experiment Station at Beltsville, the Federal Bureaus of Animal Industry and Plant Industry began coöperation in 1930 on systems of pasture management in steer production (56—1931:11).

In the Middle West

The early coöperative experiments in the production of beef cattle in western States were local and temporary, and were occasioned by special conditions which arose from time to time. The first recorded instance of Federal-State coöperation in the production problems of western beef cattle occurred in Colorado (56—1904: 66). In about 1904, when the U. S. Department of Agriculture was giving much attention to the development of the sugar-beet industry in this country, an experiment in feeding steers on sugar-beet pulp, conducted by the Colorado Agricultural Experiment Station, was financed in part by the Bureau of Animal Industry. The results were published by the State (14—97) in 1905, with acknowledgment of the financial assistance (p. 1).

In 1906 the Bureau of Animal Industry published (58—91) some results of feeding prickly pear (cactus) to cattle. This was part of a study of emergency feeding of range cattle during drought periods made by the Office of Farm Management of the Bureau of Plant Industry in collaboration with Texas stockmen. Experiments on the digestibility of the cactus, conducted in partnership by the latter Bureau and the New Mexico Agricultural Experiment Station, were published by the State station (34—69) and also by the Bureau of Animal Industry (58—106), in 1908. Later, in 1915, after more extensive feeding experiments had been carried on by the Dairy Division of the Bureau of Animal Industry in coöperation with the Office of Farm Management of the Bureau of Plant Industry, the results were published jointly (26—4:405–50).

In 1915 the Bureau of Animal Industry began an experiment in cattle breeding in coöperation with the Kansas Agricultural Experiment Station, to develop a dual-purpose (beef and milk) animal. The work was continued until 1924 and the results were then said to be in process of compilation (37:23).

In 1917 was published an account of experiments to increase cattle production on the ranges in the Southwest (47—588). The work was done by the Grazing Branch of the Forest Service on some 200,000 acres of land in Dona Ana County, New Mexico, withdrawn from entry by the Department of the Interior to form the Jornada Range Reserve of the Department of Agriculture. In 1917, also, was published a three-year study of economic wintering of cows in the corn belt, comprising a joint contribution from the Office of Farm Management and the Bureau of Animal Industry (47—615). A similar comprehensive coöperative study of costs and methods of fattening beef cattle in the corn belt was published (48—23) under joint authorship in 1927.

Appropriations were made by Congress to the Bureau of Animal Industry in 1916 for the development of a more stable farm-livestock industry in the arid and semiarid districts of the West. These caused the beginning of experiments at several points in 1916 and 1917, mostly on stations already established by the Bureau of Plant Industry, either independently or in coöperation with the States. At some of these points work was done only with beef cattle, at others with dairy cattle, or with hogs in addition to cattle, while at still others several classes of livestock were subjects of experiment.

North Dakota.—In 1916 grazing experiments with cattle were begun at the Northern Great Plains Field Station at Mandan, North Dakota, established for the Bureau of Plant Industry but conducted in coöperation with the North Dakota Agricultural Experiment Station. The study was primarily to determine the carrying capacity of the short-grass range under controlled conditions and therefore was intimately concerned with the livestock industry, although the Federal Bureau of Animal Industry was not a party. The results from 1916 to the end of the season of 1921 were published in 1923, with the words, "United States Department of Agriculture in coöperation with the North Dakota Agricultural Experiment Station," appearing in a box on the cover, and the coöperation acknowledged also in a first-page footnote (47—1170). Data for the year 1923 are given in a bulletin (47—1337) appearing in 1925, with the coöperation of North Dakota in grazing indicated in the text (p. 2), and the results included (pp. 16–87). During 1931 a project on the inheritance of milk and beef production in dual-purpose cattle was established in coöperation with the North Dakota Station at the Edgeley Substation (56—1931:14).

South Dakota.—Experiments with beef cattle were begun in 1917 at the U. S. Dry-Land Field Station at Ardmore, South Dakota, established in 1912 by the Office of Dry-Land Agriculture of the Bureau of Plant Industry. In 1927 the results to the end of 1925 were published under joint authorship of the Bureaus of Plant Industry and Animal Industry, the latter represented by both its Animal Husbandry and Dairy Divisions (48—17). The section on beef cattle was confined to steer grazing (*op. cit.*, pp. 33–36). A second publication on the livestock work at Ardmore dealt with wintering steers, and covered the results of five seasons from 1923 to 1928. It appeared under joint authorship of the two Bureaus (48—192), with the coöperation stated also in a footnote. This collaboration continues, as do the joint grazing experiments now of more than fifteen years' duration.

New Mexico–Texas.—Some ten years ago coöperative studies in the utilization of dry-land feed crops in cattle production were begun by the Bureaus of Plant Industry and Animal Industry on Plant Industry field stations in the Near Southwest. The coöperative publications appeared in 1927 and 1928. The first covered steer fattening on dry-land crops and involved the coöperation and joint authorship of the two Federal Bureaus and the New Mexico Agricultural Experiment Station, the work having been done at a Plant Industry Field Station at Tucumcari, New Mexico (48—30). The publication made no statement of the coöperation, other than authors' titles. The second bulletin (48—43) issued in 1928, contained the results of tests of feeds for fattening calves and had the same joint authorship as the one last mentioned. In addition, it contained results of experiments from 1923 to 1925 at another Plant Industry Field Station at Big Springs, Texas, in which the two Federal Bureaus had coöperated with the Texas Station also (*op. cit.*, p. 2). These experiments are still in progress, with all three agencies coöperating. More recently the two Bureaus have entered into coöperation with the Texas Station at its Beeville Substation in feeding experiments with special reference to the use of various sorghums in different forms (56—1931 :12).

Montana.—In 1924 the Department of the Interior transferred to the Department of Agriculture the Fort Keogh Military Reservation near Miles City, Montana, which had been relinquished by the War Department (17 :715). It was designated as the United States Range Livestock Experiment Station of the Bureau of Animal Industry and was devoted at first to studies in beef production on the range, including the growing of the necessary forage crops (37 :23). Later this extensive livestock station was made coöperative with the Montana Agricultural Experiment Station and other classes of livestock were added. The Department of Agriculture has created an advisory committee consisting of an animal husbandman from each of eight western State colleges of agriculture, which usually meets annually to consider the problems, procedure, and results of the livestock experiments being conducted at the coöperative station. Some of the expenses of the meeting are defrayed by the Department. Extensive and varied studies in the grazing and feeding of cattle of different ages are in progress (56—1931 :13). Somewhat similar experiments, though on a smaller scale, have been conducted by the Division of Animal Husbandry in coöperation with the Montana Station at its Northern Montana Branch Station at Havre for the past several years (56—1931 :14).

Other States.—In its annual report for 1931 (p. 10) the Bureau of Animal Industry says that research in beef production alone was conducted at twenty-four Federal and State experiment stations during that year. Twelve states—Georgia, Louisiana, Maryland, Mississippi, Missouri, Montana, New Mexico, North Dakota, South Dakota, Texas, Virginia, and West Virginia—already have been discussed. In Colorado and Wyoming, studies are being made in selected areas, in coöperation with the experiment stations of those States, on the effect on calf production of keeping breeding cows on supervised pasture rather than on open range or forest range. This work was begun in 1929 and is coöperative also with the Federal Bureau of Agricultural Economics (56—1931 :14). Investigations on dual-purpose cattle are being made in coöperation with the Indiana (Purdue) and Minnesota Agricultural Experiment Stations, along the lines already noted under North Dakota (56— 1930 :14). Some of the other ten States are among the twenty-two which are conducting coöperative investigations on the quality and palatability of meats, in coöperation also with the Federal Bureaus of Agricultural Economics and Home Economics.

The publications listed in the Literature Cited at the end of this chapter which have been cited in this section on Beef Cattle Production are Nos. 14, 17, 26, 31, 34, 35, 37, 47, 48, 49, 50, 56, 58, and 76.

DAIRY PRODUCTS RESEARCH

Because of conditions existing at the time, coöperative relations developed in the study of dairy products before they did in the field of dairy-cattle production. For this reason the two topics are treated in the order given, although this seems to reverse the logical order. From 1895 onward there was a very rapid expansion of the dairy industry in America. By 1894 there were more than 16,000,-000 dairy cows in the United States, the increase being 4,000,000 in the ten years between 1880 and 1890. The number of registered Jerseys, Holsteins, and Guernseys virtually trebled between 1885 and 1895. More than a billion pounds of butter were being made on the farms annually, but quality was not keeping pace with quantity. Factory production also was increasing rapidly and had reached an annual output of 300,000,000 pounds. The cheese industry was expanding steadily and by 1894 had reached a total of 270,000,000 pounds a year. But exports had decreased from nearly 150,000,000 pounds in 1880 to half that quantity in 1894, owing largely to prejudice aroused by the exportation of quantities of adulterated (filled) cheese. The market-milk business of the cities had developed to large proportions but with little attention to sanitary handling or the inspection of plants or supplies. Under these unsatisfactory conditions a demand developed for a Federal agency to study the situation, distribute information, and aid in improving the quality of dairy products.

For the first eleven years of its existence the Bureau of Animal Industry was concerned almost wholly with the diseases of livestock. On July 1, 1895, its Dairy Division was established and immediately began studies looking toward the improvement of dairy practices and the stimulation of dairy production in the United States. At first the Bureau had no dairy experts of its own, except the chief of the new Division. From time to time, therefore, it obtained the services of some qualified State official to make special studies and prepare the results for publication. In 1896 it began to publish on the general phases and problems of the dairy industry.

In 1896, the Dairy Division compiled dairy statistics from the data collected by the United States Census of 1890 and from other sources, and published them with interpretations (58—11). In 1896, likewise, the Division began the compilation of annual lists of officials, associations, and educational institutions connected with the dairy industry in this country. These lists were published in the circular series of the Bureau of Animal Industry (59—10, 18, 22, 26, 29, 33, 36, 40, 44, 80, 99, 115, 135, and 162) from 1896 to 1910, except 1909. In 1896, also, the Bureau published a bulletin on dairying in California, prepared by Professor Wickson of the State College of Agriculture (58—14). In 1897 appeared a discussion of the dairy industry in Missouri and Kansas by Levi Chubbuck, Secretary of the Missouri State of Board of Agriculture (58—18). Under the law of March 2, 1901, the Bureau, through its Dairy Division, began the official inspection of all dairy products offered for export on and after July 1 of that year, at the ports of Boston, New York, Chicago, and San Francisco (56—1902 :44). Through coöperation with the Bureau of the Census, then in the Department of the Interior, the chief of the Dairy Division was appointed a special agent of that Bureau to compile statistics of butter and milk, and of condensed-milk factories, for the National Census of 1900. These were published in June, 1902, as Census Bureau Bulletin No. 189 (56—1902 :45). From 1902 onward, the Division increased its activities steadily in the investigation and extension of better methods of producing and handling dairy products. The coöperative side of these activities will be presented under the headings of milk, butter, and cheese production.

Milk Production and Improvement

After the statistical and related studies which occupied the early years of the Dairy Division it began, about 1902, a program of investigation and of extension activities in the production and improvement of milk. Since the Division became a Bureau in 1924, this work has been part of the duty of its Division of Market-Milk Investigations.

Milk production.—In about 1908 the Dairy Division entered into a coöperative agreement with the Dairy Department of the Missouri Agricultural Experiment Station for an investigation of the effects of the period of lactation, feeding, and other factors on the chemical composition of milk. The results were published by the Bureau of Animal Industry (58). The first contribution covered a study of the large and small fat globules in milk (58—111) and appeared in 1909. The second concerned the estimation of the solids in milk by the use of formulas (58—134), and appeared in 1911. These were followed by three others in 1913, concerned with the effect of the stage of lactation, the breed, and the individual cow on the composition of the milk (58—155, 156, and 157). The entire series appeared under joint authorship and the coöperation was shown by the scientific titles of the authors on cover and title page and in the Letter of Transmittal by the chief of the Bureau. Apparently the coöperation was discontinued with the completion of these researches. In 1909 the Division published also on the methods of determining leucocytes in milk and the effect of heat on their number (58—117). On the cover the words "In coöperation with the Pennsylvania State Livestock Sanitary Board" are printed prominently, while the Letter of Transmittal acknowledges the collaboration both of this and of other State agencies.

Improvement of local milk supplies.—The Dairy Division of the Bureau of Animal Industry has coöperated with many other agencies in surveys of practices and resulting quality of local milk supplies, including those of cities, counties, and Federal institutions. Examples which show the type though not the quantity of such activities are given below.

The early studies made on city milk were by experts from other official agencies temporarily employed by the Dairy Division of the Bureau. In 1898 was published a study of the milk supply of Boston and other New England cities by an officer of the Massachusetts State Dairy Bureau (58—20). In 1903 the Federal Division coöperated with the United States Naval Academy in assuring the quality of its commercial milk supply after an outbreak of milk-borne disease among the cadets (56—1903:61). Following an epidemic of typhoid fever among the cadets in 1910, the Naval Academy decided to produce its own milk. The Dairy Division coöperated in the planning and construction of the plant and the selection and management of the herd (54—1920:463-70). The Division also assisted certain cities and the District of Columbia in improving their supplies of milk. In 1903 members of the Division staff published the results of a study of the milk supply of some two hundred cities and towns, in which they acknowledge the coöperation of numerous city officials whose contributions comprise a large portion (pp. 45-165) of the bulletins (58—46). In 1905 the Bureau published on the milk supply of twenty-nine southern cities, for which the study was made by a member of the Maryland Station staff (58—70). Still other studies were made by dairy experts not connected with official agencies.

Early in 1929 a representative of the Division of Market-Milk Investigations of the Bureau of Dairy Industry was detailed to coöperate with the Monroe County Department of Sanitation in a study of the quality of the milk supply of Rochester, New York. The county furnished two inspectors and one veterinarian for the work. Eight months later a checkup inspection was made to determine the resulting degree of improvement, which was found to be very marked (65—1930:33-34). In 1929 also the Division began coöperation with the United States Naval Academy in a program for the improvement of the milk from the Academy herd. This relation has been continued on the basis of a regular monthly check on the quality, including bacterial content of the milk, since the first improvement campaign was concluded.

Recently the Bureau of Dairy Industry, on request of the health authorities of Norfolk, Virginia, detailed a milk specialist to aid city milk inspectors in a survey of local conditions and avenues of improvement. The joint report was submitted to the Department of Public Welfare and to the Virginia Polytechnic Institute at Blacksburg (65—1931:24). Bureau specialists coöperated also with the health department of one of the large eastern cities in preparing a publication on the production of quality milk.

Improvement of national milk supply.—In contrast to activities with local communities and institutions, the Federal dairy agencies also have developed coöperative relations in studies and extension activities fundamental to the improvement of the quality of milk produced nationally. Some of these activities themselves have been local in scope, while others have been regional or national. Some have been incidental developments of projects in their fields.

In 1904 the Dairy Division began formal coöperation within the Storrs (Connecticut) Station in cheese making, as is discussed later. One of the early incidental results was a study of the use and the bacteriology of milking machines, published by the Bureau of Animal Industry in 1907. The bulletin (58—92) consists of two parts, of which the second contains the independent State study of the bacteriological aspects.

In 1913, the Dairy Division asked the Bureau of Standards of the Department of Commerce to determine the coefficients of expansion of market milk, single cream, and double cream, and this was done. The samples were prepared, and the fat determinations made, by the Dairy Division.

In 1917 the Bureaus of Animal Industry and Chemistry published, as a joint contribution, a guide for formulating a milk ordinance (47—585), a cover statement showing the collaboration. In 1923 the Dairy Division of the Bureau published a general discussion of the inspection of milk supplies (49—276) including score cards, farm inspection, and a recommended milk ordinance.

From 1917 to 1919 the Dairy Division coöperated with the Nebraska Agricultural Experiment Station in a study of unit requirements in the production of market milk in eastern Nebraska (47—972). The bulletin appeared in 1921 under joint authorship, with the coöperation shown on the first page in footnote and text.

In 1922, the Bureau of Animal Industry published, under joint authorship, the results of a study made by the Department of Dairy Husbandry of the University of Maryland and the Dairy Division of the Bureau on the effect of silage on the flavor and odor of milk (47—1097). The work was done at the Beltsville Experimental Farm of the Bureau, and the coöperation was noted on the first page in footnote and on the fifth page in text. In 1930 the Bureau of Dairy Industry and the Bureau of Plant Industry coöperated in a test of the effect of hempseed meal on the flavor and odor of milk.

In 1925 were published the results of a coöperative study of the effects of various factors on the creaming ability of market milk (47—1344), with the statement, "United States Department of Agriculture in coöperation with the Minnesota State Board of Health," appearing in a cover box, and the relation acknowledged in the text (p. 2). In 1926 the Bureau of Dairy Industry coöperated with the Division of Sanitation of the Minnesota Department of Health and the Department of Physics of the University of Minnesota in a study of temperature and bacterial count of milk and of foam during certain stages in the pasteurization process. The results were published in 1927 under joint authorship of the three agencies and with the coöperation stated in the text (48—18).

In 1929 a joint survey of the efficiency and economy of small refrigerating systems on dairy farms was made by the Federal Bureaus of Dairy Industry and Agricultural Engineering (the latter then still a division). This work was continued for some years thereafter (65—1930 and 1931). In California, different State agencies had coöperated in similar studies. A circular in 1925 showed coöperation by the Divisions of Agriculture, Engineering, and Dairy Industry in the State Experiment Station with the State Department of Agriculture (7—286). The second, published in 1930, was coöperative between the State Station and the Committee on Dairy Refrigeration of the California Committee on the Relation of Electricity to Agriculture (6—495).

In 1929, the Division of Market-Milk Investigations coöperated with the Federal Board for Vocational Education in presenting to the Board's regional directors the importance of the production of high-quality milk throughout the country. The two agencies then prepared an outline of a teaching project to be developed by the vocational teachers with their pupils in the many hundreds of schools under their charge.

For several years the Division of Market-Milk Investigations has coöperated widely with the Federal-State Agricultural Extension Service in many States on programs for market-milk improvement. Some of these have been designed for participation by adults and some by members of the 4-H Clubs of boys and girls. Subject-matter specialists of both agencies prepare the outlines. These then are passed upon by the Federal coördinating agency and thereafter distributed to extension workers throughout the country. Some of the first work under this project was done in Maine, where it was set going at a conference attended by Federal and State dairy officials and extension officials and by representatives of commercial agencies, including the dairy farmers. A checkup a year later showed that the proportion of Grade 1 milk had risen from 40 per cent to 57 per cent of the total. Meetings held in other States, South and North, included Federal, State, and local officials representing dairying, agricultural extension, and health agencies. In 1931 a specific project of milk improvement covering two counties in Maryland was started by the Bureau in coöperation with the State Extension Service and the State Department of Health, working with county and municipal officials (65—1931:24).

During 1931, conferences were held between the Bureau of Dairy Industry, the Public Health Service of the Treasury Department, and the Chief Coördinator of the Federal Government to determine the scope of the activities of different agencies in regard to the sanitary regulation of milk supplies. The final agreement provides for coöperation between the Bureau and the Service in putting out a set of rules to serve as a guide to States, municipalities, and communities in formulating the regulations and ordinances necessary in their given localities. A bulletin was published (52—148) in 1932 by the Federal Division of Market-Milk Investigations, discussing a milk-quality improvement program for extension workers.

Milk consumption campaigns.—Dairy production was speeded up during the World War, and at its close the problem of surplus production arose. A national campaign to stimulate the use of milk, especially among undernourished children, was started. Efforts were made also to promote the use of milk by factory workers and others in place of the beer which had come under the scope of the national prohibition of liquor. Early in 1919 educational campaigns were organized by the Division in several cities and in rural districts. Coöperation was had from commercial, civic, educational, and other agencies, public and private. The idea spread rapidly (49—250). The Dairy Division took part in the local campaigns only on the invitation of the State agricultural college, and then operated through the Federal-State Extension Service (23:198).

Butter Production and Quality

In 1902 the Dairy Division of the Bureau of Animal Industry, U. S. Department of Agriculture, began coöperation with the Navy Department by stationing Division inspectors at butter factories to inspect all butter being made and packed for Navy consumption. The coöperation has been continued and the quantity inspected annually runs as high as 10,000,000 pounds (23 :204). On a much smaller scale the same service has been rendered to the War Department (56—1902 :44). An act of May 2, 1902, provided for Federal supervision of factories making renovated butter for interstate commerce or export. Under the law the Treasury Department, through its Bureau of Internal Revenue, was responsible for the licensing of such factories, while the Department of Agriculture was charged with their inspection (56—1902 :45). This work has been continued, but the number of factories has decreased steadily (23 :204), because of the falling off in the manufacture of farm butter. By 1921 there were only eleven such factories and in 1931 only four remained (65—1931 :32).

In 1905 the Dairy Division began coöperation with the Iowa Station on the determination of the quality of cream and butter (56—1905 :57). This work was continued for a single year (23 :206) and then transferred to Washington, D. C. In 1906 the Bureau published a discussion of the manufacture and storage of butter (58—84), with the collaboration of the Iowa Station in the scoring, which was included (pp. 23–24).

In the annual report for 1907, it was recorded (p. 246) that the Dairy Division had arranged coöperation with the Minnesota Station on problems of butter production. The work was to be done at a commercial creamery at Albert Lea, Minnesota. Laboratories were equipped in a building on the creamery grounds. The distance from Washington made the location undesirable and the arrangement was discontinued about 1909 or 1910 (23 :206), and the work transferred to a creamery in Pennsylvania.

A score card for creameries was developed in the Dairy Division and extensively tested in the field. As commercial plants were scored thereunder by Division experts a copy of the resulting score was sent to the State dairy and food commissioner (56—1907 :

251). In 1909 the Dairy Division published the results of a coöperative study on the influence of the acidity of cream on the flavor of butter (58—114), acknowledging the courtesy of the Wisconsin Station in affording the use of its laboratories for the work.

In California, a few instances of official relationship have occurred. In July, 1922, the Federal Dairy Division and the Division of Dairy Industry of the University of California Agricultural Experiment Station began a coöperative investigation of butter improvement. By previous agreement the coöperation was continued for only two years, during which time the California agency obtained sufficient appropriations to carry on the work unaided. The results of this study were published in 1927 by the State station (6—443), under the title, *Standardization and Improvement of California Butter,* with the coöperation stated in the text (p. 4). In 1925 the Division of Agricultural Engineering at the California Station published *Milk Houses for California Dairies,* and acknowledged in it the services received from staff members of the Bureau of Dairy Service of the State Department of Agriculture and the Division of Dairy Industry at the California Station (7—286).

From the instances noted above it will be seen that official relations in butter production and improvement were few and sporadic. Intensive research has been conducted in this field by many agencies but mostly without coöperation, owing largely to the laboratory nature of the work. With the creation of the Federal Bureau of Dairy Industry in 1924, a Division of Dairy Manufacturing Investigations and Introduction was established. Most of its official relations have been with extension activities, and are comprehended in the term "Introduction." With the gradual shift from cotton farming to diversified farming in the old cotton belt, arising largely from boll-weevil infestation and cattle-tick eradication, that area had become interested in dairying but was without experience or training in its technic. In coöperation with the Agricultural Extension Services of Alabama, Arkansas, Florida, Mississippi, South Carolina, and Tennessee particularly, the Federal Division has aided in short-course instruction, dairy-scoring contests, butter-judging contests, and other methods of improving creamery practice and butter quality. Similar assistance has been given also to short courses in other parts of the country (65). A resulting publication on making creamery butter in the South (51—294) appeared in 1933 under joint authorship of the Federal Dairy Division and the Alabama Polytechnic Institute.

Research on the nutritive properties of butterfat is conducted by the Federal Bureau in coöperation with the University of California, with financial support from both agencies. Striking results are becoming apparent (65—1931:11).

Cheese and Cheese Making

Investigations in cheese making began much later than the studies of market-milk supply. The possibility of curing cheese at lower temperatures than usually were employed led to an experiment in cold curing in coöperation with the Wisconsin Station and the New York (Geneva) Station. The Dairy Division purchased the cheeses, and carried the expense of transportation, storage, and regular examination by experts. The Station experts selected the cheeses, arranged details, gave supervision, made chemical analyses, and recorded and reported the results. The comprehensive bulletin of 88 pages, appearing under joint authorship in 1903, comprises chiefly two sections containing the data from the two coöperating stations, each under its own authors (58—49). The Wisconsin Station published its portion of the data (78—101) also, in 1903, with the coöperation shown in the text (p. 3), and with a footnote reference to the Federal publication.

In 1908 the Dairy Division of the Bureau of Animal Industry and the Office of Experiment Stations collaborated in the compilation of descriptions and analyses of cheese varieties (58—105), which was revised and republished (58—146) in 1911. Both bulletins appeared under joint authorship. A second revision (47—608) was issued in 1918, with collaboration by the Bureau of Chemistry acknowledged.

Camembert type.—Beginning in 1904, the Dairy Division of the Bureau of Animal Industry entered into a formal coöperative agreement with the Storrs (Connecticut) Agricultural Experiment Station covering coöperative investigation of the manufacture of certain types of soft cheeses, such as Camembert and Roquefort. The Federal agency furnished three experts, a cheese-maker, a chemist, and a mycologist. The Storrs Station provided laboratories, curing rooms, and equipment, and furnished supervision.

The results of the continuing coöperative research were published promptly and a notable series of papers resulted. This is one of the few instances of Federal-State coöperation in which many of the publications were printed simultaneously by each of the two agencies. The first study, therefore, appeared under joint authorship in 1905 and covered a discussion of the Camembert type of cheese in the United States. It was publishd at about the same time by both agencies (15—35 ; 58–71), with identical titles and authors and practically identical text. Occasional words or phrases are different and the sequence of paragraphs is not always the same. The extensive letter of introduction in the Connecticut bulletin is signed only by the director of the Storrs Station but in the Federal bulletin it is signed also by the chief of the Dairy Division. The type was set independently by the two agencies. The coöperation is explained in the joint introductory letter in both papers, and is repeated at the beginning of the text in the State publication (*op. cit.*, p. 5).

The second bulletin was concerned with fungi used in cheese ripening and appeared in 1906 in the Federal series (58—82) and also in the seventeenth annual report of the Storrs Station. The third publication, containing directions for making Camembert cheese, appeared in 1907 under a Federal author but was published simultaneously by both agencies (15—46 ; 58—98), with reference to the three years of coöperation in the introductory letter by the Storrs director. The text again varies only slightly, but the headings and subheadings vary a good deal. The fourth paper, covering changes occurring in the ripening of such cheese (58—109), appeared in the Federal series in 1908 but apparently was not published by Connecticut. The fifth paper, on Camembert cheese problems, was published by both agencies (15—58 ; 58—115) in 1909 with virtually identical texts. The sixth paper, a study of the species of *Penicillium,* was published in 1910 by the Federal Bureau only (58—118). The seventh, on the enzymes of certain cheese fungi, appeared in the Federal series (58—120) in 1910 but had appeared already in the State series in the same bulletin (15—58 :375–453) as the fifth paper. At about this time the coöperation in Connecticut was discontinued and the work transferred to the Dairy Experiment Farm near Beltsville, Maryland. The Storrs Station continued research and publication in this field (15—78 and 79), the State having retained the Federal mycologist.

Cheddar type.—In about 1909 the Dairy Division, in coöperation with the Wisconsin Agricultural Experiment Station (famous for its research on dairy problems), began studies of the factors involved in the making of cheddar cheese. From the beginning the Federal Bureau furnished a bacteriologist, a cheese maker, and a chemist while the Wisconsin Station supplied the laboratories and equipment and one or more researchers, who also supervised the project. Here, as at the Storrs Station in Connecticut, some of the publications were issued more or less simultaneously by both agencies.

The first paper discussed moisture content and appeared in 1910, under joint authorship and with identical titles in both series (58—122; 79—7). The Wisconsin bulletin showed the institutional affiliations of the authors on the front cover and the coöperation in a note on the inside of the cover. The second and third papers were concerned with some chemical factors and were published in 1910 by Wisconsin only (79—10 and 11). Both were under joint authorship but the institutional relations are not shown on the cover. The second, which comprises only the middle portion of the containing bulletin, shows the coöperation in the opening paragraph, but the third, of which a Federal agent was senior author, makes no mention anywhere of the coöperation. The fourth paper, covering the factors of ripening of cheddar cheese, was published by Wisconsin (79—25) in 1912, with joint authorship and the coöperation stated in a footnote, which refers also to Wisconsin *Research Bulletins 7* and *11* and Bureau of Animal Industry *Bulletin 122* as representing coöperation. In the same year the Federal Bureau published the fifth paper, on the bacteriology of cheddar cheese (58—150), also jointly prepared and essentially the same as the State bulletin. The sixth paper, discussing the manufacture of cheddar cheese from pasteurized milk, was published in 1912 by Wisconsin (79—27) and in 1913 by the Bureau (58—165), under joint authorship. The Wisconsin bulletin showed institutional relationships on the title page but not on the cover. Coöperation was declared also in a footnote. Both publications showed that the Federal agency had had three successive bacteriologists, three successive cheese makers, and two successive chemists stationed in Wisconsin during the period covered.

Coöperation was shown in all the Federal bulletins through the institutional relations of the authors on cover and title page and by statement in the Letter of Transmittal. In 1914, soon after the founding of the *Journal of Agricultural Research* under Federal-State auspices, two papers on the bacterial ripening of cheddar cheese were published therein, under joint authorship (26—2: 167–92 and 193–216). Recently, in 1931, the Federal Bureau of Dairy Industry and the Wisconsin Station each has furnished a specialist in a coöperative program for improving the quality of Swiss cheese manufactured in Wisconsin (65—1931:31).

Miscellaneous types.—In the period of the World War, food conservation was a major activity and the Dairy Division waged a nation-wide campaign during 1918 and 1919 to promote the use of skimmed milk in making cottage cheese. The work was done in coöperation with other Federal units and with State agencies, and attained a large success (23:197).

Very recently, in 1930 and 1931, the Federal Bureau of Dairy Industry has been informally coöperating with several dairy departments of State colleges of agriculture in demonstrating new and improved methods of manufacture of grain-curd lactic-acid casein (65—1931:32).

There has been only minor coöperation between the Federal Bureau of Dairy Industry and official agencies in California. In 1925 the State Station published, under joint authorship, the results of a study of the manufacture of Roquefort-type cheese from the milk of goats (6—397). In the text (p. 20) it is declared that the development of this process in California was made possible through the close coöperation of the Federal Bureau. The Divisions of Animal Husbandry and Dairy Industry in the California Station worked together in the investigation.

There have been some small interrelations in dairy industry between the California Agricultural Experiment Station and the State Department of Agriculture. In 1925 the dairy laboratory of the Division of Chemistry of the State Department of Agriculture reported that in order to determine the limits of accuracy to be expected in the analysis of cheese, collaborative work had been carried on with the Division of Dairy Industry at the Experiment Station (10—14:258–62). Under California law, the Bureau of Dairy Control of the State Division of Animal Industry is a regulatory and statistical organization, having no research functions and normally no coöperative activities. However, in a publication of 1927 on the manufacture of Monterey cheese the Federal-State Agricultural Extension Service of the University of California acknowledges (*op. cit. infra,* p. 20) helpful assistance from the Bureau of Dairy Control in the supplying of statistics (7—13).

DAIRY CATTLE PRODUCTION

The Dairy Division of the Bureau of Animal Industry, U. S. Department of Agriculture, was organized in 1895, but for its first ten years it was concerned chiefly with the pressing problems of the improvement of the quality of dairy products, as already discussed. Later it began to give attention to the dairy cow and the management of the dairy herd. By that time dairying was well organized in the older dairy regions, and Federal activity was largely restricted to two sections, the South and the dry-land West, where dairying was new and little known. The programs carried forward in these two areas are presented below, together with minor activities in other parts of the country.

Dairy Demonstrations in the South

In 1905, the Dairy Division began a survey of dairy conditions and opportunities in the southern States. Conferences were held with the agricultural colleges to formulate plans for dairy extension in the various States. An appropriation of $20,000 was obtained from Congress and the work was begun in North Carolina, South Carolina, Georgia, Tennessee, Mississippi, and Texas, a dairy specialist being assigned to each State. Expenses of starting the work were borne wholly by the Dairy Division, with the understanding that if the plan were successful the States would gradually assume the financial support (23:191). Louisiana furnished an assistant in 1907 (56—1907:243), and Mississippi and North Carolina made appropriations in 1908 and supplied assistants in order to expand the work (56—1908:272). In 1908 Georgia published a bulletin (18—80), *Co-operative Dairy Investigations*, "by the Georgia Experiment Station and the Dairy Division, Bureau of Animal Industry, U. S. Department of Agriculture," under joint authorship and with Introduction by the Station director (pp. 1–2) in which the fact, but not the terms, of coöperation is set forth.

The coöperative study in Louisiana, begun in 1907, resulted in the publication in 1908 of the milk-production records of dairy herds in the vicinity of Hammond, under joint authorship, with a letter from the State director of experiment stations noting the coöperation (28—102). Feeding experiments were begun by the two workers in connection with the other dairy studies, with the consequence that two publications under joint authorship appeared in 1908, one on feeding molasses to calves (28—104), and the other on various cottonseed products as dairy feeds (28—110)—the latter showing the names of the coöperating agencies on the front cover for the first time. Experiments in dairying and dairy-herd management are conducted by the Bureau of Animal Industry, in coöperation with the Louisiana Station, at the Iberia Livestock Experiment Station, near Jeanerette, which was established about 1914 to help in diversifying agriculture in the sugar-cane belt. The Bureau of Plant Industry coöperates in the forage and pasturage experiments.

The early extension work covered better feeding methods, herd records, silo building, and better breeding. Gradually, calf raising, remodeling of barns, butter quality, and purebred bulls were emphasized. The formation of bull associations was promoted, as was also the development of cow-testing associations to determine milk and butterfat production in relation to the quantity of food consumed. In 1912 and 1913 the Mississippi Agricultural Experiment Station built dairy barns under coöperative Federal supervision at the McNeill Branch Station (31—158:4) and the Holly Springs Branch Station (31—165:23). By January, 1915, two assistant animal husbandmen, supplied coöperatively by the U. S. Department of Agriculture, were carried on the list of the Mississippi Station staff (31—170), as published on the inside of the front cover, where the coöperation was indicated by footnote. Additional Federal funds were obtained in 1914 for demonstrations

in livestock improvement in southern areas freed from cattle ticks
(23:193). After the organization of the agricultural extension
work in 1915, the Congress felt it increasingly inadvisable to maintain extension appropriations for subject-matter bureaus and this
type of activity was discontinued by the Dairy Division on June
30, 1920. However, substantially all of its dairy specialists were
immediately employed by the States in which they had been located, and the work was continued.

Several years ago the South Carolina Agricultural Experiment
Station established a Sandhill Substation at Pontiac, near Columbia, and entered into coöperation with the Federal Bureaus of
Animal Industry, Plant Industry, and Soils in the conduct of
experiments on dairying, forage plants, and soil management.
Buildings, equipment, and maintenance are provided by the State
agency and each Federal agency assigns one specialist to the substation. The breeding and management of the dairy herd is the
coöperative project in this field.

During 1930 the State of Tennessee deeded to the Federal Government 485 acres of land at Lewisburg, Tennessee, for use as a
United States Dairy Experiment Station. Congress made a special
appropriation to equip the station for its work. The breeding of
Jersey dairy cattle, and feeding and pasture investigations are
being pursued. The State Experiment Station coöperates in the
investigations (65—1930:3 and 30).

In 1931 the Bureau of Dairy Industry was enabled to open co-
operation with the Missouri Experiment Station in dairy-cattle
breeding and feeding on the Hatch Station, near Hannibal. The
station, once the home farm of the Honorable William H. Hatch,
representative in Congress from Missouri and father of the Hatch
Act creating the system of State agricultural experiment stations
in 1887 through Federal subsidy, was deeded by his estate to the
State of Missouri to be used for the advancement of agriculture
(65—1931:3).

Dairy Extension in the North and West

In 1910 the Dairy Division took up a dairy extension program in
the Rocky Mountain and Pacific Coast States, in coöperation with
the State colleges of agriculture and experiment stations in Ari-

zona, California, Colorado, Idaho, Montana, New Mexico, Nevada, Oregon, Utah, Washington, and Wyoming. Much of the actual work of the field men was done coöperatively with the county agricultural agents. In 1912 an independent western headquarters was established at Salt Lake City and the work directed from there until 1917, when it became a western section of the nationwide program. The work included the formation of cow-testing associations and bull associations. In coöperation with the teaching staffs of the State agricultural colleges, short courses in cheese-making and other dairy subjects have been given from time to time (23:195).

In 1915, the Dairy Division began field work in dairy extension with the States in the Middle West and North in coöperation with the various State agricultural agencies. By 1916 the work was widely established, mostly on a half-and-half basis on the side of expenses. Work was done through community organizations rather than with individual farmers, as had been the practice in the South and the Far West where conditions were less advanced (23: 195). Cow-testing associations were the major enterprise, although market-milk production and creamery practices were important phases of the extension activity. In 1920 the number of men employed for the whole country, by the Division, in cow-testing was reduced to four, who were engaged principally in the study of records from the cow-testing associations (*op. cit.*, p. 196). About the same number were engaged in promoting the formation of bull associations, the fourth man being added in 1922 (p. 197).

In 1916 the States Relation Service and the Bureau of Animal Industry, both of the U. S. Department of Agriculture, issued as a joint contribution and under joint authorship, a bulletin on judging the dairy cow. It was intended for use in secondary schools (47—434).

Dairy Demonstrations in the Great Plains

In August, 1916, the Congress made a special appropriation to the U. S. Department of Agriculture for conducting dairy demonstration work in the arid and semiarid districts of the western United States (48—116). The Dairy Division of the Bureau of Animal Industry immediately began preparations for carrying the law into effect. Advantage was taken of existing field stations maintained by the Bureau of Plant Industry either independently or in coöperation with the State agricultural experiment stations. Experiments were begun in 1917 or 1918 at several field stations. Some of these dairy experiments, although started independently of State agencies, eventually became coöperative with them. At some points experiments with beef cattle and hogs also were established at the same time, while at others only the dairy experiments were started.

These demonstrations in dry-land areas differed materially from those just described as extension activities. The extension program was carried out with farmers on their farms, in coöperation with the established extension agencies. The work described below, while called dairy demonstration, was really dairy experiment. The stations were owned by State or Federal agencies. The Dairy Division owned the cattle, fed and milked them, and sold the products. Jointly with the Bureau of Plant Industry and State agencies, it grew the pasturage and feeds employed. For all operations, cost accounts were kept, so that the entire experiment became a demonstration of what might be done with the dairy enterprise under given conditions.

At Ardmore, near the Black Hills in western South Dakota, the U. S. Dry-land Field Station was established in 1912 by the Office of Dry-land Agriculture of the Bureau of Plant Industry. Livestock experiments, including dairying, were begun in 1917. The station results to the end of 1925, including milk production, pasture experiments, and breeding experiments, were published in 1927. These dairy data comprised nearly half (pp. 40–67) of the bulletin (48—17), which contained the results of both crop and livestock studies and was under the joint authorship of six persons, two from Plant Industry and four from Animal Industry, of whom three were of the Dairy Division. Other than the scientific titles of the authors there was very little prominent recognition of the coöperation.

At Huntley, Montana, the (U. S.) Huntley Field Station was established by the Bureau of Plant Industry in 1910, on the Huntley reclamation project. Land for buildings, corrals, and irrigated pasture was made available by the Bureau of Plant Industry, buildings erected and equipped by the Dairy Division in 1917, and the dairy herd purchased in 1918. Results of dairy experiments from 1918 to 1927, inclusive, were published in 1929 by the Dairy Division (48—116), with the coöperation mentioned in the text (p. 1). Results obtained in crop and livestock production from 1927 to 1930 were published (48—353) under joint authorship by the Bureaus of Plant and Animal Industry in 1933. The station had been made an enterprise coöperative with the Montana Agricultural Experiment Station by that time, and this fact is shown by a prominent statement on the title page and again in the text (p. 1).

In 1921 the Dairy Division began work on the Woodward Dairy Experiment Farm at Woodward, Oklahoma, under a special appropriation made by Congress. The city of Woodward purchased for the purpose 160 acres of land adjoining the field station of the Bureau of Plant Industry. The Dairy Division provided buildings, equipment, and technical personnel, while the necessary crop production and financial accounting were carried on by the superintendent of the Plant Industry Station. The results of the dairying experiments from 1921 to 1926 were published in 1927 by the Bureau of Dairy Industry, and the various coöperations noted above were stated in the introductory text (51—12). Later, the dairy station was made coöperative with the Oklahoma Agricultural Experiment Station. In 1933, the results of experiments from 1928 to 1931 with Sudan grass as a hay, silage, and pasture for dairy cattle were published (48—352), and the State coöperation mentioned in a footnote, the three authors representing the Bureau of Dairy Industry.

Still later, dairy experiments were started at the Northern Great Plains Field Station, Mandan, North Dakota, a station of the Bureau of Plant Industry operated in coöperation with the State Agricultural Experiment Station. In 1930 the State gave to the Federal Department a lease on a full section of land for dairy experimentation, thus making 800 acres available for the work (65—1930:27).

Dairy Herd Improvement

Some of the work described above is concerned with the improvement of dairy herds. This is especially true of extension activities in promoting cow-testing associations and bull associations. The various field stations, also, are engaged in these activities. Special programs in herd improvement are presented below.

About 1907, the Dairy Division of the Bureau of Animal Industry entered into coöperation with the Minnesota Agricultural Experiment Station, and through it with farmers living near, on a project for breeding a strain of milking shorthorns (56—1907: 238). In 1909 Holstein cattle were added to the experiments.

In connection with the Dairy Experiment Farm at Beltsville, Maryland, near Washington, the Bureau of Animal Industry through its Dairy Division, and thus later the Bureau of Dairy Industry as established in 1924, have been engaged in developing a superior dairy herd. As the numerous field stations have been established they also have taken part in the program. One of the major features of this enterprise has been the encouragement of the use of proved dairy sires, by which is meant a bull of proved ability to transmit to his daughters a high capacity for milk and butterfat production. This requires the coöperation of State and private agencies. Young bulls of good breeding are produced in numbers at Beltsville and elsewhere and are proved through keeping full and accurate record of the performance of their daughters over a period of years. These young bulls are loaned to the dairy departments of the many State colleges of agriculture and to selected farmers, the latter under coöperative supervision by county agricultural agents or other official extension workers. These bulls are exchanged or transferred to new localities from time to time to avoid inbreeding. In 1930 it was recorded that 123 bulls from the Beltsville station were then in service. Hundreds of their progeny were under observation and test. The coöperation permits the work to be conducted on a large scale with mutual benefit. Bulls are being produced in smaller numbers at several dairy field stations discussed above.

The Bureau of Dairy Industry has given a good deal of help to the U. S. Department of Justice in the breeding and management of the dairy herds at the five Federal penitentiaries (65—1930:31).

A line of fundamental research undertaken during recent years concerns the relation between external form and internal anatomy, and between both of these and producing capacity. It covers dairy animals of both sexes and several breeds. The work is carried on

at the Beltsville Dairy Station and coöperatively with nineteen
State agricultural experiment stations, well distributed over the
nation. Both ante-mortem and post-mortem studies are made, and
the duplicates of all coöperative records are filed with the Federal
Bureau of Dairy Industry. Phases of the work comparing beef and
dairy breeds represent coöperation with the Division of Animal
Husbandry (65—1930:20–21).

Various studies in regard to dairy structures are made from
time to time by the same Bureau in collaboration with the Bureau
of Agricultural Engineering.

The publications listed in the Literature Cited at the end of this
chapter which have been cited in this section on Dairy Products
are Nos. 6, 7, 10, 15, 18, 23, 26, 28, 31, 47, 48, 49, 51, 52, 54, 56, 58,
59, 65, 78, and 79.

REINDEER

Reindeer, or caribou, have been domesticated in the Arctic areas
of the Old World for many centuries. With the wholesale slaughter
of seal and walrus in Alaskan waters, and the rapid reduction in
fur-bearing land animals, after the coming of the white man, the
Eskimo tribes faced starvation. Dr. Sheldon Jackson, Alaskan representative of the Federal Bureau of Education, suggested the
introduction and raising of reindeer as a source of meat and skins.
Through coöperation with the Revenue Cutter Service of the
Treasury Department, about ten head of reindeer were brought
from Siberia to Unalaska in 1891. In the next year some 170 head
were landed at Port Clarence, on Seward Peninsula, where the
Teller Reindeer Station was established. Introduction continued
until 1902, by which time 1280 reindeer had been brought from
Siberia (47—1089).

In 1894 the Congress made the first direct appropriation for the
work (59—55). Experienced herders from Lapland were brought
over to teach reindeer management to the Eskimos. In 1901 a special expedition of the Revenue Cutter Service brought 250 reindeer of an especially large and robust breed for the improvement
of the breeding stock. The industry grew rapidly and was gradually extended over much of western Alaska. As the herds increased,
certain diseases appeared and better methods of large-scale management became desirable.

In 1920, Congress made funds available to the Federal Bureau of Biological Survey for survey and improvement of the reindeer industry, including control of diseases. Through the coöperation of the Bureau of Education, headquarters were established at Unalakleet on Bering Sea. In the study of pests and diseases, coöperation was obtained from the Federal Bureaus of Entomology and Animal Industry, while assistance was received from the Bureau of Plant Industry in the identification of reindeer food plants. The industry has now grown to large commercial proportions.

5. SHEEP AND GOATS

INVESTIGATIONS in the production and protection of sheep and goats, involving more or less of coöperative relations with other official agencies, have been a part of the work of the Bureau of Animal Industry during most of the time since its creation in 1884. Just as for other classes of livestock, protection activities antedated production activities. The protection of sheep and goats from other environmental influences than specific diseases already has been presented under livestock protection. In 1931 it was recorded that experiments with sheep, goats, and animal fibers were being made at seventeen State and Federal stations, at one wool-scouring plant, two woolen mills, and one mohair mill, and at one hospital clinic (Johns Hopkins University) for testing the value of goat milk for infant feeding (56—1931 :14). The major portion of the Federal investigation of sheep and goats involves no relations with other official agencies.

SHEEP PRODUCTION AND IMPROVEMENT

The Division (then called Office) of Animal Husbandry, of the Federal Bureau of Animal Industry, began the breeding of Rambouillet range sheep in coöperation with the Wyoming Agricultural Experiment Station under a formal agreement effective September 1, 1906. The breeding project was located on a private ranch near Laramie. The coöperation with the Wyoming Station was discontinued on June 30, 1910, but the work at the Wyoming Station was continued until October, 1917. In that month the work of sheep breeding was transferred to the newly-established United States Sheep Experiment Station at Dubois, Idaho. In 1915, the General

Land Office of the Department of the Interior had coöperated in facilitating the selection of some 28,000 acres of sagebrush range land from the public domain for use in sheep-production investigations. Under authority of the Congress, President Wilson withdrew this area from entry and transferred it to the control of the U. S. Department of Agriculture (48—85:1–2). In 1924, coöperation was begun with the U. S. Forest Service in a study of the problems of range management, with particular reference to the effect of different methods on carrying capacity (56—1931:15).

In 1917 the Bureau of Animal Industry prepared a discussion of sheep judging as a subject of instruction in secondary schools (47—593). At the Beltsville (Maryland) Experiment Farm maintained by Animal Industry, there has been some collaboration with the Bureau of Plant Industry in the production and maintenance of sheep pastures. Experiments in feeding sheep with reference to the effects of early breeding have been conducted at the Belle Fourche Field Station in coöperation with the Bureau of Plant Industry and the South Dakota Station. At the Range Livestock Experiment Station at Miles City, Montana, coöperative with the Montana Station, other experiments in the feeding of sheep previous to lambing have been carried on for several years.

SHEEP PROTECTION FROM DISEASES

The protection of sheep from various environmental conditions already has been presented under livestock protection. Two specific diseases of sheep require discussion here, namely, scabies and liver flukes.

Sheep Scabies

Almost from the beginning of its existence, the Bureau of Animal Industry has given attention to the severe damage done to the sheep industry by sheep scab. This summary of the gigantic campaign to control and eradicate it is derived from a forty-year history prepared by the bureau (23) except as otherwise stated. In 1895 the Bureau recommended that control over sheep shipments should be applied under existing legislation, and declared that our foreign trade was imperiled by the disease. In 1896 Great Britain prohibited the importation of live sheep from the United States because of the increasing numbers of scabby sheep received. Port inspection was begun but was ineffective because disease later developed on shipboard. In June, 1897, the Department of Agriculture issued its first order making it a violation of law to receive for transportation, or to transport, sheep affected with scabies, and requiring the disinfection of carrying vehicles. Inspectors were stationed at major railroad stations leading to market centers.

In July, 1899, it was ordered that all sheep shipped from stockyards to other States for feeding purposes be dipped in some preparation that would kill the parasites. Under this order, effective in August, 1899, no sheep affected with scab, or which had been in contact with affected sheep, could be shipped in interstate commerce unless first dipped in one of the two approved mixtures, tobacco-sulfur and lime-sulfur. Livestock sanitary officers in various western States coöperated by issuing similar orders governing intrastate shipments. Federal inspectors were stationed at numerous western shipping points. A Wyoming State law of 1903 provided for coöperation by the State Board of Sheep Commissioners with the Bureau of Animal Industry in its eradication campaign in that State, and the Bureau inspectors were given State appointments also (56—1904:43). This was representative of State coöperation. These successively more comprehensive control measures accomplished results, but it gradually became evident that even the dipping program was not sufficient to accomplish the degree of control desired.

Under orders effective June 1, 1905, an eradication campaign was begun by placing a Federal quarantine on the movement of sheep in or from all the territory west of the eastern border of the States from North Dakota to Texas, inclusive, an area of 1,785,-000 square miles. A plan of coöperation between the Department of Agriculture and the various State livestock sanitary commissions was arranged. This covered the range inspection of all flocks in the entire area and the treatment of all found affected or exposed to infection. The work proceeded without interruption, except for unavoidable disruptions during the World War. As many as 60,000,000 sheep were inspected in each of the peak years up to 1913, with dippings of 12,000,000 to more than 17,000,000 in each year. Thereafter the number declined as the area gradually was cleared of the disease. By 1923, only about 33,000 square miles, comprised in three parishes in Louisiana and ten counties in California, were still under quarantine. More than 1,750,000 square miles, or over one half the area of the country, had been cleared in the eighteen years. By 1930 the entire area, with the exception of San Clemente Island off the coast of California, was clean, and in 1931 the job was finished (10—20:540–43).

During the early progress of the campaign the Federal Bureau, through its Zoölogical Division, coöperated with the South Dakota Experiment Station in a test of creosote and cresol as dips for scabby sheep (56—1907:229). The resulting State bulletin in 1908 acknowledged the coöperation in the text (43—107) and published the State laws and regulations governing the handling of scabby sheep. The experiments were interrupted in 1908 by the destruction of the sheep by dogs (56—1908:253).

Several of the major sheep States of the west, namely, California, Idaho, Montana, Nevada, Oregon, and Washington, now are free from scab. Reduction of infection continues in Arizona, Colorado, New Mexico, and Wyoming, as well as in more eastern States. Inspections in 1931 totaled nearly 22,000,000 and dippings nearly 4,000,000. The percentage of infected animals was only 2.6 per cent (56—1931:33). The work continues in coöperation with the States involved, while special work has been done on Indian Reservations in coöperation with the Office of Indian Affairs, of the Interior Department.

The wiping out of sheep scabies from a State removes burdensome restrictions on the marketing of sheep and avoids the losses caused by the disease as well as the expenditures necessary to eradication, the sheep owners having been obliged to supply the materials and physical equipment necessary to dipping, as well as the labor required to handle the animals needing treatment. While the disease has been eradicated from several States, permanent supervision and inspection is necessary to prevent its reintroduction from other areas where it still is prevalent.

Relations in California.—In California the campaign for the control and eradication of sheep scabies was begun in 1905 by the U. S. Bureau of Animal Industry through its Field Inspection Division. Federal quarantine was laid on June 1, 1905, and the control program planned and carried out in coöperation with the

State Veterinarian and his inspectors. Since the creation of the California State Department of Agriculture in 1919, the work has been done in coöperation with the Division of Animal Industry of that Department. By the end of 1930, eradication had been completed on the mainland, and in 1931 the final infection on San Clemente Island was destroyed.

Coöperation has been carried forward under a written memorandum of understanding between the U. S. Bureau and the State Division of Animal Industry, signed annually by the chiefs of these two agencies. Under this agreement, the State agrees to set aside funds anually to employ competent State inspectors, to enforce State regulations within the State similar to Federal regulations governing interstate movements, and to supply the official State quarantine and permit blanks, as well as copies of State regulations. The Federal agency agrees to furnish a competent supervising inspector to direct Federal personnel and coöperate with the State officers, to provide inspectors and other employees to the extent of the funds available, and to furnish necessary Federal blank forms. The two agencies agree to coöperate in the planning and procedure of the project, to harmonize any differences arising, and to interchange reports necessary to its proper conduct. Official headquarters were in the Federal Building at Sacramento. Federal personnel recently has consisted of one inspector in charge, five assistant veterinarians, and one clerk, with a total annual salary budget of approximately $20,000. The salary expenditures of the State agency have been said to be about one half this sum.

Liver-Fluke Control and Eradication

While occurring in both sheep and cattle, flukes are much more abundant and destructive in sheep. Work on control of this pest was begun in California in 1928 by the Zoölogical Division of the U. S. Bureau of Animal Industry, in coöperation with the Division of Animal Industry, State Department of Agriculture, and the University of California Agricultural Experiment Station. California was the first State selected for this demonstration and was chosen because of the high incidence of flukes in certain sections. The activity consists of control by treatment of infested animals, destruction of snail hosts by copper sulphate, and the draining, filling, or fencing of swampy areas. County agricultural advisors help in locating commercial coöperators among the sheep and cattle growers, with whom informal agreements are made. Control has been effective over large areas, with consequent large saving of money to sheep growers.

The annual Federal budget has grown from about $4,000 in 1929 to about $7,500 in 1931 and 1932. The work is conducted by an associate veterinarian and a junior veterinarian. The project has yielded results of both scientific and economic value. As the Zoölogical Division is primarily a research agency, it feels that the work, if maintained in California, should be taken over by the Field Inspection Division as a practical control campaign, and that the funds now contributed by the Zoölogical Division should be released in order to initiate similar work in other States. Considererable objection has been raised by Californians to any discontinuance of the project.

GOAT PRODUCTION AND PROTECTION

The Federal Bureau of Animal Industry has given minor attention to the goat industry for many years, but without many official relations in the work. In the last few years it has coöperated with the Texas Agricultural Experiment Station in the improvement of Angora goats, with especial reference to the production of improved mohair. This work is conducted both at College Station and at Substation No. 14, at Sonora, where both State and Federal personnel are located for this project (56—1931:17).

In 1929, there was published a general agricultural and economic discussion (50—50) of the Angora goat and the mohair industry under joint authorship of three bureaus in the U. S. Department of Agriculture and two bureaus of the Department of Commerce. The six authors formed the Interdepartmental Angora Goat and Mohair Committee, of which the chairman and secretary were members of the Bureau of Agricultural Economics. The Departmental coöperation was shown in a box at the top of the cover and title pages and the interbureau coöperation was shown by the scientific titles of the authors and also in a box on the inside of the front cover. The Bureaus concerned were Agricultural Economics, Animal Industry, and Forest Service, in Agriculture, and Foreign and Domestic Commerce and Standards, in Commerce. The text includes a discussion of the improvement and management of these goats and of losses from poisonous plants, predatory animals, and diseases.

The only coöperative activity conducted especially for the protection of goats is the campaign for the eradication of goat scabies in Texas, carried on jointly by the Bureau of Animal Industry and the State livestock sanitary authorities, as in the case of cattle scab and sheep scab. Of the 187,000 goats inspected in 1931, somewhat more than two per cent were infected (56—1931:33).

SHEEP AND GOAT SKINS AND FIBERS

For some years the Federal Division of Animal Husbandry has been conducting experiments in crossing Karakul sheep with other breeds and in the production of furs of the Karakul or Persianlamb type. The studies of fur value are made in coöperation with the Bureaus of Biological Survey and Home Economics (56—1931:17). The testing of wool and other animal fibers for the manufacture of pillows, mattresses, upholstery, and brushes has been conducted in collaboration with the Federal Specification Board for the purchase of materials for Government use. These tests have resulted in the production of articles meeting the exacting specifications and also in the saving of money on their purchase (56—1931:17).

The publications listed in the Literature Cited at the end of this chapter which have been cited in this section on Sheep and Goats are Nos. 10, 23, 43, 47, 48, 50, and 56.

6. SWINE

INVESTIGATIONS OF SWINE in which official relationships have developed include production and feeding studies and protection from diseases specific to these animals.

HOG AND PORK PRODUCTION

Anticipating the initiation of livestock breeding and feeding experiments, the Bureau of Animal Industry published in 1904 a comprehensive bulletin (58—47) of 298 pages on the hog industry. The Letter of Transmittal acknowledges the collaboration of the

Office of Experiment Stations and the Bureau of Statistics of the Federal Department of Agriculture and also that of the Iowa Agricultural Experiment Station. No coöperative program of hog breeding or hog feeding initiated by the Bureau appears to have developed for several years thereafter.

Hog Production

In January, 1915, the Animal Husbandry Division of the Bureau of Animal Industry began studies of fish meal as food for swine, in coöperation with the Bureau of Chemistry of the Department of Agriculture and the Bureau of Fisheries of the Department of Commerce. The work was continued over several years, new sources of supply being discovered and investigations of crustaceans (shrimp wastes) being added (23:245). Several publications resulted (47—378, 610, and 1272). Recently additional studies have been made, partly in coöperation with the New Jersey Station. These had special reference to the effect of fish meal in the hog diet on the flavor and aroma of the roasted pork (56—1931:10). (This work has been presented brieflly also in the chapter on Agricultural Chemistry.) Similar recent studies of the effect of peanuts on the flavor and aroma of pork when roasted have been conducted in coöperation with the North Carolina and Virginia Stations.

In 1917 the results of experiments in the disposal of irrigated crops through the use of hogs were published as a joint contribution of the Bureaus of Plant Industry and Animal Industry. The work was done at the Scottsbluff Experiment Farm, on the North Platte irrigation project, conducted coöperatively by the Office of Western Irrigation Agriculture and the Nebraska Agricultural Experiment Station. The bulletin (47—488) is under Plant Industry authorship, with the words, "In coöperation with the Bureau of Animal Industry," after the author's scientific title. Swine investigations were carried on also in connection with the more extensive studies of beef and dairy cattle at some of the Great Plains experiment stations established by the Bureau of Plant Industry. Results have been published from time to time from Ardmore, South Dakota (48—17:36–39) and Huntley, Montana (48—353:34–39) and the discussion of coöperation will be found under the section devoted to beef and dairy cattle.

The emergency appropriation for stimulating agriculture after the entry of the United States into the World War allowed some $250,000 to be made available for developing hog and poultry production. In coöperation with the Food Administration an increase of fifteen per cent in production was decided upon and a vigorous and successful campaign waged. Similar but larger plans were made for the autumn of 1919 but were rendered inoperative by the armistice (23 :250). As in the case of most such war activities, the campaigns were carried on in coöperation with Federal-State agricultural extension agencies.

In various other activities, both before and since the World War, the Division of Animal Husbandry has promoted better breeding, feeding, and management of swine through collaboration with extension agencies. With swine, as with poultry also, large results may be obtained in a relatively short period because of the short time required to develop the animal from birth to maturity.

Soft-Pork Studies

In connection with the efforts to develop larger livestock industries in the southern States, consequent to the disruption of cotton farming, the question of the effect of various southern concentrated feeding stuffs on the firmness of the resulting pork became important. A collaboration of most of the State agricultural experiment stations in the South in an extensive allocated program was brought about in 1919 through the efforts of the Division of Animal Husbandry of the Bureau of Animal Industry. Congress provided $20,000 in the appropriation to the Division for the fiscal year 1920 (23 :245) and State contacts were made immediately. The coöperation of Alabama, Arkansas, Georgia, Indiana, Kentucky, Louisiana, Mississippi, North Carolina, Oklahoma, Pennsylvania, South Carolina, and Texas, as well as of scientific and commercial agencies, was obtained. By agreement, all animals were sent to the Beltsville Experiment Farm in Maryland for slaughter, and all chemical analyses were made there. Conferences of representatives of the coöperating agencies were held from time to time (23 :245–46).

The first comprehensive publication (47—1407) appeared in 1926 under the title, *Some Results of Soft Pork Investigations.*

The statement, "Conducted jointly by the United States Department of Agriculture and the Agricultural Experiment Stations of Alabama, Arkansas, Georgia, Indiana, Kentucky, Mississippi, North Carolina, Oklahoma, South Carolina, Tennessee, and Texas," appeared on the cover page below the title, and also in a box on the inside of the front cover. The second publication (47—1492) appeared in 1927 with a similar display of the coöperative relations on the cover and also at various points in the text. The States concerned included Arkansas, Georgia, Indiana, Mississippi, North Carolina, and South Carolina. As outgrowth of these coöperative investigations, the Bureau of Animal Industry conducted further feeding tests independently at its Beltsville (Maryland) Experiment Farm from 1924 to 1927 and published the results (48—110) in 1929. Still later investigations conducted independently at Beltsville as part of the national investigation were published in 1933, and included Virginia as well as the States named above (48—368).

SWINE PROTECTION FROM DISEASES

The protection of swine from other environmental influences than diseases specific to these animals has been presented under general livestock protection. The principal specific disease to which hogs are susceptible is the well-known hog cholera. In recent years, however, attention has been given to the control of parasitic worms through proper sanitary measures. The connection of swine with foot-and-mouth disease, to which they are very susceptible, has been discussed, likewise, under livestock protection.

Hog Cholera

The disease of swine now universally known as hog cholera was first recognized in the United States in 1833, and has been a destructive factor in swine raising for a full century. In the first twenty years no less than ninety separate infection centers developed. By 1876 the annual loss from the disease was estimated at more than $20,000,000. European countries began to prohibit the entry of American pork. Many scientific studies of the disease were made by Government veterinarians both before and after the specific appropriations by Congress for such work, in 1878.

A bacterium believed to be the cause of the disease was discovered by Federal investigators in 1878 but no control resulted. Usually, hog cholera is somewhat periodic, becoming virulent and spreading destructively for a time and then diminishing in intensity through another period. Its ravages were among the chief reasons for the creation of the Federal Bureau of Animal Industry by the Congress in 1884.

An interesting program of Federal research was immediately developed. The bacterium occurring abundantly in cases of hog cholera was studied and renamed and a long series of researches on the production of serums and vaccines was carried out. Repeated failure finally led to the suspicion that a virulent causative agent remained undiscovered. Further research during an extremely fatal outbreak in Iowa in 1903 discovered an invisible or filterable virus and proved it to be the cause of hog cholera. On the basis of this knowledge it was possible to produce both serum and virus and to confer immunity. The results of these epochal researches were published by the Bureau (58—72 and 102; 59—41 and 43). Through the collaboration of the Patent Office, in the Department of the Interior, a patent was granted to the Department of Agriculture, giving the Government and the people of the United States the right to free use of this discovery (that is, without payment of royalties).

Federal-State coöperation.—The serum method of hog-cholera control was tested on the Animal Industry Bureau's station, and then on farms in Iowa in 1907. Plans for coöperation with the States in hog-cholera control were developed. In 1908 the proper officials of all States were invited to visit the small leased farm maintained since 1906 by the Biochemic Division of the Bureau near Ames, the seat of Iowa Agricultural College and Experiment Station. Representatives of twenty-five States responded at intervals and were instructed in methods of preparing and applying the serum. By 1913 the serum was being produced on a large scale by seven States in the central part of the country and by California, as well as in numerous commercial plants. In March, 1913, Congress passed the Virus-Serum-Toxin Act, which provided for Federal regulation and inspection of all such products before importation or interstate shipment. An appropriation of $75,000 was made also for demonstrating methods of control and eradication of hog cholera. The research program was continued to discover the ways of dissemination of the disease and to improve the methods of manufacture and the quality of the serums.

The coöperative control program was inaugurated on July 1, 1913, in selected areas in four States, Indiana, Iowa, Missouri, and Nebraska. The work had three main objects: first, to coöperate with the State agricultural colleges in instructing farmers in the methods of controlling hog cholera; second, to coöperate with State livestock sanitary officials in the enforcement of necessary quarantine regulations; and third, to coöperate in the application of the preventive serum so as to reduce or prevent losses. So successful was this initial effort that Congress appropriated $450,000 for 1914 to continue and extend the intensive control work to other States, which was done (47—584). In addition, a gigantic coöperation in demonstrations to farmers was started under the Agricultural Extension (Smith-Lever) Act. On January 1, 1916, a separate Office (later Division) of Hog-Cholera Control was created, and early in 1917 a similar Office of Virus-Serum Control was established.

In the years that have followed, the two-fold program of education or extension activities, on the one hand, and the application of intensive control methods in limited areas, on the other, has been continued with some modifications. Substantially all field activities in both lines have been coöperative with State agencies. In general, it may be said that after the World War the extension methods were diminished, so far as the Federal Bureau was concerned, whereas the area under control measures has steadily increased as education progressed, farmers became informed, veterinarians were trained in diagnosis and serum use, and State laws were improved to give adequate means of enforcing quarantines and other protective measures. During 1918 and 1919 the regular funds for the work, already large, were supplemented by generous allotments from war-emergency funds for stimulating agriculture, because pork and fats were in great demand. The total sum available in the latter year was $450,000. Beginning with fiscal year 1921, the Federal appropriations for the work were reduced, as Congress had provided large funds for agricultural extension through the Smith-Lever Act and no longer provided extension funds to the subject-matter bureaus. The regular extension forces, however, carried on much of the work. In recent years the Federal leader in each of the various States usually, though not always, has supervision of all the eradication campaigns under way in that State. In 1931, collaborative activities were carried on in 944 counties in thirty States, or in nearly one third of the counties of the country.

In California, this coöperative project, at first primarily educational in character, was established at Berkeley by the Federal Bureau in coöperation with the University of California College of Agriculture, on September 28, 1914. The Federal agency was removed to Sacramento on April 25, 1918, and certain regulatory duties in the matter of quarantine were assigned to it. A part of the educational activity was discontinued in April, 1920, because it had largely accomplished its purposes.

Since the removal of headquarters to Sacramento, there has been a triple coöperation, including the Division of Hog-Cholera Control in the U. S. Bureau of Animal Industry, the Division of Animal Industry in the State Department of Agriculture, and the coöperative Federal-State Agricultural Extension Service of the College of Agriculture in the University of California. The work is done under a four-party memorandum of understanding, signed by the Chief of the U. S. Bureau of Animal Industry and the Chief of the Office of Coöperative Extension Work, and by the Chief of the State Division of Animal Industry and the State Director of Agricultural Extension.

The Bureau of Animal Industry assigns one or more qualified veterinarians to assist in investigating reported outbreaks of hog cholera, diagnosing the disease, enforcing rules and regulations regarding quarantine and disinfection, advising swine raisers in the application of preventive measures, administering preventive treatment where other veterinary service is unavailable, and training practicing veterinarians in the proper methods of handling outbreaks and applying recognized preventive treatments. The State Division of Animal Industry obligates itself to advise swine owners where and how to obtain anti-hog-cholera serum produced by establishments operating under Federal license or State supervision, and where to obtain competent veterinarians to apply treatment, and to arrange for the serum treatments where veterinary service is lacking.

It is agreed also that the Federal representative shall be available to assist the extension forces in educational campaigns, and in coöperating with extension agents in the field under the supervision of the State director of extension. The memorandum provides that office accommodations, if desired, and such clerical help as may be necessary, shall be provided by one or the other of the coöperating State agencies. The Federal representative has office in the Federal Building in Sacramento, where he has charge also of tuberculosis control and sheep-scab eradication.

Other Diseases

Much interest in garbage-feeding of hogs was developed through the discovery of the origin of the California outbreak of foot-and-mouth disease in 1924. As a result a discussion of feeding methods and the physiological effects of garbage feeding was prepared by a representative of the Division of Hog-Cholera Control of the U. S. Bureau of Animal Industry, stationed at Sacramento. This paper was published coöperatively, under the title, "The Garbage-Fed Hog," in the *Monthly Bulletin* of the State Department of Agriculture for September, 1929 (10—18 :484–88). In 1915, the Federal Animal Husbandry Division and the Medical Corps of the United States Army published under joint authorship a discussion of beriberi and cottonseed poisoning in pigs (26—5 :489).

Some coöperative relations have developed in connection with a program to control the intestinal roundworm or ascarid, which infects both hogs and humans. In 1927 the Zoölogical Division and the Division of Hog-Cholera Control collaborated in applying in McLean County, Illinois, the swine-sanitation system developed by the Bureau (48—44). There was local coöperation by the Farm Bureau Federation (*op. cit.*, p. 5), a farmer organization working in close relation with the Federal-State Agricultural Extension Service. More recently this collaborative activity has been extended to areas in other States.

The publications listed in the Literature Cited at the end of this chapter which have been cited in this section on Swine are Nos. 10, 23, 26, 47, 48, 56, 58, and 59.

7. POULTRY AND PIGEONS

A LARGE VOLUME of research on the production and protection of poultry and eggs has been conducted by the Federal Bureau of Animal Industry and the various State agricultural experiment stations but in relatively little of it have any coöperative relations developed.

POULTRY AND EGG PRODUCTION

In August, 1904, the Bureau of Animal Industry began coöperative experiments with poultry at the Maine Agricultural Experiment Station, and these were continued until June 30, 1913 (23: 235; 56—1904:66). The station itself had begun the work in 1897. The first Federal publication (58—90), appearing in 1906, and covering breeding experiments for egg production, was a revision of *Bulletin 100* of the Maine Station and contained State results from the beginning in 1897. The succeeding publications (58— 110) comprised one bulletin in three separate but consecutively paged parts, issued in 1909, 1911, and 1914, respectively, under the general title: "A biometrical study of egg production in the domestic fowl." The three parts dealt with annual variation and seasonal distribution in egg production and the effect of variety on the physical characters of the egg.

In 1911 and 1913, the experts of the Bureau published on the improvement and the care, respectively, of the farm egg (58—141 and 160). The studies were made chiefly in Kansas and both publications acknowledge the collaboration of officials of the Kansas Station and the Kansas State Board of Health.

In 1921 the people of the community of Glendale, Arizona, and vicinity provided a sum sufficient to buy ten acres of land near that town. This land was deeded to the U. S. Department of Agriculture for permanent use as a United States Poultry Experiment Farm and it has been so operated since that time. Apparently no official relations have developed.

PROTECTION FROM DISEASES

In 1928 the Food, Drug, and Insecticide Administration and the Division of Insects Affecting Man and Animals, of the Bureau of Entomology, published jointly the results of experiments which demonstrated the ineffectiveness of internal medication for the control of external parasites of poultry (48—60). The materials were furnished and the analyses made by the Insecticide and Fungicide Board. In a study of development of certain nematodes in poultry and game birds, published by the Zoölogical Division of the Bureau of Animal Industry in 1931, assistance in obtaining material through the Animal Husbandry Division, the Bureaus of Biological Survey, Entomology, and Plant Industry, the Smithsonian Institution, and the Connecticut Game Commission, was given footnote acknowledgment (48—227).

A poultry pathological laboratory was established at Los Angeles in April, 1927, through the joint efforts of the Division of Animal Industry of the California State Department of Agriculture, the University of California, and the poultry interests of Southern California, the latter furnishing the building which housed the laboratory. The director was furnished by the State Division. The Poultry Division of the College of Agriculture of the University collaborated by paying the salary of a technician and furnishing the equipment and part of the supplies. On June 30, 1931, however, the College of Agriculture and the State Department of Agriculture agreed that the former would concentrate its efforts on research in poultry diseases in Berkeley, and the State Department would assume responsibility for the diagnostic and regulatory features at Los Angeles. Thereafter the State Department of Agriculture paid the salaries of the supervisor, pathologist, and technician and furnished the supplies and equipment. The Livestock Department of Los Angeles County has assisted through the occasional assignment of one or more veterinarians for service in the laboratory.

The Division of Animal Industry of the State Department of Agriculture opened a poultry pathological laboratory at Petaluma in December, 1930, to conduct a diagnostic service for poultry diseases. Poultry interests of the Petaluma district provided the building. Under an agreement of the State Division of Animal Industry with the counties of Sonoma, Napa, and Marin, organized as a Tri-County Poultry Sanitary District, a coöperative program for the control of poultry diseases was inaugurated at the same time. The three counties comprising the sanitary district provided

$10,000 annually to cover expenses and to be handled as a trust fund by the State Division, which assigned two veterinarians to conduct the sanitary program. Office space for the sanitary district veterinarians was provided in the poultry pathology laboratory (10—20:286–87). This activity was discontinued in 1933.

The publications listed in the Literature Cited at the end of this chapter which have been cited in this section on Poultry and Pigeons are Nos. 10, 23, 48, 56, and 58.

8. HONEYBEES

FEDERAL AND STATE agencies have conducted research and regulatory activities concerned with honeybee production and protection for many years, but very little of the work has been coöperative.

PRODUCTION

In 1921 the States Relations Service of the U. S. Department of Agriculture, through its Office of Home Economics, conducted in collaboration with the Bureau of Entomology a study of heat production by honeybees in winter, using the Office respiration calorimeter for the purpose (47—988). This followed an earlier independent study (47—93).

In 1925 the Bureau of Entomology published on the flight activities of honeybees (47—1328), a study which through coöperation with a graduate student, involved informal relations with Cornell University and the Department of Agriculture of the Union of South Africa. In 1932 the Division of Bee Culture in the Federal Bureau of Entomology published (48—326) a full discussion of breeding the honeybee under controlled conditions. No coöperation is involved but the publication is mentioned to show that bee culture is fast being placed on the same scientific plane as those branches of animal production concerned with livestock.

Under a formal memorandum of understanding between the U. S. Bureau of Entomology and the California Agricultural Experiment Station, a Pacific Coast Bee-culture Field Station was established on February 11, 1931, at University Farm, Davis. The establishing of this field station followed the action of the State Association of Bee-keepers in December, 1928, when they peti. tioned the U. S. Department of Agriculture to establish a research station in California to aid them in problems pertaining to bee culture. Under the terms of the coöperative agreement, the California Station furnishes office and laboratory space, electrical power, light, gas, water, and janitor service. Some two acres of land also are made available. The U. S. Bureau of Entomology furnishes personnel, supplies, and any special equipment needed for the studies undertaken. Provision is made for the joint planning of the research and for either joint or independent publication of results, submission of the manuscript and the giving of due credit to the other party being required where independent publication is made.

Beekeeping problems mentioned for early attention were an economic survey of the bee industry, to be conducted in coöperation with the U. S. Bureau of Agricultural Economics, and a study of pollination problems with especial reference to the distribution of bees in orchards of deciduous fruits. The former was published by the California Station (6—555) in 1933. Under the coöperative agreement, the Federal agency is committed to the expenditure of about $15,000, and the California Station to an expenditure of $4500, in the fiscal year 1931. The Federal agency allotted the sum of $13,500 for the fiscal year 1932. The field station is in charge of a Federal representative. Two other technical employees have been added, one from the staff of the State Department of Agriculture and one from the staff of the California Agricultural Experiment Station, by transfer to the Federal rolls.

In 1927, the U. S. Department of Agriculture published recommended standards for honey (49—410). In 1927, also the required grades, color standards, and packing requirements for honey, formally adopted, were published (51—24). These had been prepared jointly by the Bureaus of Entomology and Agricultural Economics.

PROTECTION FROM DISEASES

As early as 1908, the Massachusetts Hatch Agricultural Experiment Station reprinted in its *Bulletin 124,* through the courtesy of the U. S. Department of Agriculture, a bulletin on bee diseases originally published by the Federal Bureau of Entomology as its *Bulletin 75,* Part 3.

In 1920 the Bureau of Entomology conducted a study of the be-

havior of bees in colonies affected with European foulbrood (47—
804). The work was done at Cornell University, using an isolated
yard of bees and the laboratory facilities of that institution (p. 5).
No mention of the coöperation is made in the introduction or first-
page footnote. In 1930 appeared a bulletin on the fungus diseases
of the honeybee (48—149), as a joint contribution from the University of Michigan and the Federal Bureau of Entomology, with
acknowledgment of assistance received from the mycologist of the
Bureau of Chemistry and Soils in identifying the fungus species.

The publications listed in the Literature Cited at the end of this
chapter which have been cited in this section on Honeybees are
Nos. 6, 47, 48, 49, and 51.

9. SUMMARY OF COÖPERATION

THERE IS A LARGE and constantly increasing measure of official co-
operation in the numerous and diverse activities concerned with
animal industries. Some striking examples of long-continued and
prominently recognized relations occur. For convenience, the activities may be grouped into three major divisions.

DISEASE CONTROL AND ERADICATION

In no field of agricultural activity have there been more widespread and long-continued coöperative relations between Federal,
State, and county officials during the past fifty years than in the
control of animal diseases. An essential part of the protection of
animals from diseases is the Federal-State coöperative system of
border and port inspection of animals moving in international
commerce and of stockyard and shipping-point inspection of animals moving in interstate commerce. The program includes Federal coöperation with State experiment stations in research problems, with State departments of agriculture and other State and
county livestock sanitary officials in quarantine, control, and eradication campaigns, and with the Federal-State Agricultural Extension Service in popular education on the farms.

Many nation-wide or regional campaigns have been or are still
being conducted. Among instances of complete eradication by
coöperative measures may be mentioned contagious pleuropneumonia of cattle and the recurrent outbreaks of the dreaded foot-

and-mouth disease. Eradication campaigns which already have achieved a large measure of success are concerned with cattle scab, sheep scab, dourine of horses, and cattle-tick eradication to control Texas fever. Systematic, nationwide control campaigns are now being waged against hog cholera and tuberculosis of cattle.

ANIMAL PRODUCTION AND IMPROVEMENT

Activities in this field are only some thirty years old, having started fifteen or twenty years later than those in the control of animal diseases. They have centered especially on cattle, with some attention to horses and minor activities with sheep, hogs, and honeybees. The coöperative work with horses has included the breeding of cavalry remounts in coöperation with the War Department and the breeding of light and heavy draft horses in coöperation with various State agricultural experiment stations. The improvement of beef cattle has been coöperative with State experiment stations over a large part of the country, though principally in the South where a new cattle industry is being developed, and in the dry-land areas of the Middle West where the range has given way to the farm. The work has been chiefly a combination of experimentation and extension measures in connection with the feeding of beef cattle for market.

The improvement of dairy cattle has been the function of the Dairy Division of the Bureau of Animal Industry, since 1924 an independent Bureau of Dairy Industry. In coöperation with State experiment stations, the agricultural extension service, and various herd associations, it has conducted a national campaign for the improvement of dairy-herd sires and the better feeding and care of the dairy cow. Here again especial attention has been given to the development of the industry in the South and the semiarid Middle West.

DAIRY PRODUCT IMPROVEMENT

For nearly fifty years there has been Federal-State coöperation in the improvement of milk supplies and of butter and cheese manufacture. Coöperation in milk improvement has been between the former Dairy Division and present Bureau of Dairy Industry and other government agencies maintaining dairy herds, State agricultural experiment stations and extension services, the Federal Public Health Service, and municipal health authorities, looking toward proper sanitation and handling of milk. Coöperation in butter improvement has been chiefly with certain State experiment stations in methods of manufacture, including sanitation of the cream. Coöperative relationships in the manufacture and handling of cheese have been with several State experiment stations and have covered operations with the two major groups of American cheeses, the cheddar and the Camembert-Roquefort types.

RECOGNITION OF COÖPERATION

Some remarkable instances of the prominent display of the coöperative relations in long-continued series of resulting publications have occurred in the field of animal industry. One striking example is the series of more than twenty publications on animal nutrition, resulting from coöperation between the Federal Bureau of Animal Industry and the Institute of Animal Nutrition of the Pennsylvania Agricultural Experiment Station. Another striking example is the series of Federal publications resulting from coöperation between the Federal Bureau of Animal Industry and the West Virginia Experiment Station in the feeding and care of beef cattle. A third series comprised the Federal and State publications resulting from coöperation between the Federal Dairy Division and the Connecticut (Storrs) Experiment Station in the manufacture of soft cheese. The printing of the statement of coöperation in large type on the covers of most of these publications has been a gratifying example of prominent public recognition of the relationship.

10. LITERATURE CITED

1. Agnew, Mary A. Workers in subjects pertaining to agriculture in State agricultural colleges and experiment stations. U. S. Dept. Agric., Misc. Publ. 154:1–133, 1933 (also Nos. 180, 214, 234, 254, and 299).

2. Alvord, Henry E. Officials, Associations, and Educational Institutions connected with the dairy interests of the United States for the year ——— [1896–1908; 1910; 1912]. U. S. Dept. Agric., Bur. An. Indus., Circs., 1896–1908; 1910, 1912.

3. Caffey, Francis G. A brief statutory history of the United States Department of Agriculture. 26 p. October 23, 1916. (Reprinted from *Case and Comment* 22 (9 & 10):723–33; 850–56, February & March, 1916.)

4. Caine, John T., III. Packers and Stockyards Act: How it is administered. U. S. Dept. Agric., Yearbook 1926:563–65, 1927.

5. California Agricultural Experiment Station. Report of the Agricultural Experiment Station of the University of California from July 1, ———, to June 30, ———. 1884–. (The earlier reports had varying titles.)

6. California Agricultural Experiment Station. Bulletins 1–, 1884–.

7. California Agricultural Experiment Station. Circulars 1–, 1903–.

8. California (College of Agriculture) Agricultural Extension Service. Circulars 1–, 1926–.

9. California State Department of Agriculture. Annual Reports 1–11, 1920–30, inc. (Published in Calif. Dept. Agric., Mo. Bul. vols. 9–19, 1920–30.)

10. California Department of Agriculture. Monthly Bulletin of the Department of agriculture, State of California. Vol 1–, 1911/1912–.

The last issue of each volume comprises the Annual Report of the State Department of Agriculture, beginning with 1920.

11A. California Department of Agriculture. Agricultural Statutes of the State of California. Corrected to July 1, 1931. Calif. State Dept. Agric., Sacramento, 1931. (Ten parts, separately paged, except Parts One and Two.)

11B. California State Department of Agriculture. Agricultural Code (revised to September 15, 1935). 268 p. Sacramento, Supervisor of Documents, 1935.

12. Cameron, Jenks. The Bureau of Biological Survey; Its history, activities, and organization. Institute for Government Research, Service Monograph 54:[i]–x, 1–339. (Baltimore: Johns Hopkins Press, 1929)

13. Cameron, Jenks. The Bureau of Dairy Industry: Its history, activities, and organization. Institute for Government Research, Service Monograph 55: [i]–[ix], 1–74. (Baltimore: Johns Hopkins Press, 1929)

14. Colorado Agricultural Experiment Station. Bulletins 1–, 1887–.

15. Connecticut (Storrs) Agricultural Experiment Station. Bulletins 1–, 1888–.

16. Eisenhower, M. S., and A. P. Chew. The United States Department of Agriculture: its growth, structure, and functions. U. S. Dept. Agric., Misc. Publ. 88:i–iv, 1–147, 21 charts (unnumbered), September 1, 1930.

17. Gates, Otis H. [compiler]. Animal Industry, pp. 71–111, 132. *In* Laws applicable to the United States Department of Agriculture, 1923. iv, 897 p. (Washington: Government Printing Office, 1924)

18. Georgia Agricultural Experiment Station. Bulletins 1–, 1888–.

19. Greathouse, Charles H. [compiler]. Historical sketch of the U. S. Department of Agriculture: its objects and present organization. U. S. Dept. Agric., Div. of Publ., Bul. 3:1–74, front. and 2 pls., 9 unnumbered figs. (half-tones), 1898; rev. ed., same paging, 1898; sec. rev.: 1–97, front. and 2 pls., 9 unnumbered figs. (half-tones), 1907.

20. Greathouse, Charles H. Index to the yearbooks of the United States Department of Agriculture, 1894–1900. U. S. Dept. Agric., Div. Publications, Bul. 7:1–196, 1902. Index . . . 1901–05. U. S. Dept. Agric., Div. Publications, Bul. 9, 1908. Index . . . 1906–10. U. S. Dept. Agric., Div. Publications, Bul. 10, 1913.

21. Handy, R. B., and Minna A. Cannon. List by titles of publications of the United States Department of Agriculture from 1840 to June, 1901. U. S. Dept. Agric., Div. Publ., Bul. 6:1–216, 1902. (See entries 24, 25.)

22. Hilgardia. A Journal of agricultural science published by the California Agricultural Experiment Station. Vol. 1–, 1925/26–.

23. Houck, U. G. The Bureau of Animal Industry of the United States Department of Agriculture: its establishment, achievements, and current activities. xviii, 390 p., 4 pls. (portraits), 1 organization chart (p. xvi). (Published by the Author, Washington, D. C., 1924)

24. Hunt, Mabel G. List of publications of the United States Department of Agriculture from January, 1901, to December, 1925, inclusive (compiled by comparison with the originals). U. S. Dept. Agric., Misc. Publ. 9:i–vi, 1–182, 1927. (See entry 21.)

Supplementary to Bulletin No. 6, Division of Publications, issued in 1902, but duplicating that list for months of January-June, 1901.

25. Hunt, Mabel G. List of publications of the United States Department of Agriculture from January, 1926, to December, 1930, inclusive, compiled by comparison with the originals. U. S. Dept. Agric., Misc. Publ. 153:1–46, 1932.

26. Journal of Agricultural Research. Vol 1–, 1913–.

Published by the U. S. Department of Agriculture, under the direction of a joint committee representing the Department and the Association of Land-Grant Colleges and Universities.

27. Keane, Charles. The epizootic of foot-and-mouth disease in California (February 17, 1924, to June 10, 1926). Calif. Dept. Agric., Special Publ. 65:1–54, figs. 1–8, chart, 1926.

28. Louisiana Agricultural Experiment Station. Bulletins (Second Series) 1–, 1890–.

29. Merritt, Dixon. The United States Department of Agriculture: what it is and how it serves. U. S. Dept. Agric., 47 p., mim., $8\frac{1}{2}'' \times 11''$ [about 1920].

30. Merritt, Dixon. Department of Agriculture in the War. U. S. Dept. Agric., Press Service, 208 p., mim., $8\frac{1}{2}'' \times 11''$ [about 1920].

31. Mississippi Agricultural Experiment Station. Bulletins 1–, 1888–.

32. Mohler, John R. Progress in eradicating contagious animal diseases. U. S. Dept. Agric., Yearbook 1919 (Sep. 802):69–78, 8 unnumbered figs. (graphs), 1920.

33. Nevada Agricultural Experiment Station. Bulletins 1–, 1888–.

34. New Mexico Agricultural Experiment Station. Bulletins 1–, 1890–.

35. North Carolina Agricultural Experiment Station. Bulletins 1–, 1877–.

Numbers were first applied to No. 57 and lists vary slightly as to those comprised in the first 56.

36. Pennsylvania Agricultural Experiment Station. Bulletins 1–, 1887–.

37. Powell, Fred Wilbur. The Bureau of Animal Industry: its history, activities, and organization. Institute for Government Research, Service Monograph 41:1–190. (Baltimore: Johns Hopkins Press, 1927)

38. Redington, P. G., and S. P. Young. Information for the guidance of field men and coöperators of the Bureau of Biological Survey engaged in the

control of injurious rodents and predatory animals. U. S. Dept. Agric., Misc. Publ. 115:1–8, 1931.

39. Salmon, D. E. Rules and regulations governing the operations of the Bureau of Animal Industry; also the acts of Congress under which they are made. U. S. Dept. Agric., Bur. Animal Indus., Bul. 9:1–46, 1895.

40. Salmon, D. E. Bureau of Animal Industry. U. S. Dept. Agric., Yearbook 1897 (Sep. 93):236–58, 1898.

41. Salmon, D. E. Relations of Federal Government to control of contagious diseases of animals. U. S. Dept. Agric., Yearbook 1903 (Sep. 303):491–506, 1904.

42. Salmon, D. E. Animal breeding and feeding investigations by the Bureau of Animal Industry. U. S. Dept. Agric., Yearbook 1904 (Sep. 366): 527–38, pl. 71, fig. 60, 1905.

43. South Dakota Agricultural Experiment Station. Bulletins 1–, 1887–.

44. Thompson, George F. Administrative work of the Federal government in relation to the animal industry. U. S. Dept. Agric., Yearbook 1899 (Sep. 166):441–64, 1900.

45. Thompson, George Fayette. Index to literature relating to animal industry in the publications of the United States Department of Agriculture, 1837 to 1898. U. S. Dept. Agric., Div. Publ., Bul. 5:1–626, 1900.

46. U. S. Department of Agriculture. Report of the [Commissioner] Secretary of Agriculture for the year ———. 1862–.

Report of the Commissioner, 1862–88; Report of the Secretary, 1889–. From 1862 to 1920, inclusive, and for 1922 and 1923 the reports of Chiefs of Offices, Divisions, and Bureaus are included with the report of the Secretary in a consecutively paged volume. From 1921 and 1924 to date all these reports are issued separately each year, with separate paging. (See also Yearbooks.)

47. U. S. Department of Agriculture. Department Bulletins 1–1500, 1913–29.

All Bureau series of publications were discontinued on June 30, 1913, and various Departmental series were begun on July 1. This series of *Department Bulletins* was succeeded by *Technical Bulletins*, and *Miscellaneous Publications*, the issuance of which, however, began in 1927. The Department bulletins are designated simply as *Bulletins* until after No. 1100, when the word *Department* began to be inserted.

48. U. S. Department of Agriculture. Technical Bulletins 1–, 1927–.

49. U. S. Department of Agriculture. Department Circulars 1–425, 1919–27.

This series should not be confused with the series designated *Miscellaneous Circulars* (Nos. 1–, 1923–), or with the series designated simply *Circulars* (Nos. 1–, 1927–).

50. U. S. Department of Agriculture. Miscellaneous Circulars 1–110, 1923–1929.

This series should not be confused with the series designated *Department Circulars* (Nos. 1–425, 1919–27), or with the series designated simply as *Circulars* (Nos. 1–, 1927–).

51. U. S. Department of Agriculture. Circulars 1–, 1927–.

This series should not be confused with the series designated *Department Circulars* (Nos. 1–425, 1919–27), or with the series designated *Miscellaneous Circulars* (Nos. 1–110, 1923–1929).

52. U. S. Department of Agriculture. Miscellaneous Publications 1–, 1927–.

These comprise a series in which the numbers range in size from 16mo or smaller through 12mo, 8vo, and 4to, which means that bound sets rarely are complete. This series should not be confused with the concurrent series of *Miscellaneous Circulars*.

53. U. S. Department of Agriculture. Reports 1–117, 1862–1917.

Nos. 1–58 were issued 1862–98, without numbers. A list of titles and assigned numbers for this series was printed on cover pages 3 and 4 of No. 59, which was the first to bear a number.

54. U. S. Department of Agriculture. Yearbook of the Department of Agriculture, —— (year). 1894–.

From 1894 to 1928 the statistical and other data were for the year named in the title and the volume was published in the following year. Beginning with 1930, the year in the title is the year of issue, and the contained data are for the previous year, a most confusing condition. Through this change there is no volume bearing 1929 in its title.

55. U. S. Department of Agriculture. List of technical workers in the Department of Agriculture and outline of Department functions, 1931. U. S. Dept. Agric., Misc. Publ. 123:1–165. July, 1931. See also Nos. 177 (1933), 233 (1935) and 304 (1938).

56. U. S. Department of Agriculture, Bureau of Animal Industry. Report of the Chief of the Bureau of Animal Industry for —— (year). 1894–.

This series of administrative reports should not be confused with the series of technical volumes issued from 1884 to 1905 as *Annual Reports of the Bureau of Animal Industry*, First to Twenty-second.

57. U. S. Department of Agriculture, Bureau of Animal Industry. —— Annual Report of the Bureau of Animal Industry, for the year ——. 1–28 (1884–1911), 1885–1913.

These volumes of technical papers should not be confused with the series of annual administrative reports.

58. U. S. Department of Agriculture, Bureau of Animal Industry. Bulletins 1–167, 1893–1913.

59. U. S. Department of Agriculture, Bureau of Animal Industry. Circulars 1–218. 1894–1913.

60. U. S. Department of Agriculture, Bureau of Animal Industry. Miscellaneous reports.

No series of publications actually designated *Miscellaneous Reports* ever was issued by the Bureau. However, a list of about 100 papers, most of which appeared in one or another of the Departmental series of publications on animal industry, such as *Miscellaneous Reports, Reports*, and *Special Reports*, all of the Office of the Secretary, as well as *Farmers' Bulletins, Yearbook Separates*, and others, has been compiled under the general title *Miscellaneous Reports* (21:68–72).

61. U. S. Department of Agriculture, Bureau of Animal Industry. Directory of the Bureau of Animal Industry. U. S. Dept. Agric., Bur. Animal Indus. (unnumbered publ.), January, 1910. Rev. ed. quarterly to Jan. 1, 1919; rev. July 25, 1919; April 3, 1921; Oct. 1, 1923; Nov. 1, 1925; Apr. 1, 1930 (68 p.)

62. U. S. Department of Agriculture, Bureau of Biological Survey. Bulletins 1–45, 1889–1913.

63. U. S. Department of Agriculture, Bureau of Biological Survey. Circulars 1–94, 1886–1913.

64. U. S. Department of Agriculture, Bureau of Biological Survey. Directory of field activities of the Bureau of Biological Survey. U. S. Dept. Agric., Miscl. Publ. 49:1–37, fig. 1 (map), 3¼" × 5⅝", June, 1929.

65. U. S. Department of Agriculture, Bureau of Dairy Industry. Report of the Chief of the Bureau of Dairy Industry. 1925–.

66. U. S. Department of Agriculture, Office of Experiment Stations. Bulletins 1–256, 1889–1913.

67. U. S. Department of Agriculture, Forest Service. Bulletins 1–127, 1887–1913.

68. U. S. Department of Agriculture, Bureau of Plant Industry. Report of the Chief of the Bureau of Plant Industry for ———— [year]. 1901–.

From 1901 to 1920, inclusive, the reports of the Chief of the Bureau of Plant Industry were published with the annual report of the Secretary of Agriculture in the consecutively paged *Annual Report of the Department*. Since then they have appeared as separately paged pamphlets.

69. U. S. Department of Agriculture, Bureau of Plant Industry. Bulletins 1–285, 1901–13.

70. U. S. Department of Agriculture, Division of Publications. Bulletins 1–10, 1896–1913. (See also Entry Nos. 19, 20, 21, 45, and 72.)

71. U. S. Department of Agriculture, Division of Publications. Circulars 1–19, 1901–12.

72. U. S. Department of Agriculture, Division of Publications. Index to the annual reports of the U. S. Department of Agriculture for the years 1837 to 1893, inclusive. U. S. Dept. Agric., Div. Publs., Bul. 1:1–252, 1896.

73. U. S. Department of Agriculture, Division of Publications. Publications of the Bureau of Animal Industry. U. S. Dept. Agric., Div. Publs., Cir. 15. March 8, 1911. Rev. ed., October 3, 1911; December 7, 1911; January 27, 1912; April 18, 1912; November 9, 1912; February 17, 1913; June 26, 1913.

74. [U.S.] Government Printing Office, Superintendent of Documents. List of Publications of the Agriculture Department, 1862–1902. 623 p. 1904.

75. Walling, William English, and Harry W. Laidler. State Socialism: pro and con. Official documents and other authoritative selections—showing the world-wide replacement of private by governmental industry before and during the War. With a chapter on municipal socialism, by Evans Clark. (649 p.; Animal Industry, pp. 116–22) (New York: Henry Holt & Co., 1917)

76. West Virginia Agricultural Experiment Station. Bulletins 1–. 1888–.

77. Wiest, Edward. Agricultural organization in the United States. (Bureau of Animal Industry, pp. 89–110.) xxiii, 618 p. Lexington, University of Kentucky, 1923. (The University of Kentucky: Studies in Economics and Sociology, Vol. 2.)

78. Wisconsin Agricultural Experiment Station. Bulletins 1–, 1883–.

79. Wisconsin Agricultural Experiment Station. Research Bulletins 1–, 1909–.